LearningPlus®

Self-Paced Learning of Skills and Strategies

An Innovative Instructional Handbook for Building Mathematics Skills

Mathematics

More than 400 pages of instruction and practice, from basic arithmetic to measurement and logical reasoning.

ETS™ Educational Testing Service

Contents

How to Use This Handbook vii

Chapter 1: Mathematical Power

1.1 Estimation and Calculator Use **2**
   1.1.1 Using Estimation 2
   1.1.2 Using the Calculator.. 11

1.2 Communication and Problem Solving.. **14**
   1.2.1 Characteristics of Good Problem Solvers 14
   1.2.2 Problem-Solving Strategies.. 15

1. 3 Answers to Questions.. **16**

Chapter 2: Number Sense and Operations

2.1 Integers **23**
   2.1.1   Place Value 23
   2.1.2   Magnitude 23
   2.1.3   Understanding Negative Numbers 24
   2.1.4   Adding Negative Numbers 26
   2.1.5   Subtracting Negative Numbers 27
   2.1.6   Multiplying and Dividing Negative Numbers.. 28
   2.1.7   Divisibility Tests.. 30
   2.1.8   Factors 36
   2.1.9   Multiples 37
   2.1.10 Prime Numbers 39
   2.1.11 Composite Numbers 40
   2.1.12 Factoring 41
   2.1.13 Prime Factorization 42
   2.1.14 Greatest Common Factors.. 44
   2.1.15 Adding with Odd and Even Numbers 46
   2.1.16 Multiplying with Odd and Even Numbers 47
   2.1.17 Understanding Clock Arithmetic.. 48
   2.1.18 Congruence in Clock Arithmetic.. 49
   2.1.19 Adding in Clock Arithmetic 51
   2.1.20 Subtracting in Clock Arithmetic 53
   2.1.21 Multiplying in Clock Arithmetic 54

2.2 Fractions.. **56**
   2.2.1 Fractions as Part of a Whole.. 56
   2.2.2 Equivalent Fractions.. 57
   2.2.3 Scaling Up Fractions 58
   2.2.4 Scaling Down Fractions 60
   2.2.5 Fractions in Lowest Terms 61
   2.2.6 Common Denominators 62
   2.2.7 Mixed Numbers 64

      2.2.8   Improper Fractions 66
      2.2.9   Comparing Fractions to 1 67
      2.2.10 Comparing Fractions to Fractions 68
      2.2.11 Estimating Equivalent Fractions 74
      2.2.12 Adding and Subtracting Fractions 76
      2.2.13 Multiplying Fractions 79
      2.2.14 Dividing Fractions 81

2.3 Decimals **83**
      2.3.1   Decimal Numbers 83
      2.3.2   Place Value and Decimals 84
      2.3.3   Ordering Decimals 85
      2.3.4   Rounding Decimals 87
      2.3.5   Adding and Subtracting Decimals 89
      2.3.6   Multiplying Decimals 91
      2.3.7   Dividing Decimals 93
      2.3.8   Fraction/Decimal Equivalence 94

2.4 Percents **98**
      2.4.1   Meaning of Percent 98
      2.4.2   Percent as Part of a Whole 99
      2.4.3   Expressing Percents as Fractions 101
      2.4.4   Fraction/Percent Equivalence 103
      2.4.5   Decimal/Percent Equivalence 107
      2.4.6   Percents Greater Than 100% 109
      2.4.7   Percents Less Than 1% 110
      2.4.8   Calculating Percents 113
      2.4.9   Rounding Percents 115
      2.4.10 Calculations Using Percents 117
      2.4.11 Estimating Percents: Calculations 119
      2.4.12 Estimating Percents: Common Sense 121
      2.4.13 Percent Increase 123
      2.4.14 Percent Decrease 125
      2.4.15 Percents and Circle Graphs 127

2.5 Answers to Questions **130**

Chapter 3: Data Comprehension

3.1 Tables and Charts **169**
      3.1.1   Understanding Titles 169
      3.1.2   Understanding Rows 170
      3.1.3   Understanding Columns 171
      3.1.4   Reading Schedules and Tables 172
      3.1.5   Patterns in Data 173
      3.1.6   Creating Table Headings 175
      3.1.7   Organizing Data 177
      3.1.8   Generating Table Data 178

3.2 Average, Median, Mode, and Range **179**
      3.2.1   Finding the Average 179
      3.2.2   Finding the Median 180
      3.2.3   Finding the Mode 184

      3.2.4   Finding the Range 186

3.3 Basic Graphs **188**
      3.3.1   Reading Pictographs 188
      3.3.2   Reading Bar Graphs 190
      3.3.3   Reading Double Bar Graphs 192
      3.3.4   Reading Line Graphs 195
      3.3.5   Reading Scatter Plots 197
      3.3.6   Elimination with Scatter Plots 199
      3.3.7   Trends in Graphs 202
      3.3.8   Plotting Points on a Graph 203
      3.3.9   Building Pictographs 206
      3.3.10 Building Bar Graphs 209
      3.3.11 Building Line Graphs 213
      3.3.12 Building Scatter Plots 215

3.4 More Graphs **219**
      3.4.1   Reading Circle Graphs 219
      3.4.2   Reading Line Plots 220
      3.4.3   Reading Stem-and-Leaf Plots 222
      3.4.4   Clusters 223
      3.4.5   Gaps 224
      3.4.6   Outliers 225
      3.4.7   Reading Box-and-Whisker Plots 227
      3.4.8   Extremes 229
      3.4.9   Quartiles 230
      3.4.10 Comparing Box-and-Whisker Plots 231
      3.4.11 Building Circle Graphs 232
      3.4.12 Building Line Plots 234
      3.4.13 Building Stem-and-Leaf Plots 235
      3.4.14 Building Box-and-Whisker Plots 237

3.5 Answers to Questions **239**

Chapter 4: Mathematical Relationships

4.1 Ratios and Proportions **265**
      4.1.1   What is a Ratio? 265
      4.1.2   Ratios: Part to Part 266
      4.1.3   Part to Whole 268
      4.1.4   Three-Part Ratios 270
      4.1.5   Four-Part Ratios 271
      4.1.6   Ratios in Lowest Terms 273
      4.1.7   Equivalent Ratios 275
      4.1.8   What is a Proportion? 276
      4.1.9   Setting Up Proportions 278
      4.1.10 Scaling Up 280
      4.1.11 Scaling Down 281
      4.1.12 Cross Multiplying 283
      4.1.13 Ratios to Percents: Proportions 285
      4.1.14 Ratios to Percents: Calculator 286
      4.1.15 Percent of Increase 288

4.2 Number Patterns **290**
    4.2.1   Patterns in Figures 290
    4.2.2   Patterns in Sequences 292
    4.2.3   Patterns in Tables 294

4.3 Variables, Expressions, and Equations **296**
    4.3.1   Solving for Unknowns 296
    4.3.2   Evaluating Expressions 298
    4.3.3   Recognizing Equivalent Expressions 299
    4.3.4   Understanding Equations 301
    4.3.5   Manipulating Equations 303
    4.3.6   Evaluating Equations with Variables 305
    4.3.7   Exponents 307

4.4 Answers to Questions **308**

Chapter 5: Geometry and Measurement

5.1 Lines and Angles **327**
    5.1.1   Measuring Angles 327
    5.1.2   Classifying Angles 329
    5.1.3   Angle Relationships 331
    5.1.4   Familiar Angles 335
    5.1.5   Estimating Angles 337
    5.1.6   Classifying Triangles 339

5.2 Two-Dimensional and Three-Dimensional Figures **342**
    5.2.1   Polygons 342
    5.2.2   What is a Cone? 350
    5.2.3   What is a Cylinder? 351
    5.2.4   What is a Prism? 352
    5.2.5   What is a Pyramid? 353
    5.2.6   What is a Transformation? 354

5.3 Measurement and Perimeter **358**
    5.3.1   Units of Measure 358
    5.3.2   Standard Units of Measure 359
    5.3.3   Metric Units of Measure 361
    5.3.4   Converting Measures 363
    5.3.5   Perimeter 364
    5.3.6   Circumference 366
    5.3.7   Understanding Scale Factors 367

5.4 Area, Volume, and Surface Area **369**
    5.4.1   Square Units 369
    5.4.2   Understanding Area 370
    5.4.3   Area of a Rectangle 371
    5.4.4   Area of a Square 372
    5.4.5   Area of a Triangle 373
    5.4.6   Area of a Circle 374
    5.4.7   Understanding Surface Area 375
    5.4.8   Surface Area of a Rectangular Prism 376
    5.4.9   Surface Area of a Triangular Prism 378

5.4.10 Surface Area of a Cylinder 379
5.4.11 Cubic Units 381
5.4.12 Understanding Volume 382
5.4.13 Volume of a Rectangular Prism 383
5.4.14 Volume of a Triangular Prism 386
5.4.15 Volume of a Cylinder 388

5.5 Answers to Questions 390

Chapter 6: Logical Reasoning

6.1 Logic Term: *all* 408

6.2 Logic Term: *some* 410

6.3 Logic Term: *no/none* 412

6.4 Logic Term: *and* 414

6.5 Logic Term: *or* 416

6.6 Logic Terms: *if* and *then* 419

6.7 Venn Diagrams 422

6.8 Deductive Reasoning 423

6.9 Inductive Reasoning 425

6.10 Answers to Questions 426

Glossary 435

Index 447

How to Use This Handbook

The LearningPlus® Mathematics Handbook will help you learn and apply the basic mathematics skills you will need to succeed in college and in the workplace. You can use this handbook for guidance and additional practice as you complete the LearningPlus Mathematics Course. You can also use this handbook as an independent study guide to supplement other mathematics courses or activities.

Here is what you will learn in each chapter.

LearningPlus

LearningPlus is a computer-based instructional program available at many institutions. For more information about this course, refer to the inside back cover of this handbook.

Chapter 1: Mathematical Power	This chapter provides hints for using the calculator and applying estimation and problem-solving strategies.
Chapter 2: Number Sense and Operations	This chapter helps you understand and use numbers and their properties, including integers, fractions, decimals, and percents. It also helps you interpret and use equivalent forms of numbers.
Chapter 3: Data Comprehension	This chapter helps you understand, interpret, and create tables, graphs, and other data representations. It also teaches you about basic concepts of statistics, such as average, median, mode, and range.
Chapter 4: Mathematical Relationships	This chapter helps you experience and understand basic mathematical relationships by using ratios and proportions, identifying mathematical patterns, and exploring variables, expressions, and equations.
Chapter 5: Geometry and Measurement	This chapter helps you understand and use basic principles of geometry relating to lines, angles, and two- and three-dimensional figures. It also helps you explore and apply measurement concepts, including perimeter, area, volume, and surface area.
Chapter 6: Logical Reasoning	This chapter helps you learn about using logical language, Venn diagrams, deductive reasoning, and inductive reasoning.

To use the LearningPlus Mathematics Handbook effectively, follow the steps listed below.

1. Follow the numbers.

Like many handbooks, this book uses numbers to refer to chapters, sections, and subsections. For example, 3.1 refers to chapter 3, section 1. The chapters and sections are arranged in a logical sequence so you can progress from one to the next. There are also times when it makes sense to quickly refer back or ahead to other sections. When this happens, you will find the numbers useful to locate these sections.

2. Read the instruction and examples.

Each section of this handbook contains a lesson. The lesson explains a concept or skill, then shows examples. Read this information carefully before checking your understanding.

3. Refer to definitions and related topics.

Watch for definitions of critical terms in the margins. You can also look up definitions in the glossary or find terms listed in the index at the end of this handbook. In addition, some sections list topics that are related to the section. Refer to these related handbook sections for review or further information.

4. Check your understanding.

You'll find a set of questions at the end of almost every handbook section. Answer these questions to see how well you understand the explanations and examples.

5. Look up the answers and explanations.

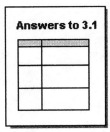

After you answer each set of questions, look in the *Answers to Questions* section at the end of the chapter. This section not only shows the answers, but also provides explanations that will help you understand the concepts better.

To locate the answers to a particular set of questions, look for the number listed above the questions. This number is the same as the section number, except that it may be followed by an *a* or *b* if there is more than one set of problems in the handbook section.

For example, if you finish the questions for section 3.1 and wish to check your answers, look under *Answers to 3.1* in the *Answers to Questions* section at the end of Chapter 3.

Chapter 1

Mathematical Power

1.1 Estimation and Calculator Use...2

    1.1.1 Using Estimation 2
    1.1.2 Using the Calculator... 11

1.2 Communication and Problem Solving 14

    1.2.1 Characteristics of Good Problem Solvers 14
    1.2.2 Problem-Solving Strategies................................... 15

1. 3 Answers to Questions 16

Learn how to use estimation, calculators, and problem-solving strategies to increase your mathematical power.

1.1 Estimation and Calculator Use

1.1.1 Using Estimation

calculate

Use mathematical operations to determine an answer to a problem.

When solving problems, it is often valuable to *estimate* an answer before you **calculate**. An estimate can be a **single value** or a **range** of values. The numbers you use to get an estimate should be easy to work with, because they are used to quickly check the reasonableness of calculated answers.

single value

A single value is one number. The single value of the expression 3 + 2 is the answer that you calculate, 5.

Example

To estimate the **product** of 313 x 12, first write the numbers in the problem as numbers that are easy to work with, then solve.

313 x 12 is about 300 x 10 or 3,000

range (as a group)

Range is *a group of numbers or values* that are defined by a high number and a low number. (To estimate 47 x 23 think:
45 x 20 = 900 and
50 x 25 = 1250, so
47 x 23 is in the range 900 — 1250.)

Estimates are also used when exact answers cannot be found. Estimates are often signaled by a word or words, or by the use of numbers that are not exact but that are meaningful.

Example

When you read the statement "there were **about 30** people at the party," the word "about" signals that the number is an estimate. The number "30" is meaningful because a party of about 30 people is easy to picture.

Here are some other words used to signal estimates:

almost	less than
approximately	nearly
at least	more than
between	perhaps
close to	roughly
just about	some

There are many strategies that can be used to estimate. Refer to the sections that follow to learn about the estimation strategies listed below.

> **Topics Related to:** Using Estimation
>
> 1.1.1.1 Estimation by Rounding
> 1.1.1.2 Estimation by Clustering
> 1.1.1.3 Estimation by Using Compatible Numbers
> 1.1.1.4 Estimation by Using Front-End Numbers

 Check Your Understanding 1.1.1a

In each of the following statements, a word or phrase signals that an estimate is being made. Underline (__) the signal word or phrase in each sentence.

Questions
1. ... making it roughly 100 times more acidic
2. ... have increased nearly tenfold
3. ... a crater more than 60 miles across
4. ... about the size of a sesame seed
5. ... to a rate at least 60 percent slower
6. ... the names of approximately 3,600 places
7. ... a temperature of almost 102°
8. ... between 10 billion and 100 billion paint chips
9. ... risk is perhaps 1 in 500
10. ... some four million visitors

Check Your Understanding 1.1.1b

Decide whether or not each of the following sentences describes an estimate. Put a check (✓) next to the correct answers in the answer column.

Question	Answer
1. Your chances of winning that lottery are one in a million.	✓ estimate ✓ not an estimate
2. One wrench and one toothbrush are in orbit around the Earth.	✓ estimate ✓ not an estimate
3. In 1989 the national debt was nearly $3 trillion.	✓ estimate ___ not an estimate
4. And the number on the winning ticket is close to 1,500!	✓ estimate ___ not an estimate
5. About half the class will be at the reunion.	✓ estimate ___ not an estimate

1.1.1.1 Estimation by Rounding

One way to estimate the answer to a problem is to **round** the numbers so they are easy to work with, and then solve using the rounded numbers. The estimate can be used to check that a calculated answer seems reasonable.

round
Rounding is a way to write complex numbers in a simple form so they are easier to work with. To estimate the answer to 3,983,423 x 6 = ? round the numbers to about 4,000,000 x 5. The answer is about 20,000,000.

 Example

To estimate the **quotient** 587 ÷ 8, first round the numbers so they are easy to work with (600 and 10 would work well), and then solve.

587 ÷ 8 = about 600 ÷ 10 = about 60

---

quotient
A quotient is the answer to a division problem. For example, 7 is the quotient of 35 and 5: 35 ÷ 5 = 7.

 Check Your Understanding 1.1.1.1

Put a check (✓) next to the correct answers in the answer column.

Question	Answer
1. Which expression is easiest to work with when estimating 4,875 + 7,217?	____ 4,880 + 7,220 ____ 4,900 + 7,200 ✗ ✓ 5,000 + 7,000
2. Which expression is easiest to work with when estimating 9,542,116 - 6,712,410?	✓ 10 million - 7 million ____ 9,500,000 - 6,700,000 ____ 9.5 million - 6.7 million
3. Which expression is easiest to work with when estimating $5,936 x 93?	____ $5.9 thousand x 90 ____ $5,900 x 90 ✓ $6,000 x 100
4. Which expression is easiest to work with when estimating 7,253 ÷ 954?	____ 7,200 ÷ 950 ✓ 7,200 ÷ 900 ____ 7,000 ÷ 900

1.1.1.2 Estimation by Clustering

Clustering is an effective estimation strategy to use when you are finding the **sum** of many numbers that are all close to a common value. To use this strategy, determine a number that all the numbers cluster around. The number should also be easy to work with.

sum

A sum is the result of the addition of two or more numbers or quantities. For example, the sum of 3 and 5 is 8.

 **Example**

You can use clustering to add these numbers:

$$83 + 63 + 61 + 70 + 73 + 69 + 79 + 80 + 71 = ?$$

First find a number that all the numbers cluster around. The number should be one that is easy to work with. A good number would be 70. Think of the equation as:

$$70 + 70 + 70 + 70 + 70 + 70 + 70 + 70 + 70 = 9 \times 70 = 630$$

 Check Your Understanding 1.1.1.2

Put a check (✓) next to the correct answers in the answer column.

Question	Answer
1. What number do the numbers in this expression cluster around? $443 + 359 + 475 + 320 + 502 + 420 = ?$	✓ 300 ✓ 400 ___ 500
2. What number do the numbers in this expression cluster around? $61 + 60 + 58 + 71 + 62 + 55 + 80 = ?$	___ 60 ✓ 70 ___ 80
3. Which expression is the best estimate of the following? $546 + 497 + 502 + 458 + 555 = ?$	___ 4 x 500 ✓ 5 x 400 ✓ 5 x 500

4. Which expression is the best estimate of the following? 1,150 + 1,223 + 1,198 + 1,276 + 1,157 = ?	___ 5 x 1,100 ___ 5 x 1,150 5 x 1,200

1.1.1.3 Estimation by Using Compatible Numbers

To estimate using the *compatible numbers* strategy, pair or group numbers that are easy to work with mentally.

Finding compatible numbers is a good estimation strategy when looking for a **sum** or **product**.

sum

A sum is the result of the addition of two or more numbers or quantities. For example, the sum of 3 and 5 is 8.

product

A product is the result of multiplying numbers.

✏️ *Example*

Compatible numbers can be used to find this sum.

34 + 46 + 23 + 41 + 51

Two groups of numbers can be made from the expression:

(34 + 23 + 41) and (46 + 51)

Each group's sum is about 100; so the answer is about 2 x 100, or about 200.

 Check Your Understanding 1.1.1.3

Put a check (✓) next to the correct answers in the answer column.

Question	Answer
1. Which of the following shows compatible numbers grouped for this sum? 23 + 48 + 96 + 27 = ?	___ (23 + 96) and (48 + 27) ___ (23 + 27) and (48 + 96) ✓ (23 + 27 + 48) and (96)
2. Which of the following shows compatible numbers grouped for this sum? 254 + 456 + 52 + 238 = ?	✓ (254 + 238) and (456 + 52) ___ (254 + 52) and (238 + 456) ___ (254 + 238 + 52) and (456)

3. Which of the following shows compatible numbers grouped for this product? 23 x 2 x 48 x 4 = ?	___ (2 x 23) and (4 x 48) ___ (2 x 4 x 23) and (48) ✓ (4 x 23) and (2 x 48)
4. Which of the following shows compatible numbers grouped for this product? 6 x 31 x 3 x 9 x 5 = ?	___ (6 x 31), (3 x 9) and (5) ✓ (6 x 5), (3 x 9) and (31) ___ (5 x 9), (3 x 6) and (31)

clustering

Clustering is an estimation strategy that finds a number all the numbers in a mathematics problem are close to in value. It is a good estimation strategy when adding long lists of numbers.

rounding

Rounding is a way to write complex numbers in a simple form so they are easier to work with. To estimate the answer to 3,983,423 x 6 = ? round the numbers to about 4,000,000 x 5. The answer is about 20,000,000.

compatible numbers

Compatible numbers are numbers that are easy to work with mentally. Compatible numbers can be number groupings that allow you to estimate an answer quickly. For example, in the expression 23 + 72 + 54 + 46, the compatible number groups are (23, 72) and (54,46). The value of each group is *about* 100, so the answer is *about* 100 x 2, or about 200.

1.1.1.4 Estimation by Using Front-End Numbers

The strategy that uses *front-end numbers* and adjustment to estimate is often used to find a more accurate estimate than could be found by **clustering**, **rounding**, or using **compatible numbers**.

The front-end strategy focuses on the first digit of a number or numbers and then requires an adjustment to the remaining numbers to arrive at the final answer.

 *Example*

The front-end strategy can be used to find an estimate for the product:

2,345 x 9 = ?

1. Multiply the front-end number (or first digit) of 2,345 times 9, then use rounding to adjust the remaining numbers:

2,000 x 9 = 18,000
345 x 9 = about 350 x 10 = 3,500

2. Add the front-end calculation to the adjustment calculation:

18,000 + 3,500 = 21,500

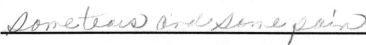

📝 *Example*

The front-end strategy can be used when adding amounts of money:

$$\$4.57 + \$23.45 + \$12.30 + \$3.65$$

1. Find the sum of the front-end numbers:

$$\$4 + \$23 + \$12 + \$3 = \$42$$

2. Use compatible numbers to find the sum of the cents:

$$(0.57 + 0.45) \text{ and } (0.30 + 0.65)$$

   Each compatible group has a value of about $1, so the value of the cents is about 2 x $1, or $2.

3. Add the front-end calculation to the adjustment calculation to determine the estimate:

$$\$42 + \$2 = \$44.$$

✔ **Check Your Understanding 1.1.1.4**

Put a check (✓) next to the correct answers in the answer column.

Question	Answer
1. Which expression uses the *front-end* strategy to estimate this sum? 321 + 235 + 456 + 763 =?	✓ (300 + 200 + 400 + 700) + (20 + 40) + 60 + 60 ___ (320 + 240 + 460 + 750) ___ (320 + 240 + 460 + 750) + (1 + 5 + 6 + 3)
2. Which expression uses the *front-end* strategy to estimate this sum? $17.52 + $11.19 + $3.53 + $6.84 = ?	___ ($17 + $11 + $3 + $6) + (0.52 + 0.19 + 0.53 + 0.84) ✓ ($17 + $11 + $3 + $6) + (0.80 + 0.20) + (0.50 + 0.50) ___ ($17 + $11 + $3 + $6)

3. Which expression uses the *front-end* strategy to estimate this product? 7,689 x 7 = ?	___ (7,600 x 7) + (50 x 7) ✓ (7,000 x 7) + (700 x 7) ___ (7,000 x 7) + (690 x 7)
4. Which expression uses the *front-end* strategy to estimate this product? $3.75 x 21 = ?	✓ (20 x $3) + (20 x 0.80) ___ (20 x $3.70) + (20 x 0.05) ___ 20 x $4

From the preceding examples, you can see that estimation strategies can be combined in many ways to estimate an answer.

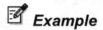 **Example**

Notice the different ways you can estimate the answer to this expression:

$$\$23.46 + \$30.45 + \$32.57 + \$19.54$$

Rounding:

You could round each dollar amount, then add. $23.46 + $30.45 + $32.57 + $19.54 = about 23 + 30 + 33 + 20 = about $106.

Clustering:

You could use clustering to find the value of groups of numbers in the expression. The numbers cluster around the value $25. The answer is about 4 x $25, or $100.

Compatible Numbers:

You could separate the numbers into two groups: (23.46 + 30.45) and (32.57 + 19.54). Each group has a sum of about $50, so the answer is about 2 x $50, or about $100.

Front-end Numbers:

First, add the front-end numbers: 23 + 30 + 32 + 19 = $104. Then use clustering to find the cents. The cents cluster around $0.50: About 4 x $0.50 = about $2. Add the front-end calculation and the adjustment calculation. The estimate is about $104 + $2, or about $106.

1.1.2 Using the Calculator

The *calculator* makes tedious computations easy. It can be used to perform basic mathematical operations involving numbers that seem difficult to compute.

Important keys on the calculator are:

Key	Function
+	addition
-	subtraction
x	multiplication
÷	division
=	equals
C	clear the calculator display
CE	clear the last entry
+/-	change between positive and negative
√	find square root

To perform a **single operation** (+, -, x, or ÷) using the calculator, enter the numbers and the operation in the order shown in the expression.

📝 Example

To complete this calculation using the calculator, follow these steps.

7,345 ÷ 56 = ?

1. Enter the number 7,345 by pressing the key for each digit.

2. Press the divide (÷) key.

3. Enter 56 by pressing the key for each digit.

4. Press the equals (=) key.

Depending on the how the calculator you are using is designed to work, your answer may be rounded or truncated (end digits cut off). Some calculators are designed to show only two digits after the decimal point. Others might show many more. For instance, when you use the calculator to complete this computation:

$$7,345 \div 56,$$

you might get 131.16 or 131.1607142857 as an answer. **You** must do the **rounding** required by a problem.

 Check Your Understanding 1.1.2a

Use a calculator to complete the calculations below. Write your answers in the answer column. **Round** your answers to two decimal places.

rules for rounding

Look at the digit to the right of the decimal place you want to round to. For example, to round the number below to two decimal places, look at the digit in the third decimal place.

1.1295337
↑
third decimal place

- If the digit is less than 5, leave the preceding digit as it is.
- If the digit is equal to or greater than 5, round the preceding digit up.
- If the digit is greater than 5, round the preceding digit up.

Question	Answer
1. 952 + 329 = ?	
2. 672.368 - 415.215 = ?	
3. $493.56 x 32 = ?	
4. 9,426 ÷ 29 = ?	

Sometimes you will need to use the calculator to perform a **series of operations**.

$$\$376 \times 15 + \$822 \div 6 = ?$$

▶ When you perform a **series of operations**, you should multiply and divide numbers before you add and subtract.

Many calculators will automatically perform the calculations in the correct order. You simply enter the numbers and operations in the order shown and then press the equals (=) key. The calculator used in the LearningPlus Mathematics Course works this way. Some calculators are not designed to work this way, however. You must multiply and divide first, jot down your intermediate answers, and then enter the numbers and add or subtract. When you use this second type of calculator, you must make sure you do your calculations in the right order or you will get the wrong answer.

series of operations

Using more than one operation to find an answer, such as adding, subtracting, multiplying, or dividing.

▶ Make sure you know which type of calculator you are using: one that automatically performs operations in the correct order, or one that doesn't. You can make up an easy test and try it on the calculator you are using so you will know how your calculator handles the **order of operations**.

✎ *Example*

To test your calculator, follow these steps:

1. Make up an easy problem that uses a series of operations. (You must use an expression that shows at least one addition or subtraction sign before a multiplication or division sign.)

    $$2 \times 3 + 4 \times 5 = ?$$

2. Complete the problem in your head or on paper by performing the operations in the correct order. In this case, you multiply first and then add the two products.

    $$2 \times 3 + 4 \times 5 = ?$$
    $$\downarrow \qquad \downarrow$$
    $$6 \ + \ 20 \ = \ 26$$

3. Next, complete the same series of operations using your calculator. Enter each number and operation in the order shown and then press the equals (=) key. Compare your answer with the one you got in step 2.

    For instance, if your calculator showed 50 for the expression above, you know your calculator doesn't automatically do the calculations in the correct order. You'll have to make sure and do this. In this case you would:

    *   Use the calculator to multiply 2 x 3.
    *   Jot down your answer (6).
    *   Use the calculator to multiply 4 x 5.
    *   After the product 20 appears, press the + key.
    *   Enter the first product (6).
    *   Then press on **equals** (=) to get your answer (26).

 Check Your Understanding 1.1.2b

Use a calculator to complete the calculations below. Write your answers in the answer column. **Round** your answers to two decimal places.

Question	Answer
1. $517.24 x 15 + $362.46 x 12 = ?	
2. 372 - 178 ÷ 7 = ?	

1.2 Communication and Problem Solving

1.2.1 Characteristics of Good Problem Solvers

We are all *problem solvers,* but it takes practice to become good mathematical problem solvers. To become a good problem solver, keep these hints in mind:

▶ **Take your time.** Read the problem carefully and connect it to any accompanying diagrams. If necessary, read a problem two or three times; identify important information; weed out unnecessary information; and put the problem in your own words. Ask how you can use what you are given to find a solution.

▶ **Use Resources.** If you need a formula, definition, or procedure, look it up. In the LearningPlus Mathematics Course, use the Handbook to review basic mathematics; then check your understanding.

▶ **Become familiar with a variety of problem-solving strategies**. Strategies are procedures such as identifying important information, drawing a diagram, estimating, setting up a proportion, breaking into subproblems, comparing with a simpler problem, guessing and testing, and working backwards.

▶ **Always check your work.** When you think you have a solution, go over your calculations to make sure you didn't make any mistakes. Use estimation to check the reasonableness of your work.

▶ **Be confident.** There are many approaches to solving a problem. If your approach leads to a solution, it is just as valid as one that someone else uses.

▶ **Keep trying.** You may need to try more than one approach before you find one that works for you. In the LearningPlus Mathematics Course, use **Clues** and **Strategies** to see hints that will help you with the problem.

 Check Your Understanding 1.2.1

Put a check (✓) next to the correct answers in the answer column.

Question	Answer
1. Ralph needs to know how to find a common denominator to solve the problem he's working on. He's forgotten how. What should he do?	___ Take more time to read the problem again. ___ Use a resource. ___ Check his work.

<table>
<tr>
<td>2. Karen was confident she knew how to solve a problem. But after she finished, she found out her answer was wrong. What should she do first?</td>
<td>

___ Use a resource.

___ Check her work.

___ Find other problem-solving strategies.

</td>
</tr>
</table>

1.2.2 Problem-Solving Strategies

Good problem solvers have learned to use several problem-solving *strategies*. Any one problem-solving strategy can be used in many different situations; however, not every strategy will help with every problem.

Some widely used and easy-to-learn strategies are listed below. As you complete the LearningPlus "Using" lessons on the computer, these and other problem-solving strategies will be used to help guide you through one solution path to the problems.

▶ **Understand the Problem.** To use this strategy, do the following:

- Carefully read the problem. Highlight or write down the given information that will help you solve the problem.

- Cross out information that won't help you solve the problem.

- Look at diagrams and tables. They contain information that will help solve the problem.

- Put the problem in your own words using only the necessary information.

▶ **Understand the Concepts.** Check your understanding of concepts or formulas used in the problem. Look them up in the Handbook. Learn all you can about them. As you do this, you may see a way to start solving the problem.

▶ **Solve a Simpler Problem.** Many problems are easier to solve if you see them as several simpler problems.

▶ **Draw a Diagram.** Geometry problems and reasoning problems are often easier to solve if you draw a picture of what you are given, and use the picture to think about what you must find.

▶ **Organize Information.** Some problems contain data. Organizing the data into a list or table may help you solve the problem.

▶ **Use a Formula or a Mathematics Sentence.** To solve some mathematics problems, you will need to write and solve a mathematics sentence or use a formula. When you use this strategy, you practice translating words into mathematical statements.

▶ **Use Logical Reasoning.** Most mathematics problems will require you to think logically. Real problem solving requires more thinking than calculation! As you use logical reasoning, you may decide that you need to use a proportion, work backwards, or use a guess-and-check approach.

▶ **Check Your Work.** Use this strategy on every mathematics problem that you solve. Double-check all calculations, and use estimation to check the reasonableness of your answer. Always ask yourself, "Could this be the answer to the problem?"

1. 3 Answers to Questions

Answers to 1.1.1a

Correct Answer
1. ... making it **roughly** 100 times more acidic
2. ... have increased **nearly** tenfold
3. ... a crater **more than** 60 miles across
4. ... **about** the size of a sesame seed
5. ... to a rate **at least** 60 percent slower
6. ... the names of **approximately** 3,600 places
7. ... a temperature of **almost** 102°
8. ... **between** 10 billion and 100 billion paint chips
9. ... risk is **perhaps** 1 in 500
10. ... **some** four million visitors

Answers to 1.1.1b

Correct Answer	Explanation
1. estimate	This statement describes your chances as "one in a million." This must be an estimate because there is no way of knowing ahead of time what will happen.
2. not an estimate	This statement states exact amounts ("one wrench and one toothbrush"). So it is not an estimate.
3. estimate	There's no way to know exactly what the national debt is at any given time, so "nearly a trillion dollars" reflects the fact that this must be an estimate.
4. estimate	This statement says "close to 1,500." So, it must be an estimate.
5. estimate	This statement refers to "about half the class." This means it is an estimate.

Answers to 1.1.1.1

Correct Answer	Explanation
1. 5,000 + 7,000	It's easiest to add numbers when you only have to add the first digits. You can easily do this calculation mentally.
2. 10 million - 7 million	It's easiest to work with 7 and 10 mentally. You don't have to worry about zeros and decimal places, either.
3. $6,000 x 100	Using this expression, all you have to do is add two zeros to $6,000 to get your estimate ($600,000).
4. 7,200 ÷ 900	Since you already know 9 x 8 = 72, this expression will be easiest to make your estimate. You can do the calculation in your head.

Answers to 1.1.1.2

Correct Answer	Explanation
1. 400	Most numbers in this expression are close to 400. One number, 320, is a bit low, but there is also another number in the set, 502, that's a bit high. So 400 is the best number to use.
2. 60	Most numbers cluster near 60 (61, 60, 58, 62). There are two other numbers above this mark (71 and 80), but there is also a number considerably below 60 (55). So, 60 still appears to be the best number.
3. 5 x 500	The numbers cluster around 500 and there are five numbers.
4. 5 x 1,200	The numbers cluster around 1,200, and there are five numbers. Also, it's easy to do this calculation in your head (you already know what 5 x 12 equals).

Answers to 1.1.1.3

Correct Answer	Explanation
1. (23 + 27 + 48) and (96)	The first set of numbers (23 + 27 + 48) equal about 100 and (96) is about 100. So, the estimate is 2 x 100, or 200.
2. (254 + 238) and (456 + 52)	Both sums are about 500. So, the estimate is 2 x 500, or 1,000.
3. (4 x 23) and (2 x 48)	Both products are about 100. So, the estimate is 100 x 100, or 10,000.
4. (6 x 5), (3 x 9) and (31)	The two products are about 30, and 31 is about 30. So, the estimate is 30 x 30 x 30, or 27,000.

Answers to 1.1.1.4

Correct Answer	Explanation
1. (300 + 200 + 400 + 700) + (20 + 40) + 60 + 60	The sum of the front-end numbers is 1,600. Using the compatible numbers strategy to figure the adjustment calculation, you can see that the last two digits of each number can be rounded and grouped to get 3 x 60, or 180. 1,600 + 180 = 1,780
2. ($17 + $11 + $3 + $6) + (0.80 + 0.20) + (0.50 + 0.50)	The sum of the front-end numbers is $37. Using the compatible numbers strategy to figure the adjustment calculation, you can see that the last two digits of each amount can be rounded and grouped to get 2 x $1, or $2. $37 + $2 = $39
3. (7,000 x 7) + (7 x 700)	The product of the front-end numbers is 49,000. By rounding the last three digits and multiplying, you get the adjustment amount (4,900). 49,000 + 4,900 = 53,900
4. (20 x $3) + (20 x 0.80)	The product of the front-end numbers is $60. By rounding the cents and multiplying, you get the adjustment amount ($16). $60 + $16 = $76

Answers to 1.1.2a

Correct Answer	Explanation
1. 1,281	Enter the numbers and operation in the order shown and then click on equals (=).
2. 257.15	In the calculator display you see 257.153. The digit after the 5 is 3, so you round down to get 257.15.

3. $15,793.92	Enter the numbers and operation in the order shown and then click on equals (=).
4. 325.03	Your calculator may have given you an answer with this many decimal places: 325.0344827586. To round your answer look at the digit in the third decimal place. It's 4. This is less than 5, so you round down.

Answers to 1.1.2b

Correct Answer	Explanation
1. $12,108.12	If you did not get this answer, do the problem again on your calculator. If you still got a different answer (for example, $97,452.72), your calculator probably does <u>not</u> perform the correct order of operations for you. You'll need to calculate both products first, jot them down, and then add these two products on the calculator.
2. 346.57	If you did not get this answer, do the problem again on your calculator. If you still got a different answer (for example, 27.71), your calculator probably does <u>not</u> perform the correct order of operations for you. You'll need to divide first (178 ÷ 7 = 25.43) and then subtract the quotient from 372.

Answers to 1.2.1

Correct Answer	Explanation
1. Use a resource.	Ralph could refer to a math handbook or math textbook to review how to find common denominators.
2. Check her work.	The first thing Karen should usually do when she gets a wrong answer is to check carefully over her work to make sure that she didn't make any mistakes in her calculations. If that doesn't seem to be the problem, then she might want to look for other ways to solve the problem.

Chapter 2

Number Sense and Operations

2.1 Integers 23

    2.1.1   Place Value 23

    2.1.2   Magnitude 23

    2.1.3   Understanding Negative Numbers 24

    2.1.4   Adding Negative Numbers 26

    2.1.5   Subtracting Negative Numbers 27

    2.1.6   Multiplying and Dividing Negative Numbers 28

    2.1.7   Divisibility Tests 30

    2.1.8   Factors 36

    2.1.9   Multiples 37

    2.1.10 Prime Numbers 39

    2.1.11 Composite Numbers 40

    2.1.12 Factoring 41

    2.1.13 Prime Factorization 42

    2.1.14 Greatest Common Factors 44

    2.1.15 Adding with Odd and Even Numbers 46

    2.1.16 Multiplying with Odd and Even Numbers 47

    2.1.17 Understanding Clock Arithmetic 48

    2.1.18 Congruence in Clock Arithmetic 49

    2.1.19 Adding in Clock Arithmetic 51

    2.1.20 Subtracting in Clock Arithmetic 53

    2.1.21 Multiplying in Clock Arithmetic 54

2.2 Fractions 56

    2.2.1   Fractions as Part of a Whole 56

    2.2.2   Equivalent Fractions 57

    2.2.3   Scaling Up Fractions 58

    2.2.4   Scaling Down Fractions 60

    2.2.5   Fractions in Lowest Terms 61

    2.2.6   Common Denominators 62

    2.2.7   Mixed Numbers 64

    2.2.8   Improper Fractions 66

    2.2.9   Comparing Fractions to 1 67

    2.2.10 Comparing Fractions to Fractions 68

    2.2.11 Estimating Equivalent Fractions 74

    2.2.12 Adding and Subtracting Fractions 76

    2.2.13 Multiplying Fractions 79

    2.2.14 Dividing Fractions 81

2.3 Decimals 83

    2.3.1 Decimal Numbers 83
    2.3.2 Place Value and Decimals 84
    2.3.3 Ordering Decimals 85
    2.3.4 Rounding Decimals 87
    2.3.5 Adding and Subtracting Decimals 89
    2.3.6 Multiplying Decimals 91
    2.3.7 Dividing Decimals 93
    2.3.8 Fraction/Decimal Equivalence 94

2.4 Percents 98

    2.4.1 Meaning of Percent 98
    2.4.2 Percent as Part of a Whole 99
    2.4.3 Expressing Percents as Fractions 101
    2.4.4 Fraction/Percent Equivalence 103
    2.4.5 Decimal/Percent Equivalence 107
    2.4.6 Percents Greater Than 100% 109
    2.4.7 Percents Less Than 1% 110
    2.4.8 Calculating Percents 113
    2.4.9 Rounding Percents 115
    2.4.10 Calculations Using Percents 117
    2.4.11 Estimating Percents: Calculations 119
    2.4.12 Estimating Percents: Common Sense 121
    2.4.13 Percent Increase 123
    2.4.14 Percent Decrease 125
    2.4.15 Percents and Circle Graphs 127

2.5 Answers to Questions 130

Improve your number sense by learning about integers, fractions, decimals, and percents, and how they relate to one another.

2.1 Integers

2.1.1 Place Value

In any number, every **digit** has a *value* based on the *place* it holds. In the number 521, the digit five represents 500 (not 5 or 50), because it is in the hundreds place. This chart shows the place values from ones to millions.

digit

Any one of the 10 counting numbers: 0, 1, 2, 3, 4, 5, 6, 7, 8, 9. All rational numbers are expressed using one or more of these digits.

millions	hundred thousands	ten thousands	thousands	hundreds	tens	ones
1,000,000	100,000	10,000	1,000	100	10	1

 Check Your Understanding 2.1.1

Put a check (✓) next to the correct answers in the answer column.

Question	Answer
1. In the number 6,329, what does the digit two represent?	___ 2000 ___ 200 ___ 20 ✓ ___ 2
2. If a building contractor says the cost of finishing a building will reach a seven-digit figure, what is the least it could cost?	___ ten thousand dollars ___ one hundred thousand dollars ___ one million dollars

2.1.2 Magnitude

The *magnitude* of a number is its distance from 0. This means that -3 and 3 have the same magnitudes.

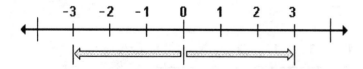

-3 is less than 3, but both numbers are the same distance from 0.

Check Your Understanding 2.1.2

Put a check (✓) next to the correct answers in the answer column.

Question	Answer
1. Which of these numbers has greater magnitude?	___ 99 ___ -121
2. Which of these numbers has the greatest magnitude?	___ 36 ___ 457 ___ -420 ___ -2
3. Which of these numbers has less magnitude?	___ 14 ___ -13
4. Which of these numbers has the least magnitude?	___ 77 ___ -1,327 ___ -390 ___ 245

Topics Related to: Magnitude

2.1.3 Understanding Negative Numbers

2.1.3 Understanding Negative Numbers

negative numbers

Numbers less than zero. Examples of negative numbers are: -5, -160, -0.23, and -1/2.

positive numbers

Numbers greater than zero. Examples of positive numbers are: 5, 160, 0.23, and 1/2

Negative numbers are the *opposite* of **positive numbers**. They are written with a negative (-) sign.

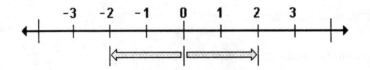

▶ This number line shows the *opposite* numbers 2 and -2. Note that they are an equal distance from 0: 2 is 2 units more than 0 and -2 is 2 units less than 0.

▶ What do you think -(-2) means? The (-) sign implies taking the opposite of the number it precedes. So -(-2) is the opposite of -2 which is +2 or simply 2.

▶ Negative numbers can be used to represent:

- temperatures lower than 0
- checkbook balances lower than 0
- stock market losses
- altitudes below sea level

▶ There are some applications where negative numbers do not make sense. They include:

- distance
- length
- weight

 Check Your Understanding 2.1.3

Put a check (✓) next to the correct answers in the answer column.

Question	Answer
1. Which pairs are *opposites*?	____ -8, 8 ____ -(-8), -8 ____ -(-(-8)), 8 ____ -(-(8)), 8
2. Which pairs are *opposites*?	____ -(-35), 35 ____ -(-35), -35 ____ -(-(-(-35))), -35 ____ -(-(-35)), 35
3. Which pairs are the *same*?	____ -(-13), 13 ____ -(-(13)), -13 ____ -(-(-13)), -13 ____ -(-(-13)), 13

2.1.4 Adding Negative Numbers

Think of adding **positive numbers**.

$$3 + 4 = 7$$

positive numbers

Numbers greater than zero. Examples of positive numbers are: 5, 160, 0.23, and 1/2.

You can think of adding **negative numbers** in the same way.

$$-3 + -4 = -7$$

negative numbers

Numbers less than zero. Examples of negative numbers are: -5, -160, -0.23, and -1/2.

If you're adding a positive number to a negative number, imagine that one (+) cancels one (-). What's left is the sign of the sum.

$$3 + -4 = -1$$

 Check Your Understanding 2.1.4

Put a check (✓) next to the correct answers in the answer column.

Question	Answer
1. Which expression adds up to 18?	___ -30 + (-8) ___ -15 + (-3) ___ 24 + (-6)
2. Which expression adds up to -23?	___ -7 + (-16) ___ -14 + 37 ___ 31 + (-8)

Topics Related to: Adding Negative Numbers

2.1.3 Understanding Negative Numbers

2.1.5 Subtracting Negative Numbers

Since **negative numbers** are the opposite of **positive numbers**, operations with negative numbers are the opposite of what you would expect with positive numbers. Use this idea to subtract negative numbers.

4 - 3   is the same as   4 + (-3)

4 - (-3)   is the same as   4 + 3

 *Rule*

One rule for subtracting negative numbers is **"change the sign and add."**

 *Example*

To compute:

-5 - 6

change the sign and add:

-5 + (-6) = -11

 Check Your Understanding 2.1.5

Put a check (✓) next to the correct answers in the answer column.

Question	Answer
1. Which expression has a **difference** of 13?	___ -7 - 6 ___ 4 - 17 ___ -7 - (-20)
2. Which expression has a difference of -27?	___ -13 - (-39) ___ 9 - 36 ___ 5 - (-32)

difference

The result of subtraction. For example, the difference of 8 - 5 is 3.

2.1.6 Multiplying and Dividing Negative Numbers

positive numbers

Numbers greater than zero.
Examples of positive numbers are:
5, 160, 0.23, and 1/2.

Consider multiplication of **positive numbers**.

$$2 \times 3$$
$$\downarrow$$
$$6$$

Now consider multiplying a positive number by a **negative number**.

$$2 \times -3$$
$$\downarrow$$
$$-(2 \times 3)$$
$$\downarrow$$
$$-6$$

negative numbers

Numbers less than zero.
Examples of negative numbers
are: -5, -160, -0.23, and -1/2.

Finally, think about multiplying two negative numbers.

$$-2 \times -3$$
$$\downarrow$$
$$(-1)(2)(-1)(3)$$
$$\downarrow$$
$$(-1)(-1)(2)(3)$$
$$\downarrow$$
$$--(1)(6)$$
$$\downarrow$$
$$6$$

Rule

Rules you can use to determine the sign of a product when multiplying negative numbers are:

An even number of negative signs will yield a positive number.

An odd number of negative signs will yield a negative number.

The same rules are true for division.

✔ **Check Your Understanding 2.1.6**

Put a check (✓) next to the correct answers in the answer column.

Question	Answer
1. Which expressions yield negative numbers?	___ -49 x 31 ___ -76 x 4 x -6 ___ -325 ÷ -3 ___ -78 ÷ -15 ÷ -7
2. Which expressions yield positive numbers?	___ -8 ÷ -34 ÷ -8 ___ -3527 ÷ -6 ___ -36 x 72 ___ -51 x 5 x -77

Topics Related to: Multiplying and Dividing Negative Numbers

2.1.3 Understanding Negative Numbers

2.1.7 Divisibility Tests

A *divisibility test* is a shortcut for deciding if one **integer** is **divisible** by another. For instance, most people can tell that 16 is divisible by 4 without doing the calculation. But can you tell if 2672 is divisible by 4 without doing the calculation?

divisible

Able to be divided without remainder by another number. For example, 12 is divisible by 6.

Topics Related to: Divisibility Tests

2.1.7.1 Divisibility Test for 2
2.1.7.2 Divisibility Test for 3
2.1.7.3 Divisibility Test for 4
2.1.7.4 Divisibility Test for 5
2.1.7.5 Divisibility Test for 9
2.1.7.6 Divisibility Test for 10

digit

Any one of the 10 counting numbers: 0, 1, 2, 3, 4, 5, 6, 7, 8, 9. All rational numbers are expressed using one or more of these digits.

2.1.7.1 Divisibility Test for 2

> 🖩 *Rule*
>
> Any **even** integer is **divisible** by 2.

In fact, divisibility by 2 is really the definition of an even number. You can identify whether an integer is even or not by just looking at it. The last **digit** of an even number is 0, 2, 4, 6, or 8.

even

An integer that can be divided by 2 without leaving a remainder.

25**4**   1,58**8**   9**2**   12,30**0**   81**6**

These numbers are all even, therefore they are all divisible by 2.

integer

An integer is any number in a set {. . . -3, -2, -1, 0, 1, 2, 3, . . .}. In other words, integers include all whole numbers, their negative opposites, and zero.

 Check Your Understanding 2.1.7.1

Put a check (✓) next to the correct answers in the answer column.

Question	Answer
1. In which series are all the numbers divisible by 2?	___ 44 51 62 138
	___ 142 48 556 874
	___ 992 314 758 21
	___ 448 392 735 286

2. In which series are all the numbers divisible by 2?	___ 876 458 341 968
	___ 124 766 628 533
	___ 228 362 721 486
	___ 556 218 244 972

Topics Related to: Divisibility Test for 2

2.1.7 Divisibility Tests

2.1.7.2 Divisibility Test for 3

> 🏫 *Rule*
>
> Any integer whose **digits** add up to a **multiple** of 3 is **divisible** by 3.

multiple

An integer that is a product of a specific number. For example, 15 is a multiple of 3 because it is a product of 3 and 5.

$$18 \longrightarrow 1 + 8 = 9$$
$$732 \longrightarrow 7 + 3 + 2 = 12$$
$$2{,}583 \longrightarrow 2 + 5 + 8 + 3 = 18$$

These three numbers all have digits whose sums are multiples of 3. Therefore, they are divisible by 3.

 Check Your Understanding 2.1.7.2

Put a check (✓) next to the correct answers in the answer column.

Question	Answer
1. In which series are all the numbers divisible by 3?	___ 42 522 623
	___ 324 48 59
	___ 62 215 531
	___ 621 372 864

2. In which series are all the numbers divisible by 3?	___ 77 282 631
	___ 273 529 342
	___ 873 492 81
	___ 831 966 425

Topics Related to: Divisibility Test for 3

2.1.7 Divisibility Tests

2.1.7.3 Divisibility Test for 4

 Rule

An integer is **divisible** by 4 if its last two **digits** form a number that is a **multiple** of 4.

4<u>08</u>   134,0<u>84</u>   2,4<u>16</u>   5,7<u>96</u>   94,8<u>52</u>

The last two digits of each of these numbers are a multiple of 4, so these numbers are divisible by 4.

✔ Check Your Understanding 2.1.7.3

Put a check (✓) next to the correct answers in the answer column.

Question	Answer
1. In which series are all the numbers divisible by 4?	___ 60 544 112 238
	___ 432 376 596 2,300
	___ 772 366 947 4,352
2. In which series are all the numbers divisible by 4?	___ 124 362 732 544
	___ 212 856 996 828
	___ 956 264 526 736

2.1.7.4 Divisibility Test for 5

🏛 *Rule*

Any integer whose last **digit** is 0 or 5 is **divisible** by 5.

2<u>0</u>   9,20<u>5</u>   39<u>0</u>   82<u>5</u>   4,79<u>5</u>   2,40<u>0</u>

The last digit of these numbers is either 0 or 5, so they are all divisible by 5.

 Check Your Understanding 2.1.7.4

Put a check (✓) next to the correct answers in the answer column.

Question	Answer
1. In which series are all the numbers divisible by 5?	___ 45 670 456 1,235 ___ 765 860 465 6,500 ___ 435 630 328 740
2. In which series are all the numbers divisible by 5?	___ 995 210 723 845 ___ 490 175 230 354 ___ 1,235 430 745 145

2.1.7.5 Divisibility Test for 9

 Rule

Any integer is **divisible** by 9 if its **digits** add up to a **multiple** of 9.

$$18 \longrightarrow 1 + 8 = 9$$
$$783 \longrightarrow 7 + 8 + 3 = 18$$
$$9{,}891 \longrightarrow 9 + 8 + 9 + 1 = 27$$

These numbers all have digits whose sums are multiples of 9. Therefore, these numbers are divisible by 9.

Check Your Understanding 2.1.7.5

Put a check (✓) next to the correct answers in the answer column.

Question	Answer
1. In which series are all the numbers divisible by 9?	___ 27 63 1,512 343 ___ 756 837 423 974 ___ 684 9,639 297 693
2. In which series are all the numbers divisible by 9?	___ 3,458 289 478 762 ___ 2,178 765 396 6,984 ___ 8,496 684 2,186 576

Topics Related to: Divisibility Test for 9

2.1.7 Divisibility Tests

2.1.7.6 Divisibility Test for 10

 Rule

Any integer whose last **digit** is 0 is **divisible** by 10.

3,05<u>0</u> 89<u>0</u> 5,18<u>0</u> 43<u>0</u> 4<u>0</u> 14,20<u>0</u>

The last digit of all these numbers is 0, so they are all divisible by 10.

Check Your Understanding 2.1.7.6

Put a check (✓) next to the correct answers in the answer column.

Question	Answer
1. In which series are all the numbers divisible by 10?	___ 650 875 340 3,495 ___ 430 820 120 460 ___ 730 950 655 345
2. In which series are all the numbers divisible by 10?	___ 3,450 860 370 310 ___ 540 355 720 280 ___ 990 560 2,250 435

Topics Related to: Divisibility Test for 10

   2.1.7 Divisibility Tests

2.1.8 Factors

product
The result of multiplying numbers.

Factors are integers that are multiplied to give a **product**. For instance, 3 and 2 are factors of 6, and 4 is a factor of 12.

All numbers except 1 have at least two factors: 1 and themselves. Many numbers have more than 2 factors.

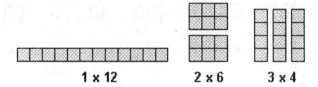

1 x 12   2 x 6   3 x 4

This diagram represents the factors of 12 (1, 2, 3, 4, 6, and 12). Notice that 12 can be divided evenly by any of its factors:

$$12 \div 6 = 2, \quad 12 \div 3 = 4, \text{ and so on.}$$

 Check Your Understanding 2.1.8

Put a check (✓) next to the correct answers in the answer column.

Question	Answer
1. Which number is a factor of 27?	___ 7 ___ 9 ___ 2 ___ 12
2. Which number is a factor of 45?	___ 8 ___ 11 ___ 15 ___ 6
3. Which numbers are factors of 48?	___ 6 ___ 7 ___ 12 ___ 3

4. Which numbers are factors of 96?	___ 11 ___ 6 ___ 8 ___ 2

Topics Related to: Factors

    2.1.9 Multiples
    2.1.12 Factoring

2.1.9 Multiples

A *multiple* is the result of multiplying a specific **factor** by another number. We usually think of a multiple in terms of that specific factor.

factor

A factor is an integer that divides another integer evenly, with no remainder. For example, 3 and 7 are factors of 21. One (1) is a factor of every number.

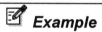 *Example*

The numbers 2, 4, 6, and 8 are all multiples of 2.

factor	multiples
2	2, 4, 6, 8, …
4	4, 8, 12, 16, …
10	10, 20, 30, 40, …
25	25, 50, 75, 100, …

This table lists some factors and a few of their multiples.

 Check Your Understanding 2.1.9

Put a check (✓) next to the correct answers in the answer column.

Question	Answer
1. Which number is a multiple of 7?	___ 102 ___ 88 ___ 98 ___ 27

2. Which number is a multiple of 9?	___ 117 ___ 77 ___ 140 ___ 28
3. Which numbers are multiples of 8?	___ 110 ___ 120 ___ 63 ___ 96
4. Which numbers are multiples of 15?	___ 55 ___ 90 ___ 105 ___ 65

Topics Related to: Multiples

2.1.8 Factors

2.1.10 Prime Numbers

A *prime* number has only two **factors**: itself and 1. The number 7 is prime because its only factors are 1 and 7.

Note that 1 is not a prime number because it only has *one* factor (itself).

Prime numbers are interesting because they are the building blocks of all other **integers**. All integers can be **factored** into a unique set of prime numbers. Prime numbers intrigue mathematicians because they have not yet found a formula for predicting when they will occur, and because very large prime numbers are difficult to find.

integers

Integers include zero, and all whole numbers (1,2, 3, ...) and their opposites, or negatives (-1, -2, -3, ...).

 Check Your Understanding 2.1.10

Put a check (✓) next to the correct answers in the answer column.

Question	Answer
1. Which number is prime?	____ 21 ____ 17 ____ 39 ____ 35
2. Which number is prime?	____ 23 ____ 45 ____ 63 ____ 15
3. Which number is prime?	____ 77 ____ 81 ____ 37 ____ 63

factored

Factoring is the process of finding a number's factors.

Topics Related to: Prime Numbers

2.1.10 Prime Factorizations
2.1.21 Factoring

2.1.11 Composite Numbers

prime

Describes an integer that has only itself and 1 as factors.

Any number (except 1) that is not **prime** is a *composite* number. A composite number is *composed* of prime numbers. The number 14 is a composite number composed of the prime factors 7 and 2.

 Check Your Understanding 2.1.11

Put a check (✓) next to the correct answers in the answer column.

Question	Answer
1. Which numbers are composite?	___ 63 ___ 49 ___ 21 ___ 53
2. Which numbers are composite?	___ 39 ___ 59 ___ 73 ___ 81

Topics Related to: Composite Numbers

2.1.8 Prime Numbers

2.1.12 Factoring

Factoring is the process of finding the **factors** of a number. Factoring is largely a trial-and-error process, but there are some techniques that can be helpful.

For example, to factor 45:

▶ Start with 1 and 45, because every number has 1 and itself as factors.
  1 x 45 = 45

▶ Is 2 a factor of 45? The **divisibility** test for 2 shows that 2 is not a factor of 45, so go on to try the next larger integer.

▶ Is 3 a factor of 45? The divisibility test for 3 shows that 3 is a factor of 45. Divide 3 into 45 to get the other factor, 15.

  3 x 15 = 45

▶ Is 4 a factor of 45? Since 45 is not divisible by 2, 4 cannot be a factor, nor can any other **multiple** of 2.

▶ Is 5 a factor of 45? Yes. So divide 45 by 5 to get the other factor, 9.

  5 x 9 = 45

▶ Since 7 x 7 is larger than 45, one of the numbers in each *factor pair* must be less than 7. All factors less than 7 are found and paired with another factor, so factoring is complete.

  The factors of 45 are: **1**, **3**, **5**, **9**, **15**, and **45**.
  The factor pairs are **1 x 45**, **3 x 15**, and **5 x 9**.

factor
A factor is an integer that divides another integer evenly, with no remainder. For example, 3 and 7 are factors of 21. One (1) is a factor of every number.

divisibility
Able to be divided without a remainder by another number. For example, 12 is divisible by 6.

 Check Your Understanding 2.1.12

Put a check (✓) next to the correct answers in the answer column.

multiple
An integer that is a product of a specific number. For example, 15 is a multiple of 3 because it is a product of 3 and 5.

Question	Answer
1. Which list shows all the factors of 40?	___ 1, 2, 4, 5, 8, 10, 20, 40 ___ 1, 2, 3, 4, 5, 8, 10, 20, 40 ___ 1, 2, 4, 5, 6, 8, 10, 20, 40 ___ 1, 2, 4, 5, 6, 10, 20, 40
2. Which list shows all the factors of 24?	___ 1, 2, 3, 4, 6, 8, 12 ___ 1, 2, 3, 4, 5, 8, 12, 24 ___ 1, 2, 3, 4, 6, 8, 12, 24 ___ 1, 2, 3, 4, 6, 7, 12, 24

Topics Related to: Factoring

2.1.7 Divisibility Tests
2.1.10 Factors

2.1.13 Prime Factorization

Every **integer** can be factored into a *unique* set of **prime factors**.

✎ *Example*

The **prime factorization** of 24 is

24 = 2 x 2 x 2 x 3.

---

prime factorization

The process of finding all the prime factors of a number.

All the factors listed are prime, and no other number has this same set of prime factors.

A common technique for finding the prime factors of a number is to use a factor tree. Place 36 at the top of the tree.

36

Then add branches for the first two factors.

Two is prime, so the branch on the left ends. Find two factors of 18 for the next branch.

Again, the branch with the prime factor (2) ends. Find two factors of 9.

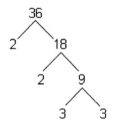

Three is prime, so this factor tree is complete. The prime factorization of 36 follows the prime branches of the factor tree: **36 = 2 x 2 x 3 x 3**.

 Check Your Understanding 2.1.13

Put a check (✓) next to the correct answers in the answer column.

Question	Answer
1. What is the prime factorization of 16?	___ 2 x 8 ___ 1 x 16 ___ 2 x 2 x 2 x 2 ___ 4 x 4
2. What is the prime factorization of 24?	___ 2 x 3 x 3 x 3 ___ 2 x 2 x 3 ___ 4 x 6 ___ 2 x 2 x 2 x 3
3. What is the missing number on the factor tree? 32 2 16 2 ? 2 4 2 2	___ 2 ___ 4 ___ 8 ___ 16

Topics Related to: Prime Factorization

2.1.10 Prime Numbers
2.1.12 Factoring

2.1.14 Greatest Common Factors

A **factor** is an **integer** that exactly *divides* another integer. Thus, a factor is also known as a *divisor*.

 *Example*

The number 6 is a factor of 12 because 12 ÷ 6 = 2 (exactly).

The number 5 is *not* a factor of 12 because 12 ÷ 5 = 2 (remainder 2).

Here are the other factors of 12: 1, 2, 3, 4, 12

A **common factor** of two or more integers is an integer that can divide both integers exactly (without remainder).

 *Example*

The number 6 is a common factor of 12 and 18 because it divides both numbers exactly.

Here are the other common factors of 12 and 18: 1, 2, 3, and 6.

This table lists the factors of 16 and 24 with the common factors highlighted.

Factors of 16	1	2		4		8	16	
Factors of 24	1	2	3	4	6	8	12	24

Eight is the *greatest* of these common factors. It is called the **greatest common factor**. GCF is an abbreviation for greatest common factor.

Check Your Understanding 2.1.14

Put a check (✓) next to the correct answers in the answer column.

Question	Answer
1. Which number is the greatest common factor (GCF) of 18 and 24?	___ 6 ___ 9 ___ 3
2. Which number is the greatest common factor (GCF) of 30 and 40?	___ 15 ___ 6 ___ 10
3. Which number is the greatest common factor (GCF) of 20 and 36?	___ 4 ___ 9 ___ 2

Topics Related to: Greatest Common Factors

2.1.12 Factoring

2.1.15 Adding with Odd and Even Numbers

integers

Integers include zero, and all whole numbers (1,2, 3, ...) and their opposites, or negatives (-1, -2, -3, ...).

sum

A sum is the result of the addition of two or more numbers or quantities. For example, the sum of 3 and 5 is 8.

odd

An odd integer leaves a remainder of 1 when divided by 2.

even

An integer that can be divided by 2 without leaving a remainder.

addends

An addend is a number that is added to another number. For example, in the equation 3 + 5 = 8, the addend is 5.

When you add **integers**, you can predict whether the **sum** will be an **even** number or an **odd** number by looking at the **addends**. The table shows the pattern. Ones represent *odd* numbers and twos represent *even* numbers.

+	1	2
1	2	3
2	3	4

+	odd	even
odd	even	odd
even	odd	even

▶ From the table, you can see that:

- **The sum of two odd numbers is even.**
- **The sum of two even numbers is even.**
- **The sum of an even number and an odd number is odd.**

▶ What do you think the sum of two odd numbers and an even number is? What about the sum of two even numbers and an odd number?

🏛 *Rule*

A sum is odd only when there is an odd number of odd **addends**.

For example, 5 + 3 + 9 = 17

 Check Your Understanding 2.1.15

Put a check (✓) next to the correct answers in the answer column.

Question	Answer
1. Which sums are odd?	___ 3 + 7 + 21 + 34 ___ 6 + 87 + 45 + 32 ___ 71 + 6 + 83 + 49 ___ 38 + 65 + 19
2. Which sums are even?	___ 16 + 85 + 71 + 27 ___ 31 + 73 + 48 + 27 ___ 94 + 17 + 81 ___ 15 + 99 + 47 + 69

Topics Related to: Adding with Odd and Even Numbers

2.1.16 Multiplying with Odd and Even Numbers

2.1.16 Multiplying with Odd and Even Numbers

When you multiply **integers**, you can predict whether the **product** will be an **even** number or an **odd** number by looking at the **factors**. The table shows the pattern. Ones represent *odd* numbers and twos represent *even* numbers.

x	1	2
1	1	2
2	2	4

→

x	odd	even
odd	odd	even
even	even	even

> **integers**
>
> Integers include zero, and all whole numbers (1, 2, 3, ...) and their opposites, or negatives (-1, -2, -3, ...).

▶ From the table, you can see that:

- **The product of two odd numbers is odd.**
- **The product of two even numbers is even.**
- **The product of an even number and an odd number is even.**

▶ What do you think the product of two odd numbers and an even number is? What about the product of two evens and an odd? And the product of three odds?

> **factor**
>
> A factor is an integer that divides another integer evenly, with no remainder. For example, 3 and 7 are factors of 21. One (1) is a factor of every number.

🏛 *Rule*

A product is odd only when all the factors are odd.

 Check Your Understanding 2.1.16

Put a check (✓) next to the correct answers in the answer column.

> **product**
>
> The result of multiplying numbers.

Question	Answer
1. Which products are odd?	___ 48 x 93
	___ 23 x 451 x 12 x 97
	___ 39 x 121 x 53 x 77
	___ 855 x 21 x 69

2. Which products are even?	___ 21 x 43
	___ 98 x 5 x 16
	___ 6 x 32 x 17 x 2
	___ 11 x 7 x 3 x 19

Topics Related to: Multiplying with Odd and Even Numbers

   2.1.15 Adding with Odd and Even Numbers

2.1.17 Understanding Clock Arithmetic

Clock arithmetic is a nickname for computing with a set of numbers that is finite or limited. This limited system of numbers is most commonly used to measure time, hence the name.

Think of a clock. The numbers begin with 1 and end with 12. No other numbers are used. There is no such thing as 13 o'clock or 162 o'clock. Once you reach 12, you begin again with 1.

 Check Your Understanding 2.1.17

Put a check (✓) next to the correct answers in the answer column.

Question	Answer
Which applications are clock systems? (Mark all that apply.)	___ years in a century
	___ miles per hour
	___ minutes in an hour

Topics Related to: Understanding Clock Arithmetic

2.1.18 Congruence in Clock Arithmetic
2.1.19 Adding in Clock Arithmetic
2.1.20 Subtracting in Clock Arithmetic
2.1.21 Multiplying in Clock Arithmetic

2.1.18 Congruence in Clock Arithmetic

Numbers in a clock system can parallel numbers in the infinite system.

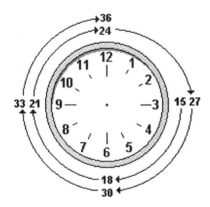

Imagine an infinite number line wrapped around a 12-hour clock. You can see that 24 and 36 are **congruent** to 12. This means if you started at 12 and counted 24 or 36 units around the clock, you would end back at 12. Try it. Place a pencil on 12. Count from 1 to 24; move your pencil one unit **clockwise** on the clock for each number you count (note that 12 is 0, not 1).

The numbers 21 and 33 are congruent to 9. This means if you started at 12 and counted 21 or 33 units **clockwise** around the clock, you would end at 9. Try it.

An easy way to figure out which numbers are congruent is to use division:

21 ÷ 12 = 1, remainder 9

33 ÷ 12 = 2, remainder 9

The remainder shows which number on the clock is congruent to 21 and 33.

congruent

Two figures are congruent if they exactly coincide when superimposed.

clockwise

In the same direction that the hands on a clock move.

Check Your Understanding 2.1.18

Put a check (✓) next to the correct answers in the answer column.

Question	Answer
1. Which number is congruent to 10 on a 12-hour clock?	___ 22 ___ 32 ___ 16 ___ 25
2. Which number is congruent to 2 on a 9-hour clock?	___ 17 ___ 38 ___ 18 ___ 28
3. Which number is congruent to 5 on a 7-hour clock? (Drawing a picture of the clock may help.)	___ 35 ___ 13 ___ 19 ___ 27
4. Which number is congruent to 6 on an 8-hour clock?	___ 48 ___ 12 ___ 20 ___ 30

Topics Related to: Congruence in Clock Arithmetic

2.1.17 Understanding Clock Arithmetic
2.1.19 Adding in Clock Arithmetic
2.1.20 Subtracting in Clock Arithmetic
2.1.21 Multiplying in Clock Arithmetic

2.1.19 Adding in Clock Arithmetic

In clock arithmetic, only a small set of numbers are used.

On a clock, the numbers begin with 1 and end with 12. Once you reach 12, you begin again with 1. Think of this when you are adding.

The clock below shows 7 + 8 = 3. Start at 7 and count around **clockwise** 8 more places.

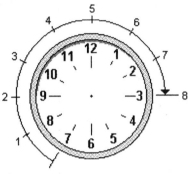

For large numbers, it may be helpful to think of adding like this:

- **Perform the addition as usual.**
  7 + 8 = 15

- **Think of how many numbers are on the clock.**
  There are 12 numbers on this clock.

- **Divide the sum by the number of numbers on the clock.**
  15 ÷ 12 = 1, remainder 3

- **Throw out the quotient (1 in this example). The remainder is the answer.**
  On a 12-clock, 7 + 8 = 3

clockwise

In the same direction that the hands on a clock move.

quotient

A quotient is the answer to a division problem. For example, 7 is the quotient of 35 and 5:

35 ÷ 5 = 7.

Check Your Understanding 2.1.19

Put a check (✓) next to the correct answers in the answer column.

Question	Answer
1. On a 12-clock, three of these expressions have the same sum. One is different. Which expression has a different sum? (Drawing a picture of a 12-clock might help you.)	___ 11 + 3 ___ 9 + 8 ___ 10 + 7 ___ 4 + 13
2. On a 9-clock, three of these expressions have the same sum. One is different. Which expression has a different sum? 8 9 1 7 2 6 3 5 4	___ 1 + 2 ___ 4 + 8 ___ 6 + 7 ___ 9 + 12
3. On a 7-clock, three of these expressions have the same sum. One is different. Which expression has a different sum? (Drawing a picture of a 7-clock might help you.)	___ 7 + 11 ___ 5 + 10 ___ 6 + 19 ___ 3 + 15

Topics Related to: Adding in Clock Arithmetic

2.1.17 Understanding Clock Arithmetic

2.1.20 Subtracting in Clock Arithmetic

Subtracting in clock arithmetic is similar in principle to adding in clock arithmetic. The difference is the direction you move. When you add, you move in the **clockwise** direction. When you subtract, you move in the **counterclockwise** direction. This clock shows 5 - 6 = 11.

Check Your Understanding 2.1.20

Put a check (✓) next to the correct answers in the answer column.

Question	Answer
1. Which expression has a difference of 9 on a 12-clock?	___ 5 - 6 ___ 3 - 7 ___ 8 - 10 ___ 2 - 5
2. Which expression has a difference of 4 on a 6-clock? (Drawing a picture of a 6-clock might help you.)	___ 1 - 5 ___ 4 - 5 ___ 2 - 4 ___ 3 - 3
3. Which expression has a difference of 7 on a 10-clock? (Drawing a picture of a 10-clock might help you.)	___ 3 - 8 ___ 9 - 7 ___ 1 - 4 ___ 5 -10

Topics Related to: Subtracting in Clock Arithmetic

2.1.17 Understanding Clock Arithmetic
2.1.19 Adding in Clock Arithmetic
2.1.21 Multiplying in Clock Arithmetic

2.1.21 Multiplying in Clock Arithmetic

Multiplying in clock arithmetic is similar to adding. Think of multiplication as successive additions. This clock shows 3 x 6 = 6.

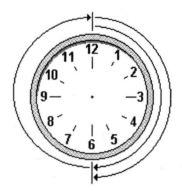

It may be helpful to think of multiplying like this:

- **Perform the multiplication as usual.**
    3 x 6 = 18

- **Think of how many numbers are on the clock.**
    There are 12 numbers on this clock.

- **Divide the sum by the number of numbers on the clock.**
    18 ÷ 12 = 1, remainder 6

- **Throw out the quotient (1 in this example). The remainder is the answer.**
    On a 12-clock, 3 x 6 = 6

Check Your Understanding 2.1.21

Put a check (✓) next to the correct answer in the answer column.

Question	Answer
1. On a 12-clock, three of these expressions have the same product. One is different. Which expression has a different product?	____ 3 x 5 ____ 3 x 9 ____ 3 x 13 ____ 2 x 13
2. On a 5-clock, three of these expressions have the same product. One is different. Which expression has a different product?	____ 4 x 6 ____ 2 x 3 ____ 3 x 13 ____ 2 x 17
3. On a 9-clock, three of these expressions have the same product. One is different. Which expression has a different product?	____ 6 x 8 ____ 2 x 7 ____ 4 x 8 ____ 5 x 10

Topics Related to: Multiplying in Clock Arithmetic

2.1.17 Understanding Clock Arithmetic
2.1.19 Adding in Clock Arithmetic

2.2 Fractions

2.2.1 Fractions as Part of a Whole

A *fraction* compares a part to a whole unit. The **numerator** of a fraction represents the *part*. The **denominator** of a fraction shows how many parts make a *whole*.

This grid is divided into 12 equal parts, or cells. Eight of the 12 cells are shaded. The fraction of the grid that is shaded is 8/12.
The numerator of this fraction (8) represents the *part* of the grid that is shaded.
The denominator (12) of this fraction represents the number of parts that make up the *whole*.

 Check Your Understanding 2.2.1

Put a check (✓) next to the correct answer in the answer column.

Question	Answer
1. What fraction of this grid is white?	___ 6/9 ___ 3/9 ___ 6/3
2. What fraction of this grid is white?	___ 16/11 ___ 5/16 ___ 11/16

2.2.2 Equivalent Fractions

Two fractions that represent the same quantity but use different numbers are *equivalent fractions*.

 *Example*

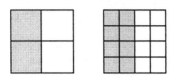

These grids represent equivalent fractions. In the left grid, 2/4 or 2 of the 4 cells are filled. In the right grid, 8/16 or 8 of the 16 cells are filled. Since the grids are equal in size and the colored area in both grids is equal, 2/4 and 8/16 are equivalent fractions.

Notice that 1 cell in the left grid is equivalent to **4** cells in the right grid. Therefore, to write 2/4 as an equivalent fraction with a **denominator** of 16, multiply the **numerator** and **denominator** of 2/4 by **4**.

$$\frac{2}{4} = \frac{2 \times \mathbf{4}}{4 \times \mathbf{4}} = \frac{8}{16}$$

▶ To compute an equivalent fraction, you can either *multiply* or *divide* the **numerator** and **denominator** of a fraction by the same number.

 Check Your Understanding 2.2.2

Put a check (✓) next to the correct answers in the answer column.

Question	Answer
1. The shaded part of this number bar represents 5/8. Which of these fractions is equivalent to 5/8?	___ 8/5 ___ 10/16 ___ 12/14

2. The shaded part of this number bar represents 3/4. Which of these fractions is equivalent to 3/4?

    ___ 9/12

    ___ 8/6

    ___ 6/9

Topics Related to: Equivalent Fractions

2.2.3 Scaling Up Fractions
2.2.4 Scaling Down Fractions
2.2.5 Fractions in Lowest Terms

2.2.3 Scaling Up Fractions

Scaling up means to multiply the **numerator** and **denominator** of a fraction by the same number. Scaling up is used to write an **equivalent fraction** with a larger numerator and denominator.

 *Example*

Scale up the fraction 3/5 to find equivalent fractions with larger numerators and denominators. Multiply 3/5 by 2/2, 3/3, 4/4, etc.

$$\frac{3 \times \mathbf{2}}{5 \times \mathbf{2}} = \frac{6}{10} \quad \text{or} \quad \frac{3 \times \mathbf{3}}{5 \times \mathbf{3}} = \frac{9}{15} \quad \text{or} \quad \frac{3 \times \mathbf{4}}{5 \times \mathbf{4}} = \frac{12}{20}$$

The fractions 3/5, 6/10, 9/15, and 12/20 are equivalent fractions.

▶ When you scale up fractions by multiplying by 2/2, 3/3, 4/4, etc., you are only changing the *appearance* of the fraction, not its *value*. This is because 2/2, 3/3, 4/4, etc. are each equal to 1, and a number times 1 equals itself.

Check Your Understanding 2.2.3

Put a check (✓) next to the correct answers in the answer column.

Question	Answer
1. To scale the fraction 3/11 up to 12/44, what number should you multiply by?	___ 4/4 ___ 3/3 ___ 11/11
2. To scale the fraction 5/9 up to 15/27, what number should you multiply by?	___ 5/5 ___ 3/3 ___ 4/4
3. To scale the fraction 2/5 up to 16/40, what number should you multiply by?	___ 10/10 ___ 8/8 ___ 4/4

Topics Related to: Scaling Up Fractions

2.2.2 Equivalent Fractions
2.2.4 Scaling Down Fractions

2.2.4 Scaling Down Fractions

Scaling down means to divide the **numerator** and **denominator** of a fraction by the same number. Scaling down is used to write an **equivalent fraction** with a smaller numerator and denominator.

 **Example**

You can scale down the fraction 24/36 to find equivalent fractions with smaller numerators and denominators. Divide 24/36 by 12/12, 6/6, 4/4, etc.

$$\frac{24 \div 12}{36 \div 12} = \frac{2}{3} \quad \text{or} \quad \frac{24 \div 6}{36 \div 6} = \frac{4}{6} \quad \text{or} \quad \frac{24 \div 4}{36 \div 4} = \frac{6}{9}$$

The fractions 24/36, 2/3, 4/6, and 6/9 are equivalent fractions.

▶ When you scale down fractions by dividing by 6/6, 4/4, 3/3, etc., you are only changing the *appearance* of the fraction, not its *value*. This is because 2/2, 3/3, 4/4, etc. are each equal to 1, and a number divided by 1 equals itself.

 Check Your Understanding 2.2.4

Put a check (✓) next to the correct answers in the answer column.

Question	Answer
1. To scale the fraction 15/35 down to 3/7, what number should you divide by?	⎯ 7/7 ___ 3/3 ___ 5/5
2. To scale the fraction 8/32 down to 1/4, what number should you divide by?	⎯ 4/4 ___ 2/2 ___ 8/8
3. To scale the fraction 12/27 down to 4/9, what number should you divide by?	⎯ 4/4 ___ 3/3 ___ 9/9

Topics Related to: Scaling Down Fractions

2.2.2 Equivalent Fractions
2.2.3 Scaling Up Fractions
2.2.5 Fractions in Lowest Terms

2.2.5 Fractions in Lowest Terms

The fractions 4/12, 2/6, and 1/3 are **equivalent fractions**. The fraction 1/3 is in *lowest terms*. It represents the same quantity as 2/6 and 4/12, but it uses the fewest number of parts and the smallest integers possible.

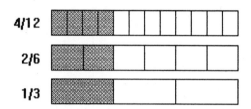

A fraction is in lowest terms when the **greatest common factor** of the **numerator** and **denominator** is 1.

▶ To reduce a fraction to lowest terms, divide the numerator and denominator by their **greatest common factor**.

---

equivalent fractions

Equivalent fractions are fractions which name the same number. For example, 12/24 and 15/30 are equivalent fractions. They are two ways of expressing 1/2.

greatest common factor

The greatest common factor is the largest factor that two or more numbers have in common. For example, the common factors of 36 and 42 are 2, 3, and 6. Six is the greatest common factor.

 Example

The greatest common factor of 4 and 12 is 4, so to reduce 4/12 to lowest terms, divide the numerator and denominator by 4.

$$\frac{4}{12} = \frac{4 \div 4}{12 \div 4} = \frac{1}{3}$$

Check Your Understanding 2.2.5

Put a check (✓) next to the correct answers in the answer column.

Question	Answer
1. Which of these fractions is in lowest terms?	___ 8/12 ___ 5/10 ___ 5/9
2. Which of these fractions is in lowest terms?	___ 4/10 ___ 6/9 ___ 5/12
3. Which of these fractions is in lowest terms, and is equivalent to 9/15?	___ 18/30 ___ 3/5 ___ 12/18

Topics Related to: Fractions in Lowest Terms

2.1.14 Greatest Common Factors
2.2.2   Equivalent Fractions
2.2.4   Scaling Down Fractions

2.2.6 Common Denominators

denominator

The denominator is the number in a fraction that represents the number of parts that make a whole. For example, in the fraction 7/13, the denominator is 13.

Common denominators are useful when adding and subtracting fractions or when comparing the relative sizes of fractions. A common denominator is a common multiple of the **denominators** of 2 or more fractions.

 Example

The number 6 is a common denominator for the fractions 1/2 and 1/3.

▶ One way to find a common denominator is to list the multiples of each of the denominators. Any multiples that all the denominators have in common are common denominators.

Multiples of 2	2	4	6	8	10	12	14	16	18
Multiples of 3	3	6	9	12	15	18	21	24	27

This chart shows some common multiples of 2 and 3: 6, 12, and 18. In other words, 6, 12, and 18 are common denominators of the fractions 1/2 and 1/3.

▶ One sure way to find a common denominator of 2 or more fractions is to multiply the denominators of the fractions.

 **Example**

To find a common denominator of 6/11, 1/2, and 3/5, multiply the denominators together: 11 x 2 x 5 = 110.

A common denominator is 110.

 Check Your Understanding 2.2.6

Put a check (✓) next to the correct answers in the answer column.

Question	Answer
1. Which numbers are common denominators of 3/4 and 5/6?	___ 10 ___ 12 ___ 16 ___ 18 ___ 24
2. Which numbers are common denominators of 1/6 and 2/9?	___ 9 ___ 15 ___ 18 ___ 27 ___ 36

Topics Related to: Common Denominators

2.2.10 Comparing Fractions to Fractions
2.2.12 Adding and Subtracting Fractions

integer

An integer is any number in a set {. . .-3, -2, -1, 0, 1, 2, 3, . . .}. In other words, integers include all whole numbers, their negative opposites, and zero.

2.2.7 Mixed Numbers

When an **integer** and a fraction together represent a single quantity, the result is a **mixed number**.

✎ *Example*

The number of filled cells in the 2 grids below can be represented by the sum of the integer 15/15 or 1 and the fraction 8/15. The mixed number is 1 8/15 which means 1 + 8/15

15/15 or 1   **8/15**

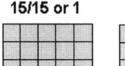

Any mixed number can also be written as an **improper fraction**, or a fraction whose numerator is greater than its denominator. The improper fraction equivalent to 1 8/15 is 23/15.

To write a mixed number as an improper fraction, follow these guidelines:

Write the whole number as a fraction.

numerator

The numerator is the number in a fraction that represents part of a whole. For example, in the fraction 7/13, the numerator is 7.

denominator

The denominator is the number in a fraction that represents the number of parts that make a whole. For example, in the fraction 7/13, the denominator is 13.

▶ The number 1 is equivalent to a fraction whose **numerator** is equal to its **denominator**: 1 = 2/2, 3/3, 4/4, . . . It follows that 2 = 4/2, 6/3, 8/4 . . . and 3 = 6/2, 9/3, 12/4 . . . etc.

▶ Use the same denominator as the fraction given.

✎ *Example*

If the mixed number is 1 8/15, write the 1 as 15/15.

Add the 2 fractions.

▶ To add 2 fractions with the same denominators, just add the numerators; keep the same denominators.

 *Example*

15/15 + 8/15 = 23/15.

 Check Your Understanding 2.2.7a

Put a check (✓) next to the correct answers in the answer column.

Question	Answer
1. Which of these statements is equivalent to 4 1/4?	___ 4/4 + 1/4 ___ 8/4 + 1/4 ___ 16/4 + 1/4
2. Which of these statements is equivalent to 6 3/8?	___ 18/8 + 3/8 ___ 48/8 + 3/8 ___ 24/8 + 3/8

 Check Your Understanding 2.2.7b

Put a check (✓) next to the correct answers in the answer column.

Question	Answer
1. The mixed number 3 1/2 = 6/2 + 1/2. Which improper fraction does it equal?	___ 7/2 ___ 6/2 ___ 5/2
2. The mixed number 5 1/5 = 25/5 + 1/5. Which improper fraction does it equal?	___ 24/5 ___ 26/5 ___ 15/5

Topics Related to: Mixed Numbers

2.2.8   Improper Fractions
2.2.12 Adding and Subtracting Fractions

2.2.8 Improper Fractions

An improper fraction has a **numerator** that is larger than or equal to its **denominator**. It represents a quantity greater than or equal to one.

✎ *Example*

The number of filled cells in the 2 grids below is represented by the improper fraction 7/4.

7/4

An improper fraction can be written as a **mixed number**. For example, all of the cells in one of the grids above are filled. Three of the 4 cells (3/4) in the other grid are filled. The improper fraction 7/4 can be written as the mixed number 1 3/4.

---

mixed number

A mixed number is an integer mixed with a fraction to represent a quantity. For example, 3 2/5 is a mixed number.

✔ Check Your Understanding 2.2.8

Put a check (✓) next to the correct answers in the answer column.

Question	Answer
1. The improper fraction 13/4 is represented by the filled cells in these grids. Which mixed number is equivalent to 13/4?	____ 3 3/4 ____ 3 1/4 ____ 12 1/4

2. The improper fraction 17/12 is represented by the filled cells in these grids. Which mixed number is equivalent to 17/12?

_____ 1 5/12

_____ 12 5/12

_____ 1 7/12

Topics Related to: Improper Fractions

2.2.7 Mixed Numbers

2.2.9 Comparing Fractions to 1

You can *compare* a fraction to 1 by looking at its **numerator** and **denominator**.

▶ If the numerator is *less than* the denominator, the fraction is *less than* 1.

Example

3/7 is less than 1.

▶ If the numerator is *equal to* the denominator, the fraction is *equal to* 1.

Example

7/7 is equal to 1.

▶ If the numerator is *greater than* the denominator, the fraction is *greater than* 1.

Example

9/7 is greater than 1.

Check Your Understanding 2.2.9

Put a check (✓) next to the correct answers in the answer column.

Question	Answer
1. Which fraction is less than 1?	___ 8/7 ___ 5/6 ___ 3/3
2. Which fraction is equal to 1?	___ 9/6 ___ 11/11 ___ 7/12
3. Which fraction is greater than 1?	___ 5/13 ___ 9/9 ___ 11/7

Topics Related to: Comparing Fractions to 1

2.2.8 Improper Fractions
2.2.10 Comparing Fractions to Fractions

2.2.10 Comparing Fractions to Fractions

Comparing the size of one fraction to another fraction is fairly simple when the fractions have the same **denominator**.

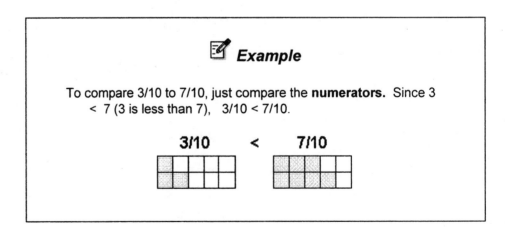

✐ *Example*

To compare 3/10 to 7/10, just compare the **numerators**. Since 3 < 7 (3 is less than 7), 3/10 < 7/10.

3/10 < **7/10**

Check Your Understanding 2.2.10

Put a check (✓) next to the correct answers in the answer column.

Question	Answer
1. Which of these fractions is greater?	___ 5/8 ___ 7/8
2. Which fraction has the greatest value?	___ 3/13 ___ 11/13 ___ 9/13
3. Which fraction has the greatest value?	___ 16/17 ___ 6/17 ___ 2/17

When the **denominators** are not the same, there is more than one way to compare the relative sizes of the fractions. One way is to use logical reasoning and estimation. Another way involves finding a **common denominator**.

To find out more about comparing fractions with different denominators, look at the related topics.

Topics Related to: Comparing Fractions to Fractions

2.2.10.1 Using Reasoning and Estimation
2.2.10.2 Using a Common Denominator

common denominator

A common denominator is a common multiple of the denominators of two or more fractions. For example, for the fractions 1/2 and 3/5, a common denominator is 10 because 10 is a multiple of both 2 and 5.

denominator

The denominator is the number in a fraction that represents the number of parts that make a whole. For example, in the fraction 7/13, the denominator is 13.

2.2.10.1 Using Reasoning and Estimation

When using *reasoning* and *estimation* to compare fractions, follow these rules.

⊞ Rule

If you compare fractions with the *same* **denominators**, then the relative sizes of the fractions depends on the **numerators**.

When the denominators are equal, the fraction with the smaller numerator is the smaller fraction.

---

denominator

The denominator is the number in a fraction that represents the number of parts that make a whole. For example, in the fraction 7/13, the denominator is 13.

numerator

The numerator is the number in a fraction that represents part of a whole. For example, in the fraction 7/13, the numerator is 7.

✎ Example

3/13 is less than 8/13 because 3 is less than 8.

⊞ Rule

If the denominators of the fractions are *not* the same, but the numerators *are* the same, then the relative sizes of the fractions depends on the denominators.

When the numerators are equal, the fraction with the larger denominator is the smaller fraction.

✎ Example

1/6 is the smallest fraction. The largest fraction is 1/4.

$$1/6 \quad < \quad 1/5 \quad < \quad 1/4$$

< means: is less than

▶ Since some fractions are used more than others, try to remember this relationship:

1/4 < 1/3 < 1/2 < 2/3 < 3/4 (< means *is less than*)

▶ Sometimes you can estimate the size of a fraction by rounding it to a fraction you *do* know the size of.

 **Example**

You can use estimation to compare 5/11 to 2/3.

5/11 is a little less than 5/10, so 5/11 is a little less than 1/2.
1/2 is less than 2/3. So, 5/11 is less than 2/3.
5/11 < 1/2 < 2/3 (< means "is less than").

▶ You can also compare fractions with different denominators by finding a **common denominator**. To see how to do this, go to section *2.2.6 Common Denominators* .

 Check Your Understanding 2.2.10.1

Put a check (✓) next to the correct answers in the answer column.

Question	Answer
1. Using estimation, which fraction is greater?	___ 5/8 ___ 1/2
2. Using estimation, which fraction is greater?	___ 2/3 ___ 11/20

Topics Related to: Using Reasoning and Estimation

2.2.2	Equivalent Fractions
2.2.6	Common Denominators
2.2.9	Comparing Fractions to 1
2.2.10.2	Using a Common Denominator

numerator

The numerator is the number in a fraction that represents part of a whole. For example, in the fraction 7/13, the numerator is 7.

2.2.10.2 Using a Common Denominator

If you compare two fractions with the *same* **denominators**, then the relative sizes of the fractions depend on their **numerators**.

 *Example*

3/13 is less than 8/13 because 3 is less than 8.

common denominator

A common denominator is a common multiple of the denominators of two or more fractions. For example, for the fractions 1/2 and 3/5, a common denominator is 10 because 10 is a multiple of both 2 and 5.

One way to compare fractions with *different* denominators is to find a **common denominator** and use it to write each fraction as an equivalent fraction.

Follow these steps to compare fractions with different denominators. The example uses the fractions 3/4 and 5/6 .

> ✏️ *Example*
>
> 1. To find a common denominator, list the multiples of each denominator, then choose the lowest one that they have in common.
>
> | Multiples of 4 | Multiples of 6 |
> |:---:|:---:|
> | 4 | 6 |
> | 8 | 12 |
> | 12 | 18 |
> | 16 | 24 |
> | 20 | 30 |
> | 24 | 36 |
>
> The first multiple that 4 and 6 have in common is 12.
>
> 2. Write each fraction as its **equivalent fraction** with the common multiple as the denominator:
>
> $$\frac{3}{4} = \frac{3 \times 3}{4 \times 3} = \frac{9}{12}$$
>
> $$\frac{5}{6} = \frac{5 \times 2}{6 \times 2} = \frac{10}{12}$$
>
> 3. Compare the numerators of the fractions with the common (equal) denominators:
>
> 9 is less than 10,
> so 9/12 (or 3/4) is less than 10/12 (or 5/6)
> and 3/4 is less than 5/6

equivalent fractions

Equivalent fractions are fractions which name the same number. For example, 12/24 and 15/30 are equivalent fractions. They are two ways of expressing 1/2.

You can also compare fractions with different denominators by using reasoning and estimation (see Topics Related to Using a Common Denominator).

 Check Your Understanding 2.2.10.2

Put a check (✓) next to the correct answers in the answer column.

Question	Answer
1. Which of these fractions has the greatest value?	____ 5/24 ____ 1/3 ____ 3/8

2. Which of these fractions has the greatest value?	___ 5/6 ___ 7/9 ___ 2/3
3. Which of these fractions has the least value?	___ 3/4 ___ 5/6 ___ 7/8

Topics Related to: Using a Common Denominator

2.2.2   Equivalent Fractions
2.2.6   Common Denominators
2.2.9   Comparing Fractions to 1
2.2.10.1   Using Reasoning and Estimation

numerator

The numerator is the number in a fraction that represents part of a whole. For example, in the fraction 7/13, the numerator is 7.

2.2.11   Estimating Equivalent Fractions

Estimating the value of fractions like 18/37 or 29/61 is a useful skill even when using a calculator.

1. Round the **numerator** to the nearest **multiple** of 5. The multiples of 5 are {5, 10, 15, 20, 25, . . .}

 **Example**

> Consider the fraction 18/37. The numerator, 18, is closer to 20 than it is to 15, so round 18 to 20.

multiple

An integer that is a product of a specific number. For example, 15 is a multiple of 3 because it is a product of 3 and 5.

2. Round the **denominator** to the nearest **multiple** of 5.

 **Example**

> The denominator of 18/37 is closer to 35 than it is to 40, so round 37 to 35. The fraction 18/37 is rounded to 20/35.

3. After rounding the fraction, reduce the rounded fraction to **lowest terms**.

 Example

18/37 is rounded to 20/35. The fraction 20/35 reduced to lowest terms is 4/7.

So the fraction 18/37 is *approximately* equal to 4/7.

▶ In summary, here is a rule for estimating fractions.

🏛 *Rule*

Round numerators and denominators, then reduce to lowest terms.

 Check Your Understanding 2.2.11

Put a check (✓) next to the correct answers in the answer column.

Question	Answer
1. What fraction is 28/49 nearest to?	____ 1/3 ____ 3/5 ____ 3/4
2. What fraction is 19/76 nearest to?	____ 1/4 ____ 1/3 ____ 3/8

Topics Related to: Estimating Equivalent Fractions

2.2.2 Equivalent Fractions

denominator

The denominator is the number in a fraction that represents the number of parts that make a whole. For example, in the fraction 7/13, the denominator is 13.

2.2.12 Adding and Subtracting Fractions

Adding Fractions with the Same Denominators

When two fractions have the *same* **denominators,** you can *add* them by simply adding their **numerators** and keeping the same denominator.

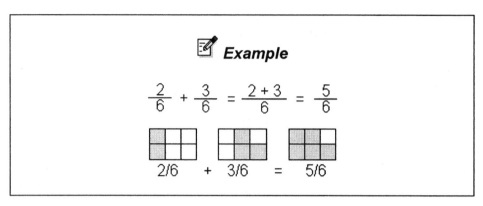

$$\frac{2}{6} + \frac{3}{6} = \frac{2+3}{6} = \frac{5}{6}$$

2/6 + 3/6 = 5/6

Similarly, you can *subtract* fractions with the *same* denominators by subtracting one numerator from the other and keeping the same denominator.

numerator

The numerator is the number in a fraction that represents part of a whole. For example, in the fraction 7/13, the numerator is 7.

Example

The fractions 5/9 and 2/9 have the same denominator. To find the difference, just subtract one numerator from the other and keep the same denominator.

$$\frac{5}{9} - \frac{2}{9} = \frac{5-2}{9} = \frac{3}{9}$$

Adding Fractions with Different Denominators

common denominator

A common denominator is a common multiple of the denominators of two or more fractions. For example, for the fractions 1/2 and 3/5, a common denominator is 10 because 10 is a multiple of both 2 and 5.

1. To add fractions that have *different* denominators, first find a **common denominator**.

Example

The fractions 1/4 and 1/3 have different denominators.

A common denominator (or common multiple of the denominators) is 12.

2. Use the common denominator and scaling to write each fraction as an **equivalent fraction**.

equivalent fractions

Equivalent fractions are fractions which name the same number. For example, 12/24 and 15/30 are equivalent fractions. They are two ways of expressing 1/2.

📝 *Example*

$$\frac{1}{4} = \frac{3}{12} \quad \text{and} \quad \frac{1}{3} = \frac{4}{12}$$

---

3. Then add the fractions that now have a common denominator.

📝 *Example*

Since 1/4 = 3/12 and 1/3 = 4/12, 1/4 + 1/3 = 3/12 + 4/12

Add 3/12 + 4/12.

$$\frac{3}{12} + \frac{4}{12} = \frac{3+4}{12} = \frac{7}{12}$$

This illustration shows how 1/4 + 1/3 is the same as 3/12 + 4/12.

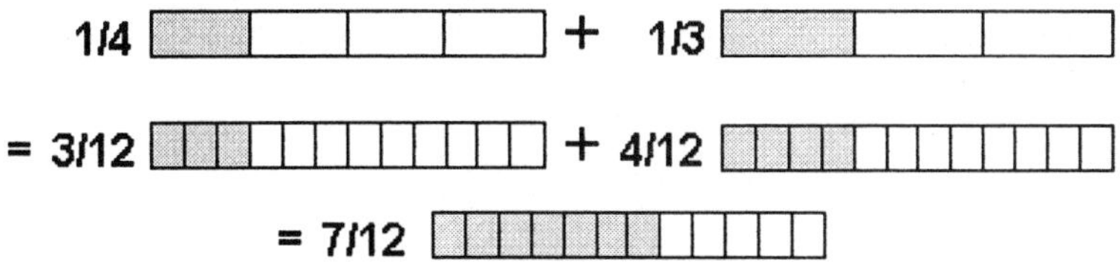

1/4 ▦□□□ + 1/3 ▦□□

= 3/12 ▦□□□□□□□□□□ + 4/12 ▦▦□□□□□□□□

= 7/12 ▦▦▦□□□□□□

These same rules apply to subtracting fractions.

 **Example**

A common denominator of 3/4 and 1/3 is 12, because 12 is a multiple of both 4 and 3. Using the common denominator, their equivalent fractions are 9/12 and 4/12.

$$\frac{3}{4} = \frac{9}{12} \quad \text{and} \quad \frac{1}{3} = \frac{4}{12}$$

Working now with 9/12 and 4/12

$$\frac{9}{12} - \frac{4}{12} = \frac{9-4}{12} = \frac{5}{12}$$

 Check Your Understanding 2.2.12

Put a check (✓) next to the correct answers in the answer column.

Question	Answer
1. Which equation correctly shows how to compute this sum: 3/4 + 3/16?	___ 12/16 + 3/16 = 15/16 ___ 6/16 + 3/16 = 9/16 ___ 3/4 + 3/16 = 6/20
2. Which equation correctly shows how to compute this difference: 5/6 - 2/9?	___ 15/18 - 6/18 = 9/18 ___ 10/12 - 3/12 = 7/12 ___ 15/18 - 4/18 = 11/18
3. Which equation correctly shows how to compute this difference: 7/8 - 2/3?	___ 14/16 - 4/6 = 2/2 ___ 21/24 - 16/24 = 5/24 ___ 21/24 - 6/24 = 15/24

Topics Related to: Adding and Subtracting Fractions

2.2.2   Equivalent Fractions
2.2.13 Multiplying Fractions
2.2.14 Dividing Fractions

2.2.13 Multiplying Fractions

When you *multiply* fractions, think of the multiplication sign (x) as "of."

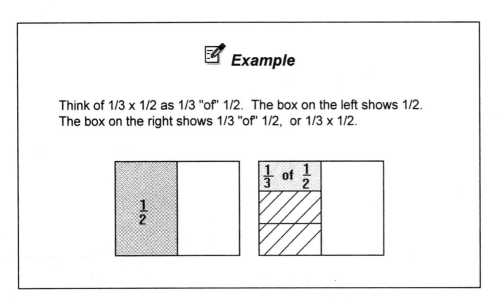

✍ *Example*

Think of 1/3 x 1/2 as 1/3 "of" 1/2. The box on the left shows 1/2.
The box on the right shows 1/3 "of" 1/2, or 1/3 x 1/2.

To multiply fractions, multiply the **numerators** together *and* multiply the **denominators** together.

 *Example*

$$\frac{1}{3} \times \frac{1}{2} = \frac{1 \times 1}{3 \times 2} = \frac{1}{6}$$

Notice that the shaded (solid shade) part of the box (1/3 x 1/2) is equal to 1/6 of the *whole* box.

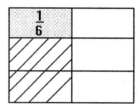

 Check Your Understanding 2.2.13

Put a check (✓) next to the correct answers in the answer column.

Question	Answer
1. What is 2/3 x 3/5?	___ 6/15 ___ 5/8 ___ 9/10
2. What is 1/4 x 3/7?	___ 4/11 ___ 7/12 ___ 3/28
3. What is 5/7 x 3/8?	___ 8/15 ___ 21/40 ___ 15/56

Topics Related to: Multiplying Fractions

2.2.2   Equivalent Fractions
2.2.5   Fractions in Lowest Terms
2.2.14 Dividing Fractions

2.2.14 Dividing Fractions

Visualizing Division with Fractions

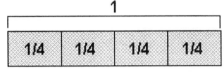

To solve 1 ÷ 1/4, ask yourself, "How many 1/4s are in 1?" There are 4 of them,
so 1 ÷ 1/4 = 4.

 Check Your Understanding 2.2.14a

Put a check (✓) next to the correct answer in the answer column.

Question	Answer
Each of these bars represents 1. Together, they represent 2. Using the bars, what is 2 ÷ 1/3? That is, how many 1/3s are in 2? ┌─1─┐ ┌─1─┐ 1/3 1/3 1/3 1/3 1/3 1/3	___ 3 ___ 6 ___ 1 1/3

Computing Division with Fractions

🏛 *Rule*

When dividing fractions, invert and multiply.

 Example

To find 3/2 ÷ 1/4

1   Invert 1/4 (or turn it upside down):

$$\frac{1}{4} \rightarrow \frac{4}{1}$$

2 Multiply 3/2 by 4/1 instead of dividing by 1/4:

$$\frac{3}{2} \div \frac{1}{4} = \frac{3}{2} \times \frac{4}{1} = \frac{12}{2} = 6$$

✔ **Check Your Understanding 2.2.14b**

Put a check (✓) next to the correct answers in the answer column.

Question	Answer
1. How many 1/8s are in 3/4?	___ 3/32 ___ 6 ___ 1/4
2. What is 9/11 ÷ 2/7?	___ 63/22 ___ 16/13 ___ 18/77

Topics Related to: Dividing Fractions

2.2.13 Multiplying Fractions

2.3 Decimals

2.3.1 Decimal Numbers

A **decimal number** is a number that uses **place value** based on powers of 10. The decimal point separates the **whole number** part of the number from the fractional part.

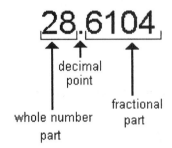

place value

Place value is the value assigned to a digit based on the place it holds relative to the decimal point. For example, in the number 7.35, the 7 has a place value of 7 *ones*, the 3 has a place value of 3 *tenths*, and the 5 has a place value of 5 *hundredths*.

whole number

A whole number is any of the numbers in the set {. . . -3, -2, -1, 0, 1, 2, 3, . . .}. The whole number part of the decimal number is to the left of the decimal point. For example, the whole number part of 19.3498 is 19.

 **Example**

Here are some examples of decimal numbers: 57.3489, 1.803, 0.783, and 0.1003.

 Check Your Understanding 2.3.1

Put a check (✓) next to the correct answer in the answer column.

Question	Answer
Which number has only the fractional part underlined?	___ <u>34</u>.104 ___ 9.<u>765</u> ___ 45.<u>65</u>

Topics Related to: Decimal Numbers

2.3.2 Place Value and Decimals

2.3.2 Place Value and Decimals

Every **digit** in a decimal number has a *value* based on the *place* it occupies.

This chart shows the place value of some digits in a decimal number.

decimal point	tenths	hundredths	thousandths	ten thousandths

 Example

In the decimal 0.528,

5 holds a value of 5 *tenths* because it is located in the *tenths* place

2 holds a value of 2 *hundredths* because it is located in the *hundredths* place

8 holds a value of 8 *thousandths* because it is located in the *thousandths* place

Collectively, the digits 5, 2 and 8 have a value of 528 *thousandths*.

---

digit

Any one of the 10 counting numbers: 0, 1, 2, 3, 4, 5, 6, 7, 8, 9. All rational numbers are expressed using one or more of these digits.

Check Your Understanding 2.3.2

Put a check (✓) next to the correct answers in the answer column.

Question	Answer
1. What is the place value of the 5 in the decimal number 0.5498?	___ tenths ___ hundredths ___ thousandths ___ ten thousandths
2. What is the place value of the 9 in the decimal number 0.5498?	___ tenths ___ hundredths ___ thousandths ___ ten thousandths

3. What is the place value of the 4 in the decimal number 0.5498?	___ tenths ___ hundredths ___ thousandths ___ ten thousandths
4. What is the place value of the 8 in the decimal number 0.5498?	___ tenths ___ hundredths ___ thousandths ___ ten thousandths

Topics Related to: Place Value and Decimals

2.3.1 Decimal Numbers

2.3.3 Ordering Decimals

Ordering decimal numbers means to list them in order from smallest to largest or from largest to smallest. Use these steps to help you compare and order decimal numbers.

> **whole number**
>
> A whole number is any of the numbers in the set { . . . -3, -2, -1, 0, 1, 2, 3, . . .}. The whole number part of the decimal number is to the left of the decimal point. For example, the whole number part of 19.3498 is 19.

1. List the numbers with all the decimal points aligned. If necessary, add zeros to the ends of some of the numbers. Adding zeros to the **end** of a decimal number does not change its value.

2.0		2.000
1.43		1.430
0.8	or	0.800
0.678		0.678
0.312		0.312
0.31		0.310
0.3		0.300

2. Order the numbers according to their **whole number** parts, from largest to smallest as in the above list, or from smallest to largest.

 ***Example***

The 2 in 2.0 is greater than the 1 in 1.43, so 2.0 is greater than 1.43.

---

3. Compare the **digits** in the tenths, hundredths, thousandths, etc. places — in that order.

 *Example*

The 8 in 0.800 is larger than the 6 in 0.678, so 0.8 is larger than 0.678.

 *Example*

For numbers like 0.312 and 0.310, the digits in the tenths and hundredths places are the same, but the digits in the thousandths places differ. Since 2 is greater than 0, 0.312 is greater than 0.310.

The number line shows the numbers ordered from smallest to largest.

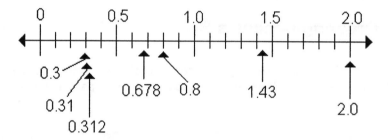

 Check Your Understanding 2.3.3

Put a check (✓) next to the correct answers in the answer column.

Question	Answer
1. Which set of numbers is ordered correctly from smallest to largest?	____ 1.33 1.4 1.298
	____ 7.6 7.718 7.73
	____ 5.2 5.138 5.217

2. Which set of numbers is ordered correctly from largest to smallest?	____ 81.129 81.23 81.13 ____ 0.438 0.399 0.51 ____ 53.8 53.73 53.724

Topics Related to: Ordering Decimals

2.3.1 Decimal Numbers
2.3.2 Place Value and Decimals

2.3.4 Rounding Decimals

The skill of *rounding* decimal numbers is used often.

 **Example**

To figure the cost per pound of 1.93 pounds of hamburger that costs $2.18, you calculate 2.18 ÷ 1.93, which equals 1.1295337. You wouldn't say that the hamburger costs $1.1295337 per pound. You would round it off to $1.13 per pound.

To round a decimal number, look at the **digit** to the right of the decimal place to which you want to round.

> **digit**
>
> Any one of the 10 counting numbers: 0, 1, 2, 3, 4, 5, 6, 7, 8, 9. All rational numbers are expressed using one or more of these digits.

Example

To round 1.1295337 to two decimal places, look at the digit in the third decimal place (thousandths place).

1.1295337
↑
third decimal place

 Rule

Some **rules for rounding** are:

- If the digit is *less than* 5, leave the preceding digit as it is.
- If the digit is *equal to or greater than* 5, round the preceding digit *up*.

 Example

In 1.1295337, the digit in the third decimal place is *greater than* 5, so round *up* to 1.13. If the digit in the third decimal place was 5, 6, 7, or 8, the decimal number would still be rounded to 1.13.

On the other hand, if the digit in the third decimal place was 4, 3, 2, 1, or 0, the decimal number would be rounded *down* to 1.12.

Check Your Understanding 2.3.4

Put a check (✓) next to the correct answers in the answer column.

Question	Answer
1. What is 31.2865 rounded to one decimal place (the nearest tenth)?	___ 31.1 ___ 31.3 ___ 31.29
2. What is 6.4572 rounded to one decimal place (the nearest tenth)?	___ 6.5 ___ 6.46 ___ 6.4
3. What is 716.2329 rounded to two decimal places (the nearest hundredth)?	___ 716.2 ___ 716.23 ___ 716.3
4. What is $3.43561 rounded to the nearest cent (the nearest hundredth)?	___ $3.40 ___ $3.43 ___ $3.44

5. What is 2.44689 lbs rounded to the nearest tenth of a pound?	____ 2.4 lbs ____ 2.45 lbs ____ 2.5 lbs
6. What is 11.54731 gallons rounded to the nearest hundredth of a gallon?	____ 11.5 gallons ____ 11.54 gallons ____ 11.55 gallons

Topics Related to: Rounding Decimals

2.3.1 Decimal Numbers
2.3.2 Place Value and Decimals

2.3.5 Adding and Subtracting Decimals

Follow these steps to *add* and *subtract* decimal numbers.

1. Write the numbers in columns so that the decimal points line up.

Adding	**Subtracting**
0.31 1.407 + 0.5	2.87 - 0.5

2. Add zeros to the numbers if necessary. Adding zeros to the end of a decimal number does not change its value.

Adding	**Subtracting**
0.31**0** 1.407 + 0.5**00**	2.87 - 0.5**0**

3. Add or subtract the numbers as if you were adding or subtracting **whole numbers**. Line up the decimal point in the answer with the other decimal points.

whole number

A whole number is any of the numbers in the set {. . . -3, -2, -1, 0, 1, 2, 3, . . .}. The whole number part of the decimal number is to the left of the decimal point. For example, the whole number part of 19.3498 is 19.

Adding	Subtracting

$$\begin{array}{r} \overset{1}{0.31\mathbf{0}} \\ 1.407 \\ +\ 0.5\mathbf{00} \\ \hline 2.217 \end{array}$$

$$\begin{array}{r} 2.87 \\ -\ 0.50 \\ \hline 2.37 \end{array}$$

Another way to add and subtract decimal numbers is to **use the calculator**. If you use the calculator, check your work by estimating the answer.

 Check Your Understanding 2.3.5a

Put a check (✓) next to the correct answer in the answer column.

Question	Answer
To add 0.8, 2.386, and 31.654 without a calculator, how should you arrange the numbers?	___ $\begin{array}{r} 0.8 \\ 2.386 \\ +\ 31.654 \\ \hline \end{array}$
	___ $\begin{array}{r} 0.8 \\ 2.386 \\ +\ 31.654 \\ \hline \end{array}$
	___ $\begin{array}{r} 0.8 \\ 2.386 \\ +\ 31.654 \\ \hline \end{array}$

 Check Your Understanding 2.3.5b

Put a check (✓) next to the correct answers in the answer column.

Question	Answer
1. What is 81.753 + 3.65?	___ 82.118 ___ 85.403 ___ 85.04
2. What is 7.76 - 0.654?	___ 7.106 ___ 7.6946 ___ 1.22

3. Which estimate most nearly approximates 7.532 + 12.69?	___ 19.9 ___ 20.1 ___ 20.2
4. The answer to 1.7689 - .931 is	___ less than 1 ___ more than 1
5. Which estimate most nearly approximates 5.814 + 6.752 + 2.399?	___ 13 ___ 14 ___ 15
6. Which estimate most nearly approximates 2.51 - 2.01111?	___ .05 ___ .50 ___ .51

Topics Related to: Adding and Subtracting Decimals

    1.1.1 Using Estimation
    2.3.6 Multiplying Decimals
    2.3.7 Dividing Decimals

2.3.6 Multiplying Decimals

Follow these steps to *multiply* decimal numbers.

1. **Round** the decimal numbers to **whole numbers** and estimate an answer. You will use your estimate later to check your exact answer.

Exact Answer	Estimate
3.024 x 1.9 ――― ?	3 x 2 ―― 6

whole number

A whole number is any of the numbers in the set {. . . -3, -2, -1, 0, 1, 2, 3, . . .}. The whole number part of the decimal number is to the left of the decimal point. For example, the whole number part of 19.3498 is 19.

2. Multiply decimal numbers just as you do whole numbers. Ignore the decimal points for now.

$$
\begin{array}{r}
3.024 \\
\times\ \ 1.9 \\
\hline
27216 \\
30240 \\
\hline
57456
\end{array}
$$

3. Count the *total* number of **digits** to the right of the decimal point in the numbers you multiplied. Your answer should have the same number of digits to the right of the decimal point. Compare the exact answer to your estimate. Are they close in value?

digit

Any one of the 10 counting numbers: 0, 1, 2, 3, 4, 5, 6, 7, 8, 9. All rational numbers are expressed using one or more of these digits.

Exact Answer

3.024 → 3 digits to the right of the decimal point
x   1.9 → 1 digit to the right of the decimal point
5.7456 → 4 digits to the right of the decimal point

Estimate

$$
\begin{array}{r}
3 \\
\times\ 2 \\
\hline
6
\end{array}
$$

Another quick way to multiply decimal numbers is to **use the calculator**. If you use the calculator, always check your work by estimating the answer.

round

Rounding is a way to write complex numbers in a simple form so that they are easier to work with. To estimate the answer to 3,983,423 x 6 = ? round the numbers to about 4,000,000 x 5. The answer is about 20,000,000.

 Check Your Understanding 2.3.6

Put a check (✓) next to the correct answers in the answer column.

Question	Answer
1. How many digits after the decimal point would the answer to 35.28 x 6.393 have?	___ 4 ___ 5 ___ 6
2. How many digits after the decimal point would the answer to 6.23 x 7.2974 have?	___ 4 ___ 5 ___ 6
3. What is 8.324 x 4.8712?	___ about 32 ___ about 36 ___ about 40
4. What is 1.645 x 9.313?	___ about 9 ___ about 18 ___ about 20

Topics Related to: Multiplying Decimals

2.3.5 Adding and Subtracting Decimals
2.3.7 Dividing Decimals

2.3.7 Dividing Decimals

Follow these steps to *divide* decimal numbers.

1. Round the decimal numbers to **whole numbers** and estimate an answer. You will use your estimate later to check your exact answer.

Exact Answer **Estimate**

$11.7 \div 1.8 = ?$ $12 \div 2 = 6$

2. Use a calculator to carry out the division.

Press 11.7, then ÷, then 1.8, then =. The answer is 6.5

3. Check your exact answer with your estimate. Your estimate should be close to your exact answer. If not, go back and check your work.

Exact Answer **Estimate**

$11.7 \div 1.8 = 6.5$ $12 \div 2 = 6$

> **whole number**
>
> A whole number is any of the numbers in the set {. . . -3, -2, -1, 0, 1, 2, 3, . . .}. The whole number part of the decimal number is to the left of the decimal point. For example, the whole number part of 19.3498 is 19.

 Check Your Understanding 2.3.7

Put a check (✓) next to the correct answers in the answer column.

Question	Answer
1. What is a reasonable estimate of 8.3 ÷ 4.2?	___ 2 ___ 3 ___ 4
2. What is a reasonable estimate of 11.8 ÷ 2.9?	___ 3 ___ 4 ___ 5

3. What is 419.657 ÷ 69.754?	___ about 5
	___ about 6
	___ about 7
4. What is 16.237998 ÷ 1.69834?	___ about 8
	___ about 12
	___ about 16

Topics Related to: Dividing Decimals

1.1.1 Using Estimation
2.3.4 Rounding Decimals
2.3.5 Adding and Subtracting Decimals
2.3.6 Multiplying Decimals

base 10

Base 10 is a number system which is based on groupings of 10. The number system we use is a base 10 system.

2.3.8 Fraction/Decimal Equivalence

A **decimal** is a **base 10** number which is written with a decimal point.

 **Example**

0.35, 4.781, and 0.0045 are decimals.

Any fraction can be written as a decimal.

For example, the *fraction* 1/100 can be written as the *decimal* 0.01.

equivalent fractions

Equivalent fractions are fractions which name the same number. For example, 12/24 and 15/30 are equivalent fractions. They are two ways of expressing 1/2.

One way to write a fraction as a decimal is to find an **equivalent fraction** with a **denominator** of 10, 100, 1,000, etc. If an equivalent fraction is not immediately obvious, you can use the calculator to divide the **numerator** by the **denominator**.

Use scaling to find an equivalent fraction with a denominator of 10, 100, 1,000, etc.

1. First look at the **denominator** of the fraction. Can you *easily* **scale up** or **scale down** the fraction to an **equivalent fraction** with a denominator of 10, 100, 1,000, etc.? Is there a number you can multiply the denominator by to get 10, 100, or 1,000?

 **Example**

3/5 can easily be scaled up to an equivalent fraction with a denominator of 10, because you can multiply 5 by 2 to get 10. Thus, you can multiply 3/5 by 2/2 (or 1) to get 6/10.

$$\frac{3}{5} = \frac{3 \times 2}{5 \times 2} = \frac{6}{10}$$

2. Next, write the equivalent fraction as a decimal. The fraction 6/10 would be written as 0.6. Remember the location of tenths, hundredths, thousandths, etc. in a decimal.

0.123
    └── thousandths
   └──── hundredths
  └────── tenths

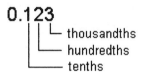 **Example**

Here are some more examples.

$$\frac{9}{10} = 0.9 \quad \text{—— tenths}$$

$$\frac{48}{100} = 0.48 \quad \text{—— hundredths}$$

$$\frac{516}{1000} = 0.516 \quad \text{—— thousandths}$$

 Check Your Understanding 2.3.8a

Put a check (✓) next to the correct answers in the answer column.

Question	Answer
1. The fraction 13/20 is equivalent to which decimal?	—— 0.65 —— 0.056 —— 0.52

2. The fraction 2/5 is equivalent to which decimal?	___ 0.1 ___ 0.25 ___ 0.4
3. The fraction 3/25 is equivalent to which decimal?	___ .09 ___ .12 ___ .25
4. The fraction 21/50 is equivalent to which decimal?	___ .42 ___ .50 ___ .71
5. The decimal .75 is equivalent to which fraction?	___ 7/10 ___ 3/4 ___ 5/7
6. The decimal 0.8 is equivalent to which fraction?	___ 4/5 ___ 5/8 ___ 8/100

numerator

The numerator is the number in a fraction that represents part of a whole. For example, in the fraction 7/13, the numerator is 7.

Use the calculator.

▶ If scaling is not immediately obvious, use the calculator to divide the **numerator** of the fraction by its **denominator**.

> 📝 *Example*
>
> Use the calculator to divide the numerator of the fraction 5/8 by its denominator: 5 ÷ 8 = 0.625. The fraction 5/8 is equivalent to the decimal 0.625.

Check Your Understanding 2.3.8b

Put a check (✓) next to the correct answers in the answer column.

Question	Answer
1. The fraction 8/23 is equivalent to which decimal?	____ 0.0347826 ____ 0.347826 ____ 0.0034782
2. The fraction 19/37 is equivalent to which decimal?	____ 0.5135135 ____ 0.0513513 ____ 0.621345
3. The fraction 7/8 is equivalent to which decimal?	____ 0.08357 ____ 0.875 ____ 0.560
4. The fraction 1/7 is equivalent to which decimal?	____ 0.01429 ____ 0.007 ____ 0.142857

Topics Related to: Fraction/Decimal Equivalence

2.3.2 Place Value and Decimals
2.4.4 Fraction/Percent Equivalence
2.4.5 Decimal/Percent Equivalence

2.4 Percents

2.4.1 Meaning of Percent

The word **percent** means "per one hundred."

 *Example*

The grid below represents a tile floor made up of 100 tiles. Fifty of the 100 tiles are shaded. So, 50 percent (or 50 per 100) are shaded and 50 percent are not shaded.

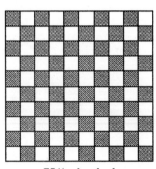

50% shaded

Percents are often written with the symbol **%**. For example, **50%** is read **fifty percent**.

 Check Your Understanding 2.4.1

Put a check (✓) next to the correct answers in the answer column.

Question	Answer
1. There are 100 trees in a park and 15 of them have just been planted. What percent of the trees have been growing in the park for a while?	____ 15% ____ 85% ____ 14%
2. Twenty-three out of 100 tomato seeds from a space station experiment did not sprout. What percent of the seeds sprouted?	____ 3% ____ 23 % ____ 77%

Topics Related to: Meaning of Percent

2.4.2 Percent as Part of a Whole
2.4.4 Fraction/Percent Equivalence

2.4.2 Percent as Part of a Whole

Percents can be used to represent a part of a whole.

percent

A percent (%) is a special kind of ratio. It compares a quantity to 100. The word percent means "per one hundred."

📝 *Example*

Imagine a cake that is cut into 4 equal pieces. The whole cake represents 100%, and each piece of the cake represents 25%.

To understand this, look at the drawing below. It represents a cake that is divided into 4 equal pieces, and then subdivided into 100 equal sections. Each section is 1% of the whole cake. Each of the four pieces contains 25 of the 100 sections, or 25% of the whole cake.

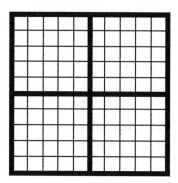

▶ To figure what percent of a whole each part is, divide 100% by the number of parts.

📝 *Example*

A box contains 25 audiotapes. What percent is each tape of the whole — all the tapes in the box?

$$100\% \div 25 = 4\%$$

Each tape represents 4% of the whole (100% or 25 tapes).

If two of the tapes are defective, what percent of the tapes is this?

$$2 \text{ tapes} \times 4\% = 8\%$$

Check Your Understanding 2.4.2

Put a check (✓) next to the correct answers in the answer column.

Question	Answer
1. A piece of paper is cut into 20 equal pieces. What percent of the original piece of paper is each piece?	___ 5% ___ 10% ___ 20%
2. A 30-foot piece of ribbon is cut into pieces that are each 10 feet long. What percent of the original ribbon is each piece?	___ 3% ___ 30% ___ 33 1/3%
3. A gardener divided her vegetable garden into five equal sections. What percent of her garden is each section?	___ 2% ___ 5% ___ 20%
4. A farmer has 25 cows. Ten of these cows are calves. What percent of the farmer's cows are calves?	___ 25% ___ 40% ___ 50%
5. A shoe store has 50 pairs of one style of sandal. Of these sandals, 15 pairs are size 6. What percent are size 6?	___ 25% ___ 30% ___ 40%
6. A classroom has 25 desks. Twenty of the desks have students using them. What percent of the desks are <u>not</u> in use?	___ 5 % ___ 20% ___ 25%

Topics Related to: Percent as Part of a Whole

2.4.1 Meaning of Percent
2.4.4 Fraction/Percent Equivalence

2.4.3 Expressing Percents as Fractions

Since the word **percent** means "per one hundred", a percent can be *expressed* as a **fraction** with a **denominator** of 100. Percents can also be expressed as fractions with denominators other than 100.

fraction

A fraction is the quotient of two quantities. It is the number that results from dividing one quantity by another. For example, 3/4 is the fraction that results from dividing 3 by 4.

✎ *Example*

▶ 75% can be expressed as the fraction 75/100.

$$75\% = \frac{75}{100}$$

▶ 75% can also be expressed as any fraction that is equivalent to 75/100.   You can use scaling to write the equivalent fractions. This example **scales down** 75/100 to 3/4 by dividing the numerator and the denominator by 25.

$$75\% = \frac{75}{100} = \frac{75 \div 25}{100 \div 25} = \frac{3}{4}$$

▶ These diagrams show how 75%, 75/100, and 3/4 are all different ways to represent the same quantity.

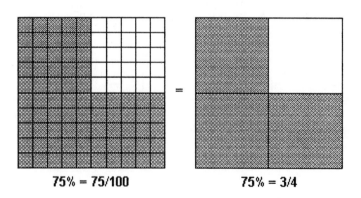

75% = 75/100   75% = 3/4

---

denominator

The denominator is the number in a fraction that represents the number of parts that make a whole. For example, in the fraction 7/13, the denominator is 13.

scale down

Scaling down a fraction or ratio means to divide the numerator and the denominator of the fraction (or each part of the ratio) by the same number. For example, you can scale down 12/15 to 4/5 by dividing both 12 and 15 by 3.

Check Your Understanding 2.4.3

Put a check (✓) next to the correct answers in the answer column.

Question	Answer
1. Which pair of fractions shows two ways to represent 30%?	___ 30/50 and 3/10 ___ 30/100 and 3/5 ___ 30/100 and 3/10
2. Which pair of fractions shows two ways to represent 40%?	___ 40/100 and 2/5 ___ 40/100 and 2/3 ___ 40/50 and 5/8
3. Finish the statement: "Sam ate 25% of the food" is the same as saying "Sam ate ____ of the food."	___ 1/25 ___ 1/8 ___ 1/4
4. Finish the statement: "The project is 60% done" is the same as saying "the project is ___ done."	___ 1/6 ___ 3/5 ___ 6/8
5. Finish the statement: "The movie is about 90% over" is the same as saying "the movie is about ___ over."	___ 9/10 ___ 5/9 ___ 2/3
6. Finish the statement: "The house is about 80% completed" is the same as saying "the house is about ___ completed."	___ 1/8 ___ 5/8 ___ 4/5

Topics Related to: Expressing Percents as Fractions

    2.2.4 Scaling Down Fractions
    2.4.1 Meaning of Percent
    2.4.2 Percent as Part of a Whole
    2.4.4 Fraction/Percent Equivalence

2.4.4 Fraction/Percent Equivalence

The word **percent** means *per one hundred*.

✒️ *Example*

If a coin is tossed 100 times and 57 of the tosses are heads, then *57 per 100* or 57% of the tosses are heads.

A fraction with a **denominator** of 100, like 57/100, can be written as a percent.

---

denominator

The denominator is the number in a fraction that represents the number of parts that make a whole. For example, in the fraction 7/13, the denominator is 13.

To write a fraction as an *equivalent percent,* you can **scale up** or **scale down**. If you can't scale up or down, you can use the calculator.

Scale up fractions to find equivalent percents.

▶ If the **denominator** of a fraction is a **factor** of 100, **scale up** to find an **equivalent fraction** with a denominator of 100.

✒️ *Example*

You can scale up 15/20 to an equivalent fraction with a denominator of 100 by multiplying by 5/5 (or 1).

$$\frac{15}{20} = \frac{15 \times 5}{20 \times 5} = \frac{75}{100} = 75\%$$

The fraction 15/20 is equivalent to 75%.

---

scale up

Scaling up a fraction or ratio means to multiply the numerator and the denominator of the fraction (or each part of the ratio) by the same number. For example, you can scale up 6/7 to 18/21 by multiplying both 6 and 7 by 3.

 Check Your Understanding 2.4.4a

Put a check (✓) next to the correct answers in the answer column.

factor

A factor is an integer that divides another integer evenly, with no remainder. For example, 3 and 7 are factors of 21. One (1) is a factor of every number.

Question	Answer
1. The fraction 6/25 is equivalent to which percent?	—— 24% —— 28% —— 30%

2. The fraction 13/20 is equivalent to which percent?	___ 13% ___ 26% ___ 65%
3. The fraction 21/50 is equivalent to which percent?	___ 21% ___ 42% ___ 51%
4. The fraction 3/5 is equivalent to which percent?	___ 30% ___ 50% ___ 60%

scale down

Scaling down a fraction or ratio means to divide the numerator and the denominator of the fraction (or each part of the ratio) by the same number. For example, you can scale down 12/15 to 4/5 by dividing both 12 and 15 by 3.

Scale down fractions to find equivalent percents.

▶ If the **denominator** of a fraction is a **multiple** of 100, **scale down** to find an **equivalent fraction** with a denominator of 100.

 Example

You can scale down 64/200 to an equivalent fraction with a denominator of 100 by dividing the numerator and the denominator by 2.

$$\frac{64}{200} = \frac{64 \div 2}{200 \div 2} = \frac{32}{100} = 32\%$$

The fraction 64/200 is equivalent to 32%.

equivalent fractions

Equivalent fractions are fractions which name the same number. For example, 12/24 and 15/30 are equivalent fractions. They are two ways of expressing 1/2.

 Check Your Understanding 2.4.4b

Draw a line to connect each item in the match column with the correct answer in the answer column.

Question	Match	Answer
1. Which percents are equivalent to each of these fractions?	32/200 32/400 40/1,000	4% 8% 16% 32%

2. Which percents are equivalent to each of these fractions?	45/300	5%
	45/500	9%
	45/900	10%
		15%
3. Which percents are equivalent to each of these fractions?	18/200	9%
	240/300	12%
	120/1,000	24%
		80%

If you can't scale up or scale down, use the calculator.

▶ You can use the calculator to find the percent that is equivalent to the fraction by dividing the **numerator** of the fraction by the **denominator**.

✍️ *Example*

To find the percent that is equivalent to the fraction 28/80, press **28 ÷ 80 =** on your calculator.

The calculator will read 0.35. The decimal number 0.35 is equivalent to 35/100, which is 35%.

Imagine moving the decimal point two places to the right to find the equivalent percent.

$$0.35 = 35\%$$

The fraction 28/80 is equivalent to 35%.

---

multiple

An integer that is a product of a specific number. For example, 15 is a multiple of 3 because it is a product of 3 and 5.

numerator

The numerator is the number in a fraction that represents part of a whole. For example, in the fraction 7/13, the numerator is 7.

Check Your Understanding 2.4.4c

Draw a line to connect each item in the match column with the correct answer in the answer column.

Question	Match	Answer
1. Which percent is most nearly equivalent to each of these fractions?	2/3 3/8 5/12	36% 38% 42% 67%
2. Which percent is most nearly equivalent to each of these fractions?	16/31 17/44 21/53	12% 39% 40% 52%
3. Which percent is most nearly equivalent to each of these fractions?	7/16 3/42 43/96	7% 9% 44% 45%

Topics Related to: Fraction/Percent Equivalence

2.2.2 Equivalent Fractions
2.2.3 Scaling Up Fractions
2.2.4 Scaling Down Fractions
2.4.5 Decimal/Percent Equivalence

2.4.5 Decimal/Percent Equivalence

A **decimal** is a **base 10** number which is written with a decimal point.

✍ *Example*

0.35, 4.781 and 0.0045 are decimals.

The decimal point separates the whole number part from the fractional part of the number.

The word **percent** means "per one hundred" or "hundredths."

Any *decimal* can be written as a *percent.* Similarly, any percent can be written as a decimal.

Decimals ▷ Percents

▶ Since percent means hundredths, you can write a decimal number as a percent by counting how many hundredths are represented by the decimal. Remember, the number which is two places to the right of the decimal point is in the hundredths position.

$$0.09 = 9 \text{ hundredths}$$
$$0.49 = 49 \text{ hundredths}$$
$$1.58 = 158 \text{ hundredths}$$
$$0.654 = 65.4 \text{ hundredths}$$

▶ Write the decimal as a fraction with a denominator of 100.

$$0.09 = 9 \text{ hundredths} = \frac{9}{100}$$
$$0.49 = 49 \text{ hundredths} = \frac{49}{100}$$
$$1.58 = 158 \text{ hundredths} = \frac{158}{100}$$
$$0.654 = 65.4 \text{ hundredths} = \frac{65.4}{100}$$

▶ Express the fraction as a percent.

$$0.09 = 9 \text{ hundredths} = \frac{9}{100} = 9\%$$
$$0.49 = 49 \text{ hundredths} = \frac{49}{100} = 49\%$$
$$1.58 = 158 \text{ hundredths} = \frac{158}{100} = 158\%$$
$$0.654 = 65.4 \text{ hundredths} = \frac{65.4}{100} = 65.4\%$$

Percents ▷ Decimals

▶ To write a percent as a decimal number, remember that percent means "per one hundred," or "hundredths."

$$97\% = 97 \text{ hundredths}$$
$$8\% = 8 \text{ hundredths}$$

▶ Then write the percent as a decimal, keeping in mind the location of hundredths in a decimal.

$$97\% = 97 \text{ hundredths } = 0.97$$
$$8\% = 8 \text{ hundredths } = 0.08$$

 Check Your Understanding 2.4.5

Draw a line to connect each item in the match column with the correct answer in the answer column.

Question	Match	Answer
1. Which decimal number is equivalent to each percent?	0.32% 3.2% 32%	0.00032 0.0032 0.032 0.32
2. Which decimal number is equivalent to each percent?	1.42% 14.2% 142%	0.0142 0.142 1.42 14.2
3. Which percent is equivalent to each decimal number?	0.0762 0.762 7.62	0.762% 7.62% 76.2% 762%

Topics Related to: Decimal/Percent Equivalence

2.3.1 Decimal Numbers
2.3.2 Place Value and Decimals
2.3.8 Fraction/Decimal Equivalence
2.4.4 Fraction/Percent Equivalence

2.4.6 Percents Greater Than 100%

percent
A percent (%) is a special kind of ratio. It compares a quantity to 100. The word percent means "per one hundred."

The filled portion of these number bars represents a **percent** that is *greater than 100%*. Each bar represents 100% and 2 1/2 bars are filled, so 250% of one bar is filled.

▶ Percents greater than 100 don't make sense in all situations.

📝 *Example*

You couldn't say: " 250% of the people surveyed preferred brand Q," because 100% is all of the people surveyed!

But you could say: "This year they surveyed 250% more people than last year," because 100% is the number of people surveyed last year.

 Check Your Understanding 2.4.6

Put a check (✓) next to the correct answers in the answer column.

Question	Answer
1. Which of these statements makes sense as a percent greater than 100%?	____ This year traffic accidents are 132% of last year. ____ Joe bought 281% of the apples in the store.

2. Which of these statements makes sense as a percent greater than 100%?	___ Lee read 168% of the books. ___ Maria's grades have improved 110% since last semester.
3. Which of these statements makes sense as a percent greater than 100%?	___ The cornfield produced 130% more than last year. ___ At least 120% of the corn is ready to be picked.

Topics Related to: Percents Greater Than 100%

2.4.1 Meaning of Percent
2.4.2 Percent as Part of a Whole
2.4.7 Percents Less Than 1%

2.4.7 Percents Less Than 1%

Use this diagram to visualize **percents** *less than 1%.*

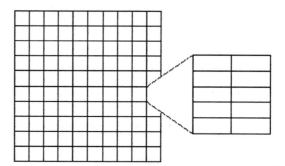

Each cell of this 100-cell grid represents 1% (1/100) of the whole.
Imagine that each cell was divided into 10 smaller cells as shown in the projection. The grid would then contain 1,000 cells (10 x 100 = 1,000).

▶ Ask yourself: If 1 cell in a 100-cell grid represents 1% (1/100), then what percent does 1 cell in a 1,000-cell grid represent? One cell in a 1,000-cell grid represents 1/1,000 or 1/10 of 1%. This can be expressed as 0.1%.

To find the fraction that is represented by a percent less than 1%, follow the steps in the example:

✎ *Example*

▶ Show the percent as a fraction with a **denominator** of 100.

$$0.4\% = \frac{0.4}{100}$$

▶ **Scale up** to a fraction with a whole number as the **numerator**:

$$\frac{0.4}{100} \times \frac{10}{10} = \frac{4}{1,000}$$

 Check Your Understanding 2.4.7a

The numerator is the number in a fraction that represents part of a whole. For example, in the fraction 7/13, the numerator is 7.

Question	Match	Answer
1. Which fraction is equivalent to each of these percents?	0.007% 0.07% 0.7%	7/100 7/1,000 7/10,000 7/100,000
2. Which fraction is equivalent to each of these percents?	0.0006% 0.006% 0.6%	6/100 6/1,000 6/100,000 6/1,000,000

denominator

The denominator is the number in a fraction that represents the number of parts that make a whole. For example, in the fraction 7/13, the denominator is 13.

numerator

The numerator is the number in a fraction that represents part of a whole. For example, in the fraction 7/13, the numerator is 7.

scale up

Scaling up a fraction or ratio means to multiply the numerator and the denominator of the fraction (or each part of the ratio) by the same number. For example, you can scale up 6/7 to 18/21 by multiplying both 6 and 7 by 3.

Check Your Understanding 2.4.7b

Put a check (✓) next to the correct answers in the answer column.

Question	Answer
1. A total of 84 students in a freshman class of 1,000 signed up to take a volleyball class. What percent of the students are signed up for volleyball?	____ 0.084% ____ 0.84% ____ 8.4% ____ 84%
2. A total of 5 people in a crowd of 1,000 are carrying umbrellas. What percent of the people are carrying umbrellas?	____ 0.005% ____ 0.05% ____ 0.5% ____ 5%
3. Of 1,000 new freshmen enrolling this year, 58 are from rural high schools. What percent of the freshmen are from rural high schools?	____ 0.058% ____ 0.58% ____ 5.8% ____ 58%
4. Out of the 10,000 eggs the chickens at High Valley Farm produced this year, 250 failed to pass inspection. What percent of the eggs failed to pass inspection?	____ 0.25% ____ 2.5% ____ 25% ____ 250%

Topics Related to: Percents Less Than 1%

2.2.3 Scaling Up Fractions
2.4.1 Meaning of Percent
2.4.2 Percent as Part of a Whole
2.4.3 Expressing Percents as Fractions
2.4.4 Fraction/Percent Equivalence
2.4.6 Percents Greater Than 100%

2.4.8 Calculating Percents

To *calculate* a **percent**, write the two **quantities** you are comparing as a **ratio**. Then use division or scaling to find an equivalent ratio expressed in hundredths. Write the ratio as a percent.

✎ *Example 1*

If you know two quantities that you want to compare, you can write a ratio. For example, a high school has an enrollment of 1,400 students. Three hundred and fifty of the students ride a bus to school. The ratio of bus students to total enrollment is:

$$\frac{\text{bus students}}{\text{total students}} = \frac{350}{1,400}$$

You can use one of these methods to find the percent:

▶ Scaling:

$$\frac{350 \div 14}{1,400 \div 14} = \frac{25}{100} = 25\%$$

When **scaling down**, divide the **numerator** and the **denominator** of the ratio by a number that will result in a denominator of 100.

▶ Division with the calculator:

$$350 \div 1400 = 0.25$$

Move the decimal point two places to the left to write the equivalent percent: 0.25 = 25%.

---

quantity

A quantity is an amount or number.

ratio

A ratio compares two or more quantities.

scale down

Scaling down a fraction or ratio means to divide the numerator and the denominator of the fraction (or each part of the ratio) by the same number. For example, you can scale down 12/15 to 4/5 by dividing both 12 and 15 by 3.

📝 **Example 2**

A fraction can be used to represent a **ratio** of two **quantities**. For example, 3 out of 4 females in a driver ed. class signed up for a car maintenance class. What percent of the females in the driver ed. class signed up?

▶ Scaling:

$$\frac{3}{4} \times \frac{25}{25} = \frac{75}{100} = 75\%$$

When **scaling up**, multiply the **numerator** and the **denominator** of the ratio by a number that will result in a denominator of 100.

▶ Division with the calculator:

$$3 \div 4 = 0.75$$

Move the decimal point two places to the right to find the equivalent percent: 75%.

 Check Your Understanding 2.4.8

Put a check (✓) next to the correct answers in the answer column.

Question	Answer
1. In the neighborhood of Foxwood, 1,600 people travel to work each day. Of these people, 320 carpool. What percent of the workers carpool?	___ 0.2% ___ 2% ___ 20%
2. On Ivy Circle, 2 out of 5 households take a morning paper. What percent of the households take a morning paper?	___ 4% ___ 40% ___ 45%
3. During the last 20 days, 12 days were cloudy. What percent of the days were cloudy during this time period?	___ 24% ___ 48% ___ 60%

scale up

Scaling up a fraction or ratio means to multiply the numerator and the denominator of the fraction (or each part of the ratio) by the same number. For example, you can scale up 6/7 to 18/21 by multiplying both 6 and 7 by 3.

4. Of the 600 voters polled, 180 voted against the new flood control proposal. What percent voted against the proposal?	___ 30% ___ 40% ___ 53%

Topics Related to: Calculating Percents

2.2.3 Scaling Up Fractions
2.2.4 Scaling Down Fractions
2.4.4 Fraction/Percent Equivalence
2.4.5 Decimal/Percent Equivalence
2.4.10 Calculations Using Percents

2.4.9 Rounding Percents

Some fractions do not yield an exactly equivalent **percent**.

percent

A percent (%) is a special kind of ratio. It compares a quantity to 100. The word percent means "per one hundred."

✎ *Example*

14/23 does not equal an exact percent. Its equivalent decimal is 0.60869 . . . and more digits follow! The equivalent percent is between 60% and 61%. A close estimate is arrived at through the following steps:

1 Use a calculator to divide 14 by 23.

$$14 \div 23 = 0.6086956$$

2 **Round** the resulting decimal number to the nearest hundredth. Round up to 0.61 because the **digit** in the thousandths place (8) is closer to 10 than to 1.

3 Write the rounded decimal (0.61) as an equivalent percent.

$$0.61 = 61/100 = 61\%$$

Check Your Understanding 2.4.9

Put a check (✓) next to the correct answers in the answer column.

Question	Answer
1. Five of every 7 persons surveyed said they agreed with a plan to restrict the operation of woodburning stoves on days when the air pollution is bad. What is the nearest approximation of the percentage of people that agree with this plan?	___ 0.71% ___ 70% ___ 71%
2. Eight of 13 movie theaters showed comedies on March 18. What is the nearest approximation of the percentage of theaters that showed comedies?	___ 0.62% ___ 61% ___ 62%
3. A basketball team won 17 out of its last 26 games. What is the nearest approximation of the team's winning percentage?	___ .66% ___ 64% ___ 65%
4. A very conscientious girl scout visited 131 households and sold cookies to 72 of those households. What is the nearest approximation of the percentage of households that bought cookies?	___ 5.5% ___ 55% ___ 56%

Topics Related to: Rounding Percents

2.3.4 Rounding Decimals
2.4.5 Decimal Percent Equivalence

2.4.10 Calculations Using Percents

percent

A percent (%) is a special kind of ratio. It compares a quantity to 100. The word percent means "per one hundred."

Percent can be used as a means to determine a number, quantity, or value. It can be used to determine the solution to the following two types of problems: "What is 35% of 200?" and "31 is 62% of what?" Examples of how to solve both types of problems are given below.

 Example

What is 20% of $10,500?

A new economy car is purchased for $10,500. It depreciates 20% in value in the first year. How much *less* is the car worth after one year?

Ask yourself: What is 20% of $10,500?

To solve this type of problem, do the following:
- Write the percent as its equivalent decimal:
  20% = 20/100 = 0.20
- Multiply the original number by the decimal equivalent.
  $10,500 x 0.20 = $2,100

The car is worth $2,100 less after one year.

 Check Your Understanding 2.4.10a

Put a check (✓) next to the correct answers in the answer column.

Question	Answer
1. Jane buys a bike for $500. When she sells the bike it is worth 26% less than when she bought it. How much has the bike depreciated in value?	___ $13 ___ $130 ___ $140
2. Tortilla chips at the grocery store were $1.99/bag last week. The price this week has dropped by 31%. How much has the price of chips dropped?	___ 65¢ ___ 6¢ ___ 62¢

3. It cost Marcel $600/month in living expenses to attend school last year. If the cost of living has increased 4% since last year, how much more per month can he expect to spend this year?	___ $2.40 ___ $24.00 ___ $240.00

 **Example**

230 is 40% of what?

A brick mason completed about 40% of the brick work on a fireplace on a certain day. If he used 230 bricks to do this, how many bricks does he need for the entire job (from start to finish)?

Ask yourself: 230 is 40% of what?

To solve this type of problem, do the following:
- Write the percent as its equivalent decimal.
  $$40\% = 40/100 = 0.40$$
- Write an equation.
  $$0.40 \times [\ ] = 230$$
- Use the calculator and solve for the unknown.
  $$[\ ] = 230 \div 0.40$$
  $$[\ ] = 575$$

575 bricks are needed to build the fireplace.

 Check Your Understanding 2.4.10b

Put a check (✓) next to the correct answers in the answer column.

Question	Answer
1. A writer finished approximately 33% of the book he was working on. If he wrote nine chapters, how many chapters will be in the completed book?	___ 22 ___ 24 ___ 27
2. A software salesperson sold 85% of her goal for the month. If she sold 357 software packages, what was her original sales goal?	___ 320 ___ 303 ___ 420

3. Fitzwater City's transportation authority reports that 15,000 people, or 8% of the city's population, ride the bus each week. What is the population of Fitzwater City?	—— 120,000 —— 187,500 —— 1,200,000

Topics Related to: Calculations Using Percents

2.3.6 Multiplying Decimals
2.3.7 Dividing Decimals
2.4.5 Decimal/Percent Equivalence
2.4.8 Calculating Percents
2.4.13 Percent Increase
2.4.14 Percent Decrease

2.4.11 Estimating Percents: Calculations

Sometimes you may not need to find the exact amount represented by a given **percent**.

percent

A percent (%) is a special kind of ratio. It compares a quantity to 100. The word percent means "per one hundred."

📝 *Example*

If a clothing store advertises 25% off an original price of $49.95, a customer can *estimate* the amount of money that would be saved. To arrive at a good estimate follow these steps:

▶ Round the original price to the nearest dollar amount: $50.00

▶ Determine the fraction that is equivalent to 25%: 1/4

▶ Ask yourself: What is 1/4 of $50.00? Think: 1/2 of $50 is $25. Therefore, 1/4 of $50 is 1/2 of 25, or $12.50. The sale price is $12.50 off the regular price.

Sometimes it may not be practical to round a price to the nearest dollar amount.

 **Example**

If the price of a new suit is $137.99 and the advertised sale price is 42% off, it may not be practical to estimate 42% of $138. These steps make the task simpler:

1 Round $138 to the nearest $10 ($140) and 42% to the nearest 10% (40%).
2 Break $140 into $100 and $40 and find 40% of each:

    40% of $100 = $40 and
    40% of $40 = $16,
    so 40% of $140 = $40 + $16 = $56.

The sale price is approximately $56 off the original price.

 Check Your Understanding 2.4.11

Put a check (✓) next to the correct answers in the answer column.

Question	Answer
1. A coat that originally sold for $159.99 is advertised at 20% off the original price. Which estimate most nearly approximates the amount saved if the coat is purchased at the sale price?	___ $16 ___ $32 ___ $40
2. Tickets to the theater are $48. Students are able to obtain them at 5% off the original price. Which estimate most nearly approximates the amount saved by a student purchasing a ticket?	___ $0.25 ___ $2.50 ___ $25.00
3. If Stacey takes the bus on a weekday, she can save 12% on the cost of a $60 ticket. Which estimate most nearly approximates the cost of a $60 ticket on a weekday?	___ $6 ___ $50 ___ $54

4. Doyle wants to buy a sweater that is 30% off the sticker price of $39.50. Which estimate most nearly approximates the cost of the sweater?	___ $12 ___ $28 ___ $30

Topics Related to: Estimating Percents: Calculations

2.3.4   Rounding Decimals
2.3.6   Multiplying Decimals
2.4.3   Expressing Percents as Fractions
2.4.5   Decimal/Percent Equivalence
2.4.10 Calculations Using Percents

2.4.12 Estimating Percents: Common Sense

To estimate is to determine an approximate value. There are many ways to estimate **percents**. One involves *common sense* in everyday situations.

percent

A percent (%) is a special kind of ratio. It compares a quantity to 100. The word percent means "per one hundred."

✒️ *Example 1*

A store owner who has been in business for one month may reasonably predict a 150% increase of sales within a year. A percent increase of 100% means that sales doubled. An increase of 150% means that sales more than doubled. This is a reasonable prediction. Sales are very low because many people are not yet aware of the store's existence. As more people become familiar with the store, sales should increase significantly.

✒️ *Example 2*

On the other hand, it may not be reasonable to assume that within a year, there will be a 150% increase in the number of high school students in an established community where the population has remained fairly constant. Common sense will tell a person that if a community's population shows no significant increase, then student population which comprises a part of the community will not increase significantly either.

Example 3

Another example of common sense in everyday situations involves **interest**. For example, a savings and loan company may want to increase its profits by increasing the interest it charges on its loans. But if it raises its interest rate significantly higher than competing companies, it runs the risk of losing customers who will want to be charged the least expensive rate they can find.

✔ Check Your Understanding 2.4.12

Put a check (✓) next to the correct answers in the answer column.

Question	Answer
1. Approximately 700 new residents moved to the town of Blackstone, which last year had a population of 7,500 residents before the new residents moved in. Which is the best commonsense prediction for the percent increase of students in the town's schools?	___ 10% ___ 40% ___ 50%
2. What is the best commonsense prediction for the annual percent increase in sales at a store that just opened two months ago?	___ 10% ___ 40% ___ 110%
3. The annual rainfall in Drybone is usually about 3 inches per year. In wet years, Drybone may get as much as 10 inches per year. What percent increase in rainfall would be a commonsense prediction for a year which was projected to be wetter than usual?	___ 100% ___ 200% ___ 300%

Topics Related to: Estimating Percents: Common Sense

2.4.4   Fraction/Percent Equivalence
2.4.5   Decimal/Percent Equivalence
2.4.6   Percents Greater Than 100%
2.4.8   Calculating Percents
2.4.13 Percent Increase
2.4.14 Percent Decrease

2.4.13 Percent Increase

Percent *increase* compares:

the amount that a quantity or value *increases*
with
the original quantity or value before the increase.

 *Example*

A girl scout troop sold 240 boxes of cookies in one year and 300 boxes of cookies the next year. The increase is 300 - 240, or 60 boxes. The percent increase compares the increase (60 boxes) with the number that was sold the previous year (240 boxes).

To determine the percent increase:

1. Write the comparison as a fraction:

$$\frac{\text{increase}}{\text{original quantity}} = \frac{60}{240}$$

2. Determine the decimal equivalent of the fraction:

$$\frac{60}{240} = 0.25$$

3. Write the decimal as its equivalent percent:

$$0.25 = 25\%$$

4. The percent increase in sales is 25%.

Check Your Understanding 2.4.13

Put a check (✓) next to the correct answer in the answer column.

Question	Answer
1. There were about 25,000 cans of food donated to the food bank in the spring. The following spring about 30,000 cans were donated. What was the percent increase in the number of cans donated to the food bank?	___ 16% ___ 20% ___ 25%
2. Last year about 50,000 people voted in the mayoral election. This year nearly 55,000 people voted in the same election. What was the percent increase in the number of votes cast?	___ 8% ___ 10% ___ 15%
3. Owen's power bill showed that last year he used 204 kilowatt hours of electricity compared with 246 this year. What percent increase does this represent?	___ 15% ___ 21% ___ 30%
4. Last year the tax on Marilyn's car was $125. This year the tax is $150. What percent did her taxes increase?	___ 10% ___ 15% ___ 20%

Topics Related to: Percent Increase

2.4.4 Fraction/Percent Equivalence
2.4.5 Decimal/Percent Equivalence
2.4.8 Calculating Percents
2.4.14 Percent Decrease

2.4.14 Percent Decrease

Percent *decrease* compares:

> the amount that a quantity or value *decreases*
>> with
>
> the original quantity or value before the decrease.

✍ *Example*

A Little League baseball team sold 20 T-shirts in May and 17 T-shirts in June. The decrease from May to June is 20 - 17, or 3 T-shirts. The percent decrease compares the decrease (3 T-shirts) with the number sold in May (20 T-shirts).

To determine the percent decrease:

1. Write the comparison as a fraction.

$$\frac{\text{decrease}}{\text{original quantity}} = \frac{3}{20}$$

2. Determine the decimal equivalent of the fraction.

$$\frac{3}{20} = 0.15$$

3. Write the decimal as an equivalent percent.

$$0.15 = 15\%$$

4. The percent decrease in sales from May to June is 15%.

Check Your Understanding 2.4.14

Put a check (✓) next to the correct answers in the answer column.

Question	Answer
1. The price of tomatoes dropped from 59¢/lb to 41¢/lb. What percent did the price of tomatoes decrease?	___ 22% ___ 31% ___ 44%
2. There were 46 students enrolled in a graphic design class in the fall semester. In the winter semester, 25 students signed up to take the class. What was the percent decrease in the number of students taking the class in the winter?	___ 39% ___ 42% ___ 46%
3. An audio shop sold 1,248 classical music tapes last year and only 987 this year. What was the percent decrease in classical music audiotape sales?	___ 15% ___ 21% ___ 30%
4. Lucille had a $148 phone bill one month and a $33 phone bill the next. What percent did her phone bill decrease from one month to the next?	___ 65% ___ 73% ___ 78%

Topics Related to: Percent Decrease

2.4.4   Fraction/Percent Equivalence
2.4.5   Decimal/Percent Equivalence
2.4.8   Calculating Percents
2.4.13 Percent Increase

2.4.15 Percents and Circle Graphs

Circle graphs are often used to show data that is expressed in percents.   The whole circle represents 100%, and if the graph were marked into 100 equal sections, each section would represent 1%.

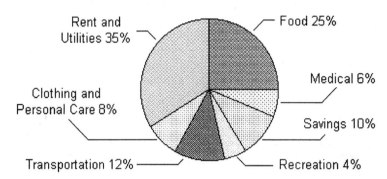

This graph shows John's budget in **percents**. The whole circle represents 100% of his monthly after-tax income. The sections of the graph show the breakdown of his income in percents.

The information in the graph can be used to determine how much money John budgets in each area.

✎ *Example*

If John's monthly income (after taxes) is $1,200, how much money does he budget for food each month?

The circle graph shows that John spends 25% of his income on food. Ask yourself: 25% of $1,200 is how many dollars?

25% x $1,200 = 0.25 x $1,200 = $300.

Refer to Topics Related to: "Calculations Using Percents" to review how to solve this type of problem.

percent

A percent (%) is a special kind of ratio. It compares a quantity to 100. The word percent means "per one hundred."

Check Your Understanding 2.4.15a

Refer to this graph of John's budget to answer the questions that follow.

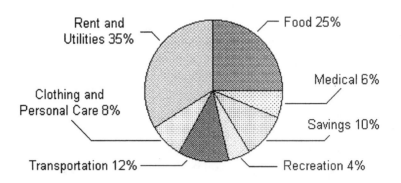

Put a check (✓) next to the correct answers in the answer column.

Question	Answer
1. If John's monthly income (after taxes) is $1,200, how much does he budget for rent and utilities each month?	___ $350 ___ $400 ___ $420
2. Based on John's $1,200/month income, how much does he budget for clothing, personal care, and transportation per month?	___ $200 ___ $240 ___ $260
3. John received a raise of $50/month (after taxes). So his monthly income went up to $1,250/month. If he leaves his budgeted percent for savings the same, how much more will he be able to put in savings each month with this raise?	___ $5 ___ $50 ___ $125

Topics Related to: Percents and Circle Graphs

2.2.4 Scaling Down Fractions
2.4.2 Percent as Part of a Whole
2.4.5 Decimal/Percent Equivalence
2.4.8 Calculations Using Percents

Check Your Understanding 2.4.15b

Refer to the graph below to answer the questions that follow. This circle graph shows the percent of people enrolled in classes at the 25th Street Community Center last year.

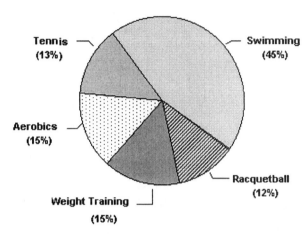

Draw a line to connect each item in the match column with the correct answer in the answer column.

Question	Match	Answer
1. What percent of people were enrolled in these combined categories?	racquetball/ weight training	15%
		27%
	weight training/ aerobics	28%
	tennis/aerobics	30%

Put a check (✓) next to the correct answers in the answer column.

Question	Answer
2. Last year a total of 2,213 people enrolled in classes at the 25th Street Community Center. How many people took swimming lessons last year? (Round to the nearest whole number.)	___ 332 ___ 996 ___ 1,221
3. Of the 2,213 people who enrolled in classes last year, how many people took weight training and aerobics classes? (Round to the nearest whole number.)	___ 332 ___ 528 ___ 664

2.5 Answers to Questions

Answers to 2.1.1

Correct Answer	Explanation
1. 20	In the number 6,329, the two is in the tens place. 2 x 10 = 20.
2. one million dollars	One million (1,000,000) has 7 digits.

Answers to 2.1.2

Correct Answer	Explanation
1. -121	The number -121 is 121 units from 0, so its magnitude is 121. The number 99 is only 99 units from 0. A magnitude of 121 is greater than a magnitude of 99.
2. 457	The number 457 is 457 units from 0. The numbers 36, -420, and -2 are 36, 420, and 2 units respectively from 0. The number 457 has the greatest magnitude. It is furthest from 0.
3. -13	The number -13 is 13 units from 0, so its magnitude is 13. A magnitude of 13 is less than a magnitude of 14.
4. 77	The number 77 is 77 units from 0. The numbers 245, -390, and -1,327, are 245, 390, and 1,327 units respectively from 0. The number 77 has the least magnitude. It is closest to 0.

Answers to 2.1.3

Correct Answer	Explanation
1. -8, 8 -(-8), -8 -(-(-8)), 8	-8 and 8 are opposites. -(-8) is the same as 8. Its opposite is -8. -(-(-8)) is the same as -8. Its opposite is 8.
2. -(-(35)), -35 -(-(-(-35))), -35 -(-(-35)), 35	-(-(35)) is the same as 35. Its opposite is -35. -(-(-(-35))) is the same as 35. Its opposite is -35. -(-(-35)) is the same as -35. Its opposite is 35.
3. -(-13), 13 -(-(-13)), -13	-(-13) is the same as 13. -(-(-13)) is the same as -13.

Answers to 2.1.4

Correct Answer	Explanation
1. 24 + (-6)	24 + (-6) = 18
2. -7 + (-16)	-7 + (-16) = -23

Answers to 2.1.5

Correct Answer	Explanation
1. -7 - (-20)	The expression -7 - (-20) is the same as -7 + 20, which equals 13.
2. 9 - 36	The expression 9 - 36 equals -27.

Answers to 2.1.6

Correct Answer	Explanation
1. -49 x 31 -78 ÷ -15 ÷ -7	You do not need to perform the computation to see that the results will be negative. An odd number of negative signs means the product or quotient will be negative.
2. -3527 ÷ -6 - 51 x 5 x -77	You do not need to perform the computation to see that the results will be positive. An even number of negative signs means the product or quotient will be positive.

Answers to 2.1.7.1

Correct Answer	Explanation
1. 142 48 556 874	These numbers are even, and they are divisible by 2.
2. 556 218 244 972	These numbers are even, and they are divisible by 2.

Answers to 2.1.7.2

Correct Answer	Explanation
1. 621 372 864	The digits of each of these numbers add up to a multiple of 3, so the numbers are all divisible by 3. 621 ⟶ 6 + 2 + 1 = 9 372 ⟶ 3 + 7 + 2 = 12 864 ⟶ 8 + 6 + 4 = 18
2. 873 492 81	The digits of each of these numbers add up to a multiple of 3, so the numbers are all divisible by 3. 873 ⟶ 8 + 7 + 3 = 18 492 ⟶ 4 + 9 + 2 = 15 81 ⟶ 8 + 1 = 9

Answers to 2.1.7.3

Correct Answer	Explanation
1. 432 376 596 2,300	The last two digits of each of these numbers is a multiple of 4, so the numbers are all divisible by 4. 4<u>32</u> 3<u>76</u> 5<u>96</u> 2,3<u>00</u> Note that a number ending in two zeros, such as 2,300, is divisible by 4. Because 4 is a multiple of 0 $(4 \times 0 = 0$ and $0 \div 4 = 0)$.
2. 212 856 996 828	The last two digits of each of these numbers is a multiple of 4, so the numbers are all divisible by 4. 2<u>12</u> 8<u>56</u> 9<u>96</u> 8<u>28</u>

Answers to 2.1.7.4

Correct Answer	Explanation
1. 765 860 465 6,500	The last digit of each of these numbers is 0 or 5, so the numbers are all divisible by 5.
2. 1,235 430 745 145	The last digit of each of these numbers is 0 or 5, so the numbers are all divisible by 5.

Answers to 2.1.7.5

Correct Answer	Explanation
1. 684 9,639 297 693	The digits of each of these numbers add up to a multiple of 9, so the numbers are all divisible by 9. 684 $\longrightarrow$ $6 + 8 + 4 = 18$ 9,639 $\longrightarrow$ $9 + 6 + 3 + 9 = 27$ 297 $\longrightarrow$ $2 + 9 + 7 = 18$ 693 $\longrightarrow$ $6 + 9 + 3 = 18$

2. 2,178 765 396 6,984	The digits of each of these numbers add up to a multiple of 9, so the numbers are all divisible by 9. 2,178 $\longrightarrow$ 2 + 1 + 7 + 8 = 18 765 $\longrightarrow$ 7 + 6 + 5 = 18 396 $\longrightarrow$ 3 + 9 + 6 = 18 6,984 $\longrightarrow$ 6 + 9 + 8 + 4 = 27

Answers to 2.1.7.6

Correct Answer	Explanation
1. 430 820 120 460	The last digit of each of these numbers is 0, so all the numbers are divisible by 0.
2. 3,450 860 370 310	The last digit of each of these numbers is 0, so all the numbers are divisible by 0.

Answers to 2.1.8

Correct Answer	Explanation
1. 9	The number 9 divides into 27 evenly, so it is a factor. 27 ÷ 9 = 3
2. 15	The number 15 divides into 45 evenly, so it is a factor. 45 ÷ 15 = 3
3. 3, 6, 12	The numbers 3, 6, and 12 divide into 45 evenly, so they are factors. 48 ÷ 3 = 16 48 ÷ 6 = 8 48 ÷ 12 = 4

4. 2, 6, 8	The numbers 2, 6, and 8 divide into 96 evenly, so they are factors. $$96 \div 2 = 48$$ $$96 \div 6 = 16$$ $$96 \div 8 = 12$$

Answers to 2.1.9

Correct Answer	Explanation
1. 98	The number 7 multiplied by 14 is 98, so 98 is a multiple of 7.
2. 117	The number 9 multiplied by 13 is 117, so 117 is a multiple of 9.
3. 96, 120	The number 8 multiplied by 12 is 96. The number 8 multiplied by 15 is 120. Therefore, 96 and 120 are multiples of 8.
4. 90, 105	The number 15 multiplied by 6 is 90. The number 15 multiplied by 7 is 105. Therefore, 90 and 105 are multiples of 15.

Answers to 2.1.10

Correct Answer	Explanation
1. 17	The number 17 is prime because it has only two factors: 1 and 17.
2. 23	The number 23 is prime because it has only two factors: 1 and 23.
3. 37	The number 37 is prime because it has only two factors: 1 and 37.

Answers to 2.1.11

Correct Answer	Explanation
1. 21, 49, 63	The number 21 is composite because it has 4 factors: 1, 3, 7, and 21. The number 49 is composite because it has 3 factors: 1, 7 and 49. The number 63 is composite because it has 5 factors: 1, 3, 7, 9, and 63. The number 53 is not composite because it has only 2 factors: 1 and 53.
2. 39 and 81	The number 39 is composite because it has 4 factors: 1, 3, 13, and 39. The number 81 is composite because it has 3 factors: 1, 9 and 81. The number 59 is not composite because it has only 2 factors: 1 and 59. The number 73 is not composite because it has only 2 factors: 1 and 73.

Answers to 2.1.12

Correct Answer	Explanation
1. 1, 2, 4, 5, 8, 10, 20, 40	The number 40 is divisible by all of these numbers. The factor pairs are 1 x 40, 2 x 20, 4 x 10, and 5 x 8.
2. 1, 2, 3, 4, 6, 8, 12, 24	The number 24 is divisible by all of these numbers. The factor pairs are 1 x 24, 2 x 12, 3 x 8, and 4 x 6.

Answers to 2.1.13

Correct Answer	Explanation
1. 2 x 2 x 2 x 2	This is the prime factorization of 16, because each factor is prime and the product of the factors is 16.
2. 2 x 2 x 2 x 3	This is the prime factorization of 24 because each factor is prime and the product of the factors is 24.

3. 8	If 2 is one of two factors of 16, the other must be 8. $2 \times 8 = 16$

Answers to 2.1.14

Correct Answer	Explanation
1. 6	The common factors of 18 and 24 are 1, 2, 3, and 6. The greatest of these common factors is 6.
2. 10	The common factors of 30 and 40 are 1, 2, 5, 6, and 10. The greatest of these common factors is 10.
3. 4	The common factors of 20 and 36 are 1, 2, and 4. The greatest of these common factors is 4.

Answers to 2.1.15

Correct Answer	Explanation
1. 3 + 7 + 21 + 34 71 + 6 + 83 + 49	You don't need to do the calculation to answer this question. Just count the number of odd addends. Since there are three odd addends in each of these expressions, their sums are odd. $$3 + 7 + 21 + 34 = 65$$ $$71 + 6 + 83 + 49 = 209$$
2. 94 + 17 + 81 15 + 99 + 47 + 69	There are two odd addends and one even addend in this expression, so the sum is even. $$94 + 17 + 81 = 192$$ There are four odd addends in this expression, so the sum is even. $$15 + 99 + 47 + 69 = 230$$

Answers to 2.1.16

Correct Answer	Explanation
1. 39 x 121 x 53 x 77 855 x 21 x 69	You don't need to multiply to answer this question. Just check to see if all the factors are odd. All the factors are odd in these expressions, so the products are also odd. 39 x 121 x 53 x 77 = 19,258,239 855 x 21 x 69 = 1,238,895
2. 98 x 5 x 16 6 x 32 x 17 x 2	There are even factors in these expressions, so the products are even. 98 x 5 x 16 = 7,840 6 x 32 x 17 x 2 = 6,528

Answers to 2.1.17

Correct Answer	Explanation
years in a century minutes in an hour	Both of these applications have a finite, or limited, set of numbers. There are 100 years in a century and 60 minutes in an hour.

Answers to 2.1.18

Correct Answer	Explanation
1. 22	22 ÷ 12 = 1 remainder 10, so 22 is congruent to 10 on a 12-hour clock.
2. 38	38 ÷ 9 = 4 remainder 2, so 38 is congruent to 2 on a 9-hour clock.
3. 19	19 ÷ 7 = 2 remainder 5, so 19 is congruent to 5 on a 7-hour clock.
4. 30	30 ÷ 8 = 3 remainder 6, so 30 is congruent to 6 on an 8-hour clock.

Answers to 2.1.19

Correct Answer	Explanation
1. 11 + 3	On a 12-clock, 11 + 3 = 2, because (14 ÷ 12 = 1, remainder 2). The other choices sum to 5.
2. 6 + 7	On a 9-clock, 6 + 7 = 4, because (13 ÷ 9 = 1, remainder 4). The other choices sum to 3.
3. 5 + 10	On a 7-clock, 5 + 10 = 1, because (15 ÷ 7 = 2, remainder 1). The other choices sum to 4.

Answers to 2.1.20

Correct Answer	Explanation
1. 2 - 5	On a 12-clock, 2 - 5 = 9.
2. 2 - 4	On a 6-clock, 2 - 4 = 4.
3. 1 - 4	On a 10-clock, 1 - 4 = 7.

Answers to 2.1.21

Correct Answer	Explanation
1. 2 x 13	On a 12-clock, 2 x 13 = 2 (26 ÷ 12 = 2 remainder 2). The other expressions equal 3.

2. 2 x 3	On a 5-clock, 2 x 3 = 1 (6 ÷ 5 = 1 remainder 1). The other expressions equal 4.
3. 6 x 8	On a 9-clock, 6 x 8 = 3 (48 ÷ 9 = 5 remainder 3). The other expressions equal 5.

Answers to 2.2.1

Correct Answer	Explanation
1. 6/9	The denominator of this fraction refers to a whole which is divided into 9 parts. This grid is divided into 9 parts. There are 6 white cells, so 6/9 of the grid is white.
2. 11/16	The denominator of this fraction refers to a whole which is divided into 16 parts. This grid is divided into 16 parts. There are 11 white cells, so 11/16 of the grid is white.

Answers to 2.2.2

Correct Answer	Explanation
1. 10/16	5/8 = 10/16 To write 5/8 as the equivalent fraction 10/16, multiply both the numerator and the denominator of 5/8 by 2. $$\frac{5}{8} = \frac{5 \times 2}{8 \times 2} = \frac{10}{16}$$

2. 9/12	3/4 = 9/12
	To write 3/4 as the equivalent fraction 9/12, multiply both the numerator and the denominator of 9/12 by 3. $$\frac{3}{4} = \frac{3 \times \mathbf{3}}{4 \times \mathbf{3}} = \frac{9}{12}$$

Answers to 2.2.3

Correct Answer	Explanation
1. 4/4	If you scale up 3/11 by 4/4, the result is 12/44. $$\frac{3}{11} = \frac{3 \times 4}{11 \times 4} = \frac{12}{44}$$
2. 3/3	If you scale up 5/9 by 3/3, the result is 15/27. $$\frac{5}{9} = \frac{5 \times 3}{9 \times 3} = \frac{15}{27}$$
3. 8/8	If you scale up 2/5 by 8/8, the result is 16/40. $$\frac{2}{5} = \frac{2 \times 8}{5 \times 8} = \frac{16}{40}$$

Answers to 2.2.4

Correct Answer	Explanation
1. 5/5	If you scale down 15/35 by 5/5, the result is 3/7. $$\frac{15 \div 5}{35 \div 5} = \frac{3}{7}$$

2. 8/8	If you scale down 8/32 by 8/8, the result is 1/4. $$\frac{8 \div 8}{32 \div 8} = \frac{1}{4}$$
3. 3/3	If you scale down 12/27 by 3/3, the result is 4/9. $$\frac{12 \div 3}{27 \div 3} = \frac{4}{9}$$

Answers to 2.2.5

Correct Answer	Explanation
1. 5/9	The fraction 5/9 is in lowest terms because the greatest common factor of 5 and 9 is 1.
2. 5/12	The fraction 5/12 is in lowest terms because the greatest common factor of 5 and 12 is 1.
3. 3/5	The fraction 3/5 is in lowest terms and is equivalent to 9/15. $$9/15 \div 3/3 = 3/5$$

Answers to 2.2.6

Correct Answer	Explanation
1. 12, 24	The numbers 12 and 24 are common denominators of 3/4 and 5/6 — they are common multiples of 4 and 6.
2. 18, 36	The numbers 18 and 36 are common denominators of 1/6 and 2/9 — they are common multiples of 6 and 9.

Answers to 2.2.7a

Correct Answer	Explanation
1. 16/4 + 1/4	The number 4 equals the fraction 16/4, so 4 1/4 equals 16/4 + 1/4.
2. 48/8 + 3/8	The number 6 equals the fraction 48/8, so 6 3/8 equals 48/8 + 3/8.

Answers to 2.2.7b

Correct Answer	Explanation
1. 7/2	The mixed number 3 1/2 = 6/2 + 1/2 = 7/2.
2. 26/5	The mixed number 5 1/5 = 25/5 + 1/5 = 26/5.

Answers to 2.2.8

Correct Answer	Explanation
1. 3 1/4	The three filled grids represent 3 and the 1 filled cell represents 1/4. Another way to think about this is: 13 ÷ 4 = 3 remainder 1.
2. 1 5/12	The filled grid represents 1 and the 5 filled cells represent 5/12. Another way to think about this is: 17 ÷ 12 = 1 remainder 5.

Answers to 2.2.9

Correct Answer	Explanation
1. 5/6	The numerator (5) is less than the denominator (6), so 5/6 is less than 1.
2. 11/11	The numerator and denominator are equal, so 11/11 is equal to 1.
3. 11/7	The numerator (11) is greater than the denominator (7), so 11/7 is greater than 1.

Answers to 2.2.10

Correct Answer	Explanation
1. 7/8	The denominators are the same (8), so to compare 5/8 and 7/8, look at their numerators: 7 is greater than 5, so 7/8 is greater than 5/8.
2. 11/13	The denominators are the same (13), so to compare 3/13, 9/13, and 11/13 look at their numerators: 11 is greater than 3 and 9, so 11/13 has the greatest value.
3. 16/17	The denominators are the same (17), so to compare 2/17, 6/17, and 16/17 look at their numerators: 16 is greater than 2 and 6, so 16/17 has the greatest value.

Answers to 2.2.10.1

Correct Answer	Explanation
1. 5/8	The fraction 5/8 is a little greater than 4/8, which equals 1/2. So 5/8 is greater than 1/2. That is, 5/8 > 4/8 or 5/8 > 1/2 (> means "is greater than").
2. 2/3	The fraction 11/20 is a little greater than 10/20, which equals 1/2. So 11/20 is greater than 10/20. That is, 11/20 > 10/20 or 11/20 > 1/2 (> means "is greater than"). 2/3 is greater than 1/2.

Answers to 2.2.10.2

Correct Answer	Explanation
1. 3/8	Using the common denominator of 24, the equivalent fractions are: 5/24 = 5/24, 1/3 = 8/24, and 3/8 = 9/24. Of these equivalent fractions (5/24, 8/24, and 9/24), 9/24 has the largest numerator, so 3/8 has the greatest value.
2. 5/6	Using the common denominator of 18, the equivalent fractions are: 5/6 = 15/18, 7/9 = 14/18, and 2/3 = 12/18. Of these equivalent fractions (15/18, 14/18, and 12/18), 15/18 has the largest numerator, so 5/6 has the greatest value.
3. 3/4	Using the common denominator of 24, the equivalent fractions are: 3/4 = 18/24, 5/6 = 20/24, and 7/8 = 21/24. Of these equivalent fractions (18/24, 20/24, and 21/24), 18/24 has the smallest numerator, so 3/4 has the least value.

Answers to 2.2.11

Correct Answer	Explanation
1. 3/5	If you round 28 to 30 and 49 to 50, and then reduce 30/50 to lowest terms (divide by 10), you get 3/5.
2. 1/4	If you round 19 to 20 and 76 to 80, and then reduce 20/80 to lowest terms (divide by 20), you get 1/4.

Answers to 2.2.12

Correct Answer	Explanation
1. 12/16 + 3/16 = 15/16	Using a common denominator of 16, the fraction 3/4 = 3/4 x 4/4 = 12/16, so 3/4 + 3/16 equals 12/16 + 3/16 = 15/16.

2. 15/18 - 4/18 = 11/18	Using a common denominator of 18, 5/6 = 15/18 and 2/9 = 4/18, so 5/6 - 2/9 equals 15/18 - 4/18 = 11/18.
3. 21/24 - 16/24 = 5/24	Using a common denominator of 24, 7/8 = 21/24 and 2/3 = 16/24, so 7/8 - 2/3 equals 21/24 - 16/24 = 5/24.

Answers to 2.2.13

Correct Answer	Explanation
1. 6/15	Multiply the denominators together and multiply the numerators together: $$\frac{2}{3} \times \frac{3}{5} = \frac{6}{15}$$
2. 3/28	Multiply the denominators together and multiply the numerators together: $$\frac{1}{4} \times \frac{3}{7} = \frac{3}{28}$$
3. 15/56	Multiply the denominators together and multiply the numerators together: $$\frac{5}{7} \times \frac{3}{8} = \frac{15}{56}$$

Answers to 2.2.14a

Correct Answer	Explanation
6	$2 \div 1/3 = 6$. There are six 1/3s in these two bars.

Answers to 2.2.14b

Correct Answer	Explanation
1. 6	*How many 1/8s are there in 3/4?* This is the same as asking what is 3/4 ÷ 1/8? 3/4 ÷ 1/8 = 3/4 x 8/1 = 24/4, or 6.
2. 63/22	9/11 ÷ 2/7 = 9/11 x 7/2 = 63/22, or 2 19/22.

Answers to 2.3.1

Correct Answer	Explanation
9.<u>765</u>	The underlined part of the decimal is the fractional part. It represents 765 thousandths, or 765/1,000.

Answers to 2.3.2

Correct Answer	Explanation
1. tenths	The number 5 holds a value of 5 tenths because it is located in the tenths place.
2. thousandths	The number 9 holds a value of 9 thousandths because it is located in the thousandths place.
3. hundredths	The number 4 holds a value of 4 hundredths because it is located in the hundredths place.
4. ten thousandths	The number 8 holds a value of 8 10 thousandths because it is located in the 10 thousandths place.

Answers to 2.3.3

Correct Answer	Explanation
1. 7.6 7.718 7.73	These numbers are listed from smallest to largest.

2.	53.8 53.73 53.724	These numbers are listed from largest to smallest.

Answers to 2.3.4

Correct Answer	Explanation
1. 31.3	To round 31.2865 to one decimal place, look at the digit in the second decimal place (8). Since 8 is greater than 5, 31.2865 is rounded up to 31.3.
2. 6.5	To round 6.4572 to one decimal place, look at the digit in the second decimal place (5). Since 5 is equal to 5, 6.4572 is rounded up to 6.5.
3. 716.23	To round 716.2329 to two decimal places, look at the digit in the third decimal place (2). Since 2 is less than 5, 716.2329 is rounded to 716.23.
4. $3.44	To round $3.43561 to two decimal places, look at the digit in the third decimal place (5). Since 5 is equal to 5, $3.43561 is rounded to $3.44.
5. 2.4 lbs	To round 2.44689 pounds to one decimal place, look at the digit in the second decimal place (4). Since 4 is less than 5, 2.44689 is rounded to 2.4.
6. 11.55 gallons	To round 11.54731 gallons to two decimal places, look at the digit in the third decimal place (7). Since 7 is greater than 5, 11.54731 is rounded up to 11.55.

Answers to 2.3.5a

Correct Answer	Explanation
0.8 2.386 <u>31.654</u>	Line up the decimal points before adding decimal numbers.

Answers to 2.3.5b

Correct Answer	Explanation
1. 85.403	Write the numbers in columns with decimal points lined up. Add a zero to 3.65 (3.650). Then add the numbers as you would whole numbers: $$\begin{array}{r} 81.753 \\ +\ 3.650 \\ \hline 85.403 \end{array}$$ Remember the decimal point is the sum.
2. 7.106	Write the numbers in columns with decimal points lined up. Add a zero to 7.76 (7.760). Then subtract the numbers as you would whole numbers: $$\begin{array}{r} \overset{0\ 1}{7.7\cancel{6}0} \\ -\ 0.654 \\ \hline 7.106 \end{array}$$ Remember the decimal point is the difference.
3. 20.2	To find an estimate to the nearest tenth for 7.532 + 12.69, round both numbers to the nearest tenth (7.5 + 12.7). Then add them together to get 20.2.
4. less than one	One way to decide if the answer to 1.7689 - .931 is less than 1 or more than 1 is to round both numbers to the nearest tenth (1.8 - .9) and subtract in your mind. The answer is .8 so the answer is less than 1.
5. 15	To find an estimate to the nearest whole number for 5.814 + 6.752 + 2.399, round all three numbers to the nearest whole number (6 + 7 + 2). Then add them together to get 15.
6. .50	To find an estimate to the nearest hundredth for 2.51 - 2.01111, round both numbers to the nearest hundredth (2.51 - 2.01). Then subtract to get .50.

Answers to 2.3.6

Correct Answer	Explanation
1. 5	There are 2 digits to the right of the decimal point in 35.28 and there are 3 digits to the right of the decimal point in 6.393. Since 2 + 3 = 5, there will be 5 digits to the right of the decimal point in 35.28 x 6.393.
2. 6	There are 2 digits to the right of the decimal point in 6.23 and there are 4 digits to the right of the decimal point in 7.2974. Since 2 + 4 = 6, there will be 6 digits to the right of the decimal point in 6.23 x 7.2974.
3. about 40	To estimate 8.324 x 4.8712 to the nearest whole number, round to the nearest whole number (8 x 5) and multiply. You get 40.
4. about 18	To estimate 1.645 x 9.313 to the nearest whole number, round to the nearest whole number (2x 9) and multiply. You get 18.

Answers to 2.3.7

Correct Answer	Explanation
1. 2	Round 8.3 to 8 and 4.2 to 4. 8 ÷ 4 = 2. So 2 is a good estimate. The actual quotient is 1.976.
2. 4	Round 11.8 to 12 and 2.9 to 3. 12 ÷ 3 = 4. So 4 is a good estimate. The actual quotient is 4.069.
3. about 6	Round 419.657 ÷ 69.754 to 420 ÷ 70. Divide to get 6. The actual quotient is 6.016.
4. about 8	Round 16.237998 ÷ 1.69834 to 16 ÷ 2. Divide to get 8. The actual quotient is 9.56109.

Answers to 2.3.8a

Correct Answer	Explanation
1. 0.65	The fraction 13/20 is equivalent to 65/100, or 0.65. $$\frac{13}{20} = \frac{13 \times 5}{20 \times 5} = \frac{65}{100} = 0.65$$
2. 0.4	The fraction 2/5 is equivalent to 4/10, or 0.4. $$\frac{2}{5} = \frac{2 \times 2}{5 \times 2} = \frac{4}{10} = 0.4$$
3. .12	The fraction 3/25 is equivalent to 12/100, or .12. $$\frac{3}{25} = \frac{3 \times 4}{25 \times 4} = \frac{12}{100} = .12$$
4. .42	The fraction 21/50 is equivalent to 42/100 or, .42. $$\frac{21}{50} = \frac{21 \times 2}{50 \times 2} = \frac{42}{100} = .42$$
5. · 3/4	The decimal .75 can be written 75/100. When you scale down this fraction by dividing the numerator and denominator by 25, you get 3/4.
6. 4/5	The decimal .8 can be written 80/100. When you scale down dividing the numerator and denominator by 20, you get 4/5.

Answers to 2.3.8b

Correct Answer	Explanation
1. 0.347826	The fraction 8/23 is equivalent to 8 ÷ 23, which equals 0.347826.
2. 0.5135135	The fraction 19/37 is equivalent to 19 ÷ 37, which equals 0.5135135.
3. 0.875	The fraction 7/8 is equivalent to 7 ÷ 8, which equals 0.875.
4. 0.142857	The fraction 1/7 is equivalent to 1 ÷ 7, which equals 0.142857.

Answers to 2.4.1

Correct Answer	Explanation
1. 85%	If 15 of the 100 trees have just been planted, then 85 of the trees have been growing in the park for a while (100 - 15 = 85). Eighty-five per one hundred is 85%.
2. 77%	If 23 of the 100 seeds did not sprout, then you know that 77 did (100 - 23 = 77). You know that 77 per one hundred is 77%.

Answers to 2.4.2

Correct Answer	Explanation
1. 5%	There are now 20 pieces of paper. Each piece of paper is 1/20 of 100% (1/20 = 5/100 = 5%).
2. 33%	Three feet is 100% of the original length of ribbon; so 1 foot is 1/3 of 100% (10/30 = 1/3 = 33 1/3%).
3. 20%	The garden is divided into 5 equal sections. Each section is 1/5 of 100% (1/5 = 20/100 = 20%).

4. 40%	The farmer has 25 cows. Each cow is 1/25 of the whole herd (100%), or 4%. Ten calves, 10 x 4% equal 40% of the herd.
5. 30%	The shoe store has 50 pairs of a certain style of sandal. Each pair is 1/50 of the whole inventory (100%) of sandals, or 2%. If 15 pairs of sandals are size 6, this represents 15 x 2%, or 30% of the store's inventory of this style of sandal.
6. 20%	The classroom has 25 desks; so each desk represents 1/25 of 100%, or 4%. Twenty of the desks are being used; so this means 5 desks are not in use (25 - 20 = 5). Five desks represents 5 x 4%, or 20% of the desks.

Answers to 2.4.3

Correct Answer	Explanation
1. 30/100 and 3/10	The fraction 30/100 represents 30%. You can scale down 30/100 by 10/10 to the fraction 3/10, which also represents 30%.
2. 40/100 and 2/5	The fraction 40/100 represents 40%. You can scale down 40/100 by 20/20 to the fraction 2/5, which also represents 40%.
3. 1/4	25% is the same as 25/100. You can scale down this fraction by 25/25 to get 1/4.
4. 3/5	60% is the same as 60/100. You can scale down this fraction by 20/20 to get 3/5.
5. 9/10	90% is the same as 90/100. You can scale down this fraction by 10/10 to get 9/10.
6. 4/5	80% is the same as 80/100. You can scale down this fraction by 20/20 to get 4/5.

Answers to 2.4.4a

Correct Answer	Explanation
1. 24%	The fraction 6/25 =24/100 = 24%. $$\frac{6}{25} = \frac{6 \times 4}{25 \times 4} = \frac{24}{100} = 24\%$$
2. 65%	The fraction 13/20 = 65/100 = 65%. $$\frac{13}{20} = \frac{13 \times 5}{20 \times 5} = \frac{65}{100} = 65\%$$
3. 42%	The fraction 21/50 = 42/100= 42% $$\frac{21}{50} = \frac{21 \times 2}{50 \times 2} = \frac{42}{100} = 42\%$$
4. 60%	The fraction 3/5=60/100=60% $$\frac{3}{5} = \frac{3 \times 20}{5 \times 20} = \frac{60}{100} = 60\%$$

Answers to 2.4.4b

Correct Answer	Explanation

1. 32/200 -----16%
    32/400 ----- 8%
    40/1000 --- 4%
	The fraction 32/200 = 16/100 =16%.
	The fraction 32/400 = 8/100 = 8%.
	The fraction 40/1000 = 4/100 = 4%.
	
	Here is an example of how to scale down to get your answers.
	
	$$\frac{32}{400} = \frac{32 \div 4}{400 \div 4} = \frac{8}{100} = 8\%$$

2. 45/300 ----15%
   45/500 ---- 9%
   45/900 ---- 5%
	The fraction 45/300 = 15/100 = 15%.
	The fraction 45/500 = 9/100 = 9%.
	The fraction 45/900 = 5/100 =5%.
	
	Here is an example of how to scale down to get your answers.
	
	$$\frac{45}{500} = \frac{45 \div 5}{500 \div 5} = \frac{9}{100} = 9\%$$

3. 18/200 ----- 9%
  240/300 --- 80%
  120/1,000 --12%
	The fraction 18/200 = 9/100 = 9%.
	The fraction 240/300 = 80/100 = 80%.
	The fraction 120/1,000 = 12/100 = 12%.
	
	Here is an example of how to scale down to get your answers.
	
	$$\frac{18}{200} = \frac{18 \div 2}{200 \div 2} = \frac{9}{100} = 9\%$$

Answers to 2.4.4c

Correct Answer	Explanation

1. 2/3 --------- 67%
  3/8 -------- 38%
  5/12 ------ 42%
	The fraction 2/3 = 0.667 = 67%.
	The fraction 3/8 = 0.375 = 38%.
	The fraction 5/12 = 0.417 = 42%.

2. 16/31 ----- 52%
  17/44 ---- 39%
  21/53 --- 40%
	The fraction 16/31 = 0.516 = 52%.
	The fraction 17/44 = 0.386 = 39%.
	The fraction 21/53 = 0.396 = 40%.

3. 7/16 ------ 44%
  3/42 ----- 7%
  43/96 --- 45%
	The fraction 7/16 = 0.4375 = 44%.
	The fraction 3/42 = 0.0714 = 7%.
	The fraction 43/96 = 0.447 = 45%.

Answers to 2.4.5

Correct Answer	Explanation
1. 0.32% ------ 0.0032 3.2% ------- 0.032 32% -------- 0.32	0.32% = .32/100 = 0.0032 3.2% = 3.2/100 = 0.032 32% = 32/100 = .32
2. 1.42% ------- 0.0142 14.2% ------ 0.142 142% ------- 1.42	1.42% = 1.42/100 = 0.0142 14.2% = 14.2/100 = 0.142 142% = 142/100 = 1.42
3. 0.0762 ------ 7.62% 0.762 --------- 76.2% 7.62 ------------ 762%	0.0762 = 7.62 hundredths = 7.62/100 = 7.62% 0.762 = 76.2 hundredths = 76.2/100 = 76.2% 7.62 = 762 hundredths = 762/100 = 762%

Answers to 2.4.6

Correct Answer	Explanation
1. This year traffic accidents are 132% of last year.	This statement makes sense. Last year's number of traffic accidents represent 100% and this year's accidents are 132% of last year's.
2. Maria's grades have improved 110% since last semester.	This statement makes sense. Maria's grades last semester represent 100% and her grades this semester are 110% of last semester's grades.
3. The cornfield produced 130% more than last year.	This statement makes sense. The 100% represents the corn produced last year and the corn produced this year is 130% of last year's crop.

Answers to 2.4.7a

Correct Answer	Explanation
1. 0.007% ----- 7/100,000 0.07% ------ 7/10,000 0.7% -------- 7/1,000	0.007% = 0.007/100 x 1,000/1,000 = 7/100,000 0.07% = 0.07/100 x 100/100 = 7/10,000 0.7% = 0.7/100 x 10/10 = 7/1,000

<table>
<tr>
<td>
2.
0.0006% ---- 6/1,000,000
0.006% ------ 6/100,000
0.6% ---------- 6/1,000
</td>
<td>
0.0006% = 0.0006/100 x 10,000/10,000 = 6/1,000,000
0.006% = 0.006/100 x 1,000/1,000 = 6/100,000
0.6% = 0.6/100 x 10/10 = 6/1,000

Write the percent as a hundredth. Then scale up to a fraction with a whole number as the numerator by multiplying the numerator and denominator by the same amount.
</td>
</tr>
</table>

Answers to 2.4.7b

Correct Answer	Explanation
1. 8.4%	The percentage 8.4% is the same as 84/1,000 (84 students signed up for the volleyball class out of a freshman class of 1,000).
2. 0.5%	The percentage 0.5% is the same as 5/1,000 (5 people carrying umbrellas in a crowd of 1,000).
3. 5.8%	If 1,000 freshmen is 100%, then what percent of 1,000 is one freshman? One is 1/1,000. If you scale down by dividing the numerator and denominator by 10, you get 0.1/100 or 0.1%. So 58 x 0.1% is 5.8%
4. 2.5%	If 10,000 eggs is 100%, then what percent of 10,000 is one egg? It's 1/10,000. If you scale down by dividing the numerator and denominator by 100, you get 0.01/100 or 0.01%. So, 250 eggs are 250 x 0.01%, or 2.5% of the whole.

Answers to 2.4.8

Correct Answer	Explanation
1. 20%	The fraction 320/1,600 scales down to 20/100 or 20%. $$\frac{320 \div 16}{1,600 \div 16} = \frac{20}{100} = 20\%$$
2. 40%	The fraction 2/5 scales up to 40/100 or 40%. $$\frac{2}{5} \times \frac{20}{20} = \frac{40}{100} = 40\%$$
3. 60%	The fraction 12/20 scales up to 60/100 or 60%. $$\frac{12}{20} = \frac{12 \times 5}{20 \times 5} = \frac{60}{100} = 60\%$$
4. 30%	The fraction 180/600 scales down to 30/100 or 30%. $$\frac{180}{600} = \frac{180 \div 6}{600 \div 6} = \frac{30}{100} = 30\%$$

Answers to 2.4.9

Correct Answer	Explanation
1. 71%	The decimal equivalent of 5/7 is 0.7142857. Rounding to the nearest hundredth gives you 0.71, which equals 71%.
2. 62%	The decimal equivalent of 8/13 is 0.6153846. Rounding to the nearest hundredth gives you 0.62, which equals 62%.
3. 65%	The decimal equivalent of 17/26 is 0.6538462. Rounding to the nearest hundredth gives you 0.65, which equals 65%.

4. 55%	The decimal 72/131 is 0.5496183. Rounding to the nearest hundredth gives you .55, which equals 55%.

Answers to 2.4.10a

Correct Answer	Explanation
1. $130	The bike is worth 26% less than when Jane bought it. 26% of $500 is equivalent to 0.26 x $500, which is $130.
2. 62¢	The chips have dropped 31% in price. 31% of $1.99 is equivalent to 0.31 x $1.99, which is 62¢.
3. $24.00	Marcel can expect to spend $24.00 more this year. 4% of $600 is equivalent to .04 x $600, which is $24.00.

Answers to 2.4.10b

Correct Answer	Explanation
1. 27	The number of chapters in the finished book equals 9 chapters ÷ 0.33 = 27 chapters. Another way to solve this problem is to use logic. If approximately 33% equals 9 chapters, then 100% equals 9 x 3 chapters = 27 chapters.
2. 420	The number of software packages sold equals 357 packages ÷ 0.85 = 420 software packages.
3. 187,500	The total population equals 15,000 people ÷ 0.08 = 187,500 people.

Answers to 2.4.11

Correct Answer	Explanation
1. $32	One way you might have done this is to: 1. Round up $159.99 to $160. 2. Find 10% of $160, and then multiply that amount by 2 (to find 20%).
2. $2.50	One way you might have done this is to: 1. Round up $48 to $50. 2. Find 10% of $50, and then half that much again (to find 5%).
3. $54	One way you might have done this is to: 1. Round 12% down to 10%. 2. Find 10% of 60, which is $6. 3. Subtract $6 from 60, which is $54.
4. $28	One way you might have done this is to: 1. Round $39.50 to $40. 2. Find 10% of $40 ($4), and then multiply that amount by 3 (3 x $4= $12). 3. Subtract $12 from $40, which is $28.

Answers to 2.4.12

Correct Answer	Explanation
1. 10%	The population rose by approximately 10%. It is reasonable to assume the same percent increase in student population.
2. 110%	Sales are probably very low because the business has just started. It is reasonable to assume that sales will more than double within the year.

3. 200%	If Drybone usually gets about 3 inches of rain per year, a 100% increase would mean that the rainfall doubles to about 6 inches (3 + 3). So a 200% increase means Drybone would get about 9 inches (3 + 3 + 3). That's close to 10 inches, the amount that falls in wet years.

Answers to 2.4.13

Correct Answer	Explanation
1. 20%	Here's one way to complete this problem: 1. Figure the amount of increase. (30,000 - 25,000 = 5,000) 2. Then divide the increase by the original quantity. (5,000/25,000 = 5/25 = 1/5 = 0.20) 0.20 equals 20%.
2. 10%	Here's one way to complete this problem: 1. Figure the amount of increase. (55,000 people - 50,000 people = 5,000 people) 2. Then divide the increase by the original quantity. (5,000/50,000 = 1/10 = 0.10) 0.10 equals 10%.
3. 21%	Here's one way to complete this problem: 1. Figure the amount of increase. (246 kilowatts - 204 kilowatts = 42 kilowatts) 2. Then divide the increase by the original quantity. (42/204 = 0.2059) 0.2059 approximately equals 21%.

4. 20%	Here's one way to complete this problem:
	1. Figure the amount of increase. ($150 - $125 = $25)
	2. Then divide the increase by the original quantity. ($25/$125 = 1/5 = 0.20)
	0.20 equals 20%

Answers to 2.4.14

Correct Answer	Explanation
1. 31%	Here's one way to complete this problem: 1. Figure the amount of decrease. (59¢ - 41¢ = 18¢) 2. Then divide the decrease by the original quantity. (18¢/ 59¢ = 0.3051) 0.3051 is approximately equal to 31%.
2. 46%	Here's one way to complete this problem: 1. Figure the amount of decrease. (46 students - 25 students = 21students) 2. Then divide the decrease by the original quantity. (21/46 = .04565) 0.4565 is approximately equal to 46%.
3. 21%	Here's one way to complete this problem: 1. Figure the amount of decrease. (1,248 tapes - 987 tapes = 261 tapes) 2. Then divide the increase by the original quantity. (261/1,248 = 0.2091) 0.2091 is approximately equal to 21%.

4. 78%	Here's one way to complete this problem: 1. Figure the amount of decrease. ($148 - $33 = $115) 2. Then divide the decrease by the original quantity. ($115/$148 = 0.77702) 0.77702 is approximately equal to 78%.

Answers to 2.4.15a

Correct Answer	Explanation
1. $420	Look at the pie graph to find the percent budgeted for rent and utilities (35%). Then ask yourself: 35% of $1,200 is what amount? 35% x $1,200 = .35 x $1,200 = $420
2. $240	Look for the percent budgeted for clothing and personal care and transportation (8% + 12% =20%). 20% x $1,200 = .20 x $1,200 = $240

3. $5	Find the difference in the dollar amount budgeted for savings before the raise and after the raise.
	
	Look for the amount budgeted for savings (10%).
	
	Amount before raise:
	    10% x $1,200 = .10 x $1,200 = $120
	Amount after raise:
	    10% x $1,250 = .10 x $1,250 = $125
	
	$125 - $120 = $5
	
	John will save $5/month more after the raise.

Answers to 2.4.15b

Correct Answer	Explanation
1. racquetball/ weight training ---- 27% weight training/ aerobics ----------- 30% tennis/ aerobics ----------- 28%	Look for the percent listed for each category on the pie graph. Then add the amounts for the combined categories together to come up with the combined percentages. For example, racquetball is 12% and weight training shows 15%. So together they account for 27% of the students who enrolled.
2. 996	Look for the percent enrolled in swimming (45%). Then ask yourself: 45% of 2,213 people is how many people? 45% x 2,213 = .45 x 2,213 = 995.85 995.85 is approximately 996 people.
3. 664	You know that weight training and aerobics together accounted for 30% of the people enrolled. 30% x 2,213 = .30 x 2,213 = 663.9 663.9 is approximately 664 people.

Chapter 3

Data Comprehension

3.1 Tables and Charts... 169

    3.1.1 Understanding Titles 169
    3.1.2 Understanding Rows 170
    3.1.3 Understanding Columns...................................... 171
    3.1.4 Reading Schedules and Tables 172
    3.1.5 Patterns in Data 173
    3.1.6 Creating Table Headings 175
    3.1.7 Organizing Data 177
    3.1.8 Generating Table Data 178

3.2 Average, Median, Mode, and Range 179

    3.2.1 Finding the Average 179
    3.2.2 Finding the Median... 180
    3.2.3 Finding the Mode 184
    3.2.4 Finding the Range 186

3.3 Basic Graphs 188

    3.3.1 Reading Pictographs.. 188
    3.3.2 Reading Bar Graphs 190
    3.3.3 Reading Double Bar Graphs 192
    3.3.4 Reading Line Graphs 195
    3.3.5 Reading Scatter Plots 197
    3.3.6 Elimination with Scatter Plots............................ 199
    3.3.7 Trends in Graphs 202
    3.3.8 Plotting Points on a Graph 203
    3.3.9 Building Pictographs 206
    3.3.10 Building Bar Graphs 209
    3.3.11 Building Line Graphs 213
    3.3.12 Building Scatter Plots 215

3.4 More Graphs 219

    3.4.1 Reading Circle Graphs....................................... 219
    3.4.2 Reading Line Plots 220
    3.4.3 Reading Stem-and-Leaf Plots 222
    3.4.4 Clusters.. 223
    3.4.5 Gaps... 224
    3.4.6 Outliers... 225
    3.4.7 Reading Box-and-Whisker Plots 227
    3.4.8 Extremes.. 229
    3.4.9 Quartiles... 230
    3.4.10 Comparing Box-and-Whisker Plots.................... 231

3.4.11   Building Circle Graphs 232
3.4.12   Building Line Plots... 234
3.4.13   Building Stem-and-Leaf Plots.. 235
3.4.14   Building Box-and-Whisker Plots.. 237

3.5 Answers to Questions 239

Learn about basic statistics and how to interpret and create tables, graphs, and other data representations.

3.1 Tables and Charts

3.1.1 Understanding Titles

The *title* is the first part of a table that you should read. It tells you what is shown in the table. Many people look at the **data** in a table before they read the title. Then they have a difficult time understanding what the table represents.

World Cup Soccer, Winners and Runners-Up: 1978 - 1990
(*Indicates Home Country Winner)

YEAR	WINNER	SCORE	RUNNER-UP	SCORE	SITE
1978	Argentina*	3	Netherlands	1	Buenos Aires
1982	Italy	3	West Germany	1	Madrid
1986	Argentina	3	West Germany	2	Mexico City
1990	West Germany	1	Argentina	0	Rome

Look at the title of this table. It tells you that the table contains the winners and runners-up of the World Cup soccer tournament from 1978 to 1990.

  Check Your Understanding 3.1.1

Put a check (✓) next to the correct answers in the answer column.

Question	Answer
1. An asterisk means	____ the winner scored the most goals in a final. ____ the country that has won the most World Cup finals. ____ the winner was playing in its home country.
2. The title says that this table shows	____ the semifinalists from 1978 to 1990. ____ the finalists from 1978 to 1990. ____ the finalists in 1978 and 1990.

data

Data is a collection of information such as facts or numbers. It is often used to form some sort of conclusion. For example, Company XYZ earned a profit of $5 million two years ago and $5.6 million the following year. From this data the company can conclude that during the second year its profits increased by $0.6 million.

Topics Related to: Understanding Titles

3.1.2 Understanding Rows
3.1.3 Understanding Columns

3.1.2 Understanding Rows

The *rows* of a table are the horizontal sections which are generally read from left to right. The first row in this table is shaded.

Merton's Most Improved Restaurant: Gray's Restaurant Award 1990 - 1994

DATE	1990	1991	1992	1993	1994
RESTAURANT	Brown's	Lamb's	Stewpot	Lamb's	The Roof
STAR RATING	*****	***	***	****	****

This table has three rows.

- The first row, labeled DATE, shows the dates from 1990 to 1994.
- The second row, labeled RESTAURANT, shows the restaurants in the town of Merton that were awarded Gray's Restaurant Award.
- The third row, labeled STAR RATING, shows the number of stars that were awarded to each restaurant (based on the quality of the food).

 Check Your Understanding 3.1.2

Put a check (✓) next to the correct answers in the answer column.

Question	Answer
1. Which row in this table should you look at to determine which restaurant had the most awards?	____ row 1 ____ row 2 ____ row 3
2. Which row in this table should you look at to see the highest rating a restaurant was awarded between 1990 and 1994?	____ row 1 ____ row 2 ____ row 3

Topics Related to: Understanding Rows

3.1.1 Understanding Titles
3.1.3 Understanding Columns

3.1.3 Understanding Columns

The *columns* of a table are the vertical sections that are generally read from top to bottom. The third column of this table is shaded.

World Cup Soccer, Winners and Runners-Up: 1978 - 1990
(*Indicates Home Country Winner)

YEAR	WINNER	SCORE	RUNNER-UP	SCORE	SITE
1978	Argentina*	3	Netherlands	1	Buenos Aires
1982	Italy	3	West Germany	1	Madrid
1986	Argentina	3	West Germany	2	Mexico City
1990	West Germany	1	Argentina	0	Rome

This table has four columns.

- The first column, labeled YEAR, shows the years the World Cup was held.
- The second column, labeled WINNER, shows the names of the winning teams.
- The third column, labeled SCORE, shows the scores of the winning teams.
- The fourth column, labeled RUNNER-UP, shows the names of the countries that were runners-up.
- The fifth column, labeled SCORE, shows the scores of the runners-up.
- The sixth column, labeled SITE, shows the cities where the World Cup final was held.

 Check Your Understanding 3.1.3

Put a check (✓) next to the correct answers in the answer column.

Question	Answer
1. Which column shows the countries that won the World Cup?	____ column 2 ____ column 4 ____ column 6
2. Which column lists the scores of the runners-up?	____ column 1 ____ column 3 ____ column 5

Topics Related to: Understanding Columns

3.1.1 Understanding Titles
3.1.2 Understanding Rows

title

The title is the first part of a table or graph that you should read. It tells you what is shown in the table or graph, and is usually above or below the table.

3.1.4 Reading Schedules and Tables

To read a *schedule* or *table,* first look at the **title**, and then go to the **rows** and **columns** to interpret the information.

World Cup Soccer, Winners and Runners-Up: 1978 - 1990
(*Indicates Home Country Winner)

YEAR	WINNER	SCORE	RUNNER-UP	SCORE	SITE
1978	Argentina*	3	Netherlands	1	Buenos Ai
1982	Italy	3	West Germany	1	Madrid
1986	Argentina	3	West Germany	2	Mexico C
1990	West Germany	1	Argentina	0	Rome

rows

Rows are the horizontal sections of a table. Rows are usually read from left to right.

▶ For example, if you want to find the winner of the World Cup in 1986:

- First, look at the title of the table (World Cup Soccer, Winners and Runners-Up: 1978 - 1990) to be certain it is the table you want.

- Second, go to the column labeled WINNER.

- Third, move down the column until you come to the row labeled 1986.

- Fourth, notice that the **cell** where the column and the row meet shows the name Argentina.

columns

Columns are the vertical sections of a table. Columns are usually read from top to bottom.

 Check Your Understanding 3.1.4

Put a check (✓) next to the correct answers in the answer column.

cell

The place in a table or chart where the row and the column meet.

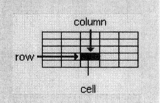

Question	Answer
1. Which team was the runner-up in the World Cup in 1982?	____ Italy ____ Madrid ____ West Germany ____ Argentina

2. What are the column and row headings for the cell that shows the World Cup final was played in Madrid?	___ WINNER and 1986 ___ SITE and 1982 ___ SITE and 1978

Topics Related to: Reading Schedules and Tables

    3.1.1 Understanding Titles
    3.1.2 Understanding Rows
    3.1.3 Understanding Columns

data

Data is a collection of information such as facts or numbers. It is often used to form some sort of conclusion. For example, Company XYZ earned a profit of $5 million two years ago and $5.6 million the following year. From this data the company can conclude that during the second year its profits increased by $0.6 million.

3.1.5 Patterns in Data

When looking at a table, it is interesting to look for a *pattern* or a trend in the **data**. Patterns can show increases or decreases in the data over time. For example, the table below shows average weekly earnings of construction workers between 1984 and 1990. Notice how the earnings increase over time.

Average Weekly Earnings of Construction Workers, 1984 - 1990

YEAR	1984	1985	1986	1987	1988	1989	1990
AVERAGE WEEKLY EARNINGS (In dollars)	458.51	464.46	466.75	480.44	495.73	512.41	526.40

Source: U.S. Dept. of Labor

Several other kinds of patterns are useful to watch for when examining data. To understand these patterns, look at the data from the table when it is plotted on a number line. Note that the numbers have been rounded to make the following plot.

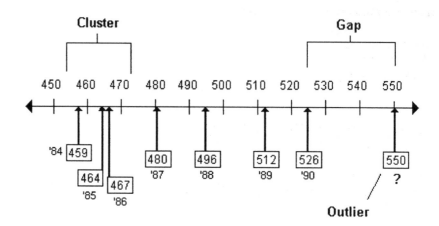

One type of pattern to look for is a **cluster**.

cluster

A cluster is a group of values in a set of data. For example, in the set 36, 22, 23, 18, 10, the values 22 and 23 form a cluster.

Notice on the number line that the values for the first three years (1984-1986) cluster together more than the values for the later years (1987-1990). This information may tell you something.

For example, in this case it tells you that construction workers' wages didn't increase as much during these years as the later years. You might want to ask why. Was the economy slow at this time? Did the housing market slump during these years?

gap

A gap refers to the space between two clusters of data or between a cluster and an outlier.

Also, watch for **gaps** in data.

Suppose the next year's data was quite a bit higher than for the previous years. The gap between the rest of the data and this **outlier** also tells you something. You know there was a dramatic increase in construction workers' salaries. Once again, you might want to find out why. Was there a sudden burst in the economy? Did interest rates go down?

outlier

An outlier is a value that is significantly removed from a cluster.

 Check Your Understanding 3.1.5

Put a check (✓) next to the correct answers in the answer column.

Question	Answer
1. Use the pattern in the table to project the average weekly earnings of construction workers in 1991. Which of these numbers is the most reasonable?	___ $513.43 ___ $539.33 ___ $597.12
2. According to the data, between which years was there the largest increase in construction workers' salaries?	___ 1986 and 1987 ___ 1988 and 1989 ___ 1989 and 1990

Topics Related to: Patterns in Data

3.4.4 Clusters
3.4.5 Gaps
3.4.6 Outliers

3.1.6 Creating Table Headings

To make a table, first decide what the *table headings* will be. The headings are the labels used for the **columns** and **rows**. The headings must be organized in a logical order.

▶ For example, if you were asked to organize the information in the following paragraph into a table, what would be the headings for the rows and columns?

columns

Columns are the vertical sections of a table. Columns are usually read from top to bottom.

> *The Lakeview Pumpkin Growers' Association holds an annual contest to find the heaviest pumpkin. In 1989, Marge Tonks won with a pumpkin that weighed 269 pounds. Su Wong's pumpkin weighed 287 pounds in 1990 (a Lakeview record), Pete Johnson's pumpkin was 265 pounds in 1991, and Al Gomez's pumpkin was 270 pounds in 1992. Kim Polanich entered in 1993, winning with a pumpkin that weighed 281 pounds, still not topping Wong's weight. In 1994, Amy Kleiner won with a 284-pound pumpkin, coming closest to the Lakeview record.*

▶ If you were to organize this information into a table, you might label the rows with the headings **Winner** and **Pumpkin Weight**. You might label the columns with the headings **Years**.

rows

Rows are the horizontal sections of a table. Rows are usually read from left to right.

Check Your Understanding 3.1.6

Put a check (✓) next to the correct answers in the answer column.

Question	Answer
1. If you wanted a table that only represented the people who won and the size of their pumpkins, what would you use for your headers?	___ **Years**, **Winner**, and **Pumpkin Weight** ___ **Winner** and **Pumpkin Weight** ___ **Years** and **Pumpkin Weight** ___ **Years** and **Winner**
2. If you wanted a table that only showed the size of the winning pumpkin between 1989 and 1994, what would you use for your headers?	___ **Years**, **Winner**, and **Pumpkin Weight** ___ **Winner** and **Pumpkin Weight** ___ **Years** and **Pumpkin Weight** ___ **Years** and **Winner**

Topics Related to: Creating Table Headings

3.1.7 Organizing Data

3.1.7 Organizing Data

Data should be *organized* so that information in the table is easy to find and the important **data** stands out.

Lakeview Pumpkin Growers' Association Awards, 1989 - 1994.

Year	1989	1990	1991	1992	1993	1994
Winner	Tonks	Wong	Johnson	Gomez	Polanich	Kleiner
Pumpkin Weight (lbs)	269	287	265	270	281	284

Data can be organized from greatest to least, alphabetically, in order of time, or in a standard order (such as name, street, city, etc.). For example, this table is ordered chronologically from 1989 to 1994.

 Check Your Understanding 3.1.7

Put a check (✓) next to the correct answers in the answer column.

Question	Answer
1. How would you organize the data in the table if you wanted to organize the table by winning pumpkin weight?	____ alphabetically ____ by date ____ heaviest to lightest
2. How would you organize the data in the table if you wanted to organize the table by the names of the winners?	____ alphabetically ____ by date ____ heaviest to lightest

Topics Related to: Organizing Data

   3.1.6 Creating Table Headings
   3.1.8 Generating Table Data

data

Data is a collection of information such as facts or numbers. It is often used to form some sort of conclusion. For example, Company XYZ earned a profit of $5 million two years ago and $5.6 million the following year. From this data the company can conclude that during the second year its profits increased by $0.6 million.

3.1.8 Generating Table Data

Data in a table can be used to find additional data or information.

Catalog Order Form

Description	Order No.	Quantity	Item Price	Total Price
Packaging Tape	0900-1221	3	$2.50	$7.50
Masking Tape	0900-1225	6	$2.00	
Invisible Tape	0900-1312		$1.50	$15.00

For example, this table is an incomplete order form. To arrive at a total price for the packaging tape, the item price of $2.50 was multiplied by the quantity of 3.

$2.50 x 3 = $7.50

 Check Your Understanding 3.1.8

Refer to the following catalog order form to answer the questions below.

Catalog Order Form

Description	Order No.	Quantity	Item Price	Total Price
Packaging Tape	0900-1221	3	$2.50	$7.50
Masking Tape	0900-1225	6	$2.00	
Invisible Tape	0900-1312		$1.50	$15.00

Put a check (✓) next to the correct answers in the answer column.

Question	Answer
1. What is the total price of the masking tape?	___ $15.00 ___ $12.00 ___ $8.00 ___ $2.00
2. What is the quantity of invisible tape?	___ 15 ___ 5 ___ 10 ___ 12

Topics Related to: Generating Table Data

    3.1.6 Creating Table Headings
    3.1.7 Organizing Data

3.2 Average, Median, Mode, and Range

3.2.1 Finding the Average

The **average** of a set of numbers is also known as the **arithmetic mean,** or simply the **mean**.

▶ To find the average of a set of numbers, first find the **sum** of the numbers. Then divide the sum by the number of items in the set.

$$\text{Average} = \frac{\text{(sum of a set of numbers)}}{\text{(number of items in the set)}}$$

✎ *Example*

For example

Set of Numbers = {10, 14, 21, 9, 11}

Sum = 10 + 14 + 21 + 9 + 11 = 65.
Number of numbers in the set = 5.
Average = 65 ÷ 5 = 13.
The average of this set of numbers is **13**.

 Check Your Understanding 3.2.1

Put a check (✓) next to the correct answers in the answer column.

Question	Answer
1. What is the average of this set of numbers? Set of Numbers = {4, 9, 11}	___ 3 ___ 24 ___ 6 ✓ 8

2. What is the average of this set of numbers? Set of Numbers = {7, 8, 11, 10}	✓ 9 ___ 7 ___ 13 ___ 11

3. Here are the weights of several pumpkins. What is the average weight of the pumpkins?
 	
  (in lbs)
 	
  269, 287, 265, 270, 281, 284
	___ 265 lbs
	✓ 276 lbs
	___ 270 lbs
	___ 268 lbs

Topics Related to: Finding the Average

3.2.2 Finding the Median
3.2.3 Finding the Mode
3.2.4 Finding the Range

3.2.2 Finding the Median

The word **median** means **middle**, so the median of a set of numbers ordered from smallest to largest is the middle number.

▶ To find the median of a set of numbers, first order the numbers from smallest to largest.

 *Example*

Set A = {7, 9, 5, 10, 4}
Set B = {4, 17, 3, 9, 6, 11}

Set A ordered from smallest to largest is {4, 5, 7, 9, 10}.

Set B ordered from smallest to largest is {3, 4, 6, 9, 11, 17}.

▶ If there is an *odd* number of terms in the set, the median is the middle number.

✍ *Example*

Set A (below) has an odd number of terms (5).

Median
↓
Set A = {4, 5, 9, 7, 10}

The median of Set A is the middle number, or **9**.

▶ If there is an *even* number of terms in the set, the median is the **average** of the *two* middle numbers.

✍ *Example*

Set B (below) has an even number of terms (6).

Set B = {3, 4, 6, 9, 11, 17}

The median is the average of these two numbers.

To find the average of the middle two numbers:

- First add the numbers: 6 + 9 = 15.
- Then divide by two: 15 ÷ 2 = **7.5**.

The median of Set B is 7.5. Note that the median of a set of numbers is not always a number in the set.

---

average

To find the average or "mean" of a group of numbers, first add the numbers, then divide the sum by the number of terms you added. For example, the average of 6, 7, and 2 is 5.
6 + 7 + 2 = 15 (Since you are adding 3 numbers, 3 is the number of terms.)
15 ÷ 3 = 5

Check Your Understanding 3.2.2a

Put a check (✓) next to the correct answers in the answer column.

Question	Answer
1. What is the median of this set of numbers? {4, 6, 9, 3, 13}	___ 4 ✓ 6 ___ 9 ___ 3 ___ 13
2. Here are some test scores. What is the median of the scores? {7, 5, 9, 4, 10, 12, 1}	✓ 7 ___ 5 ___ 9 ___ 4 ___ 10 ___ 12 ___ 1
3. Here are the prices of the used cars on Henry Lemon's used-car lot. What is the median price? $10,500 $6,200 $3,100 $6,250 $2,300 $4,280 $8,240 $6,590 $1,590	___ $4,280 ✓ $6,200 ___ $6,250 ___ $6,590

Check Your Understanding 3.2.2b

Put a check (✓) next to the correct answers in the answer column.

Question	Answer
1. What is the median of this set of numbers? {5, 11, 7, 9}	___ 7 ___ 10 ✓ 8 ___ 9
2. Here are the ages of a construction crew. What is the median age? 37, 19, 26, 24, 41, 34	___ 34 ___ 26 ✓ 30 ___ 29

Topics Related to: Finding the Median

   3.2.1 Finding the Average
   3.2.3 Finding the Mode
   3.2.4 Finding the Range

3.2.3 Finding the Mode

The **mode** is the number or numbers that occur most frequently in a set of numbers.

▶ A set of numbers may have only one mode.

📝 *Example*

{8, 9, 3, 8, 4, 8, 8, 3}

The mode of this set is **8** because it occurs more frequently than any other number in the set.

▶ A set of numbers can have *more than one mode*.

📝 *Example*

{7, 3, 6, 10, 10, 4, 3}

The numbers 4, 6, and 7 only occur once in this set of numbers. The numbers 10 and 3 occur twice, more frequently than the other numbers. So the modes of this set of numbers are **10** and **3**.

▶ If all the numbers in a set occur an equal number of times, there is *no mode*.

📝 *Example*

{8, 14, 7, 3, 15, 20}

Each number in this set occurs only once, so this set does not have a mode.

Check Your Understanding 3.2.3a

Put a check (✓) next to the correct answers in the answer column.

Question	Answer
1. What is the mode of this set of numbers? {3, 6, 5, 6, 3, 6, 7, 6}	✓ 6 ___ 3 ___ 5
2. What is the mode of the heights of these men? 6' 1", 5' 11", 5' 10", 5' 11", 6' 2", 6' 1", 6' 3"	___ 6' 1" ✓ 5' 11" and 6' 1" ___ 5' 11" ___ 6' 1" and 6' 2"

Check Your Understanding 3.2.3b

Put a check (✓) next to the correct answers in the answer column.

Question	Answer
1. How many modes does this set of numbers have? {5, 3, 8, 14, 11, 6}	✓ none ___ one ___ two ___ three
2. How many modes does this set of test scores have? 70%, 40%, 95%, 40%, 90%, 95%, 70%, 65%	___ none ___ one ___ two ✓ three

---

Topics Related to: Finding the Mode

3.2.1 Finding the Average
3.2.2 Finding the Median
3.2.4 Finding the Range

3.2.4 Finding the Range

The **range** of a set of numbers is the distance between the largest and the smallest numbers in the set. Since a distance is always a positive value, the range must always be a positive number.

🏛 *Rule*

Range = Largest Number - Smallest Number

📝 *Example*

This set of numbers {1, 2, 3, 5, 7, 9} is marked on the number line below.

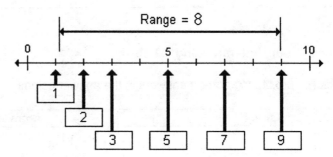

The range of this set of numbers is: 9 - 1 = **8**.

📝 *Example*

This set of numbers {-8, -7, -5, -3} is marked on the number line below.

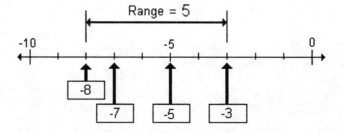

The range of this set of numbers is: (-3) - (-8) = 5.

Check Your Understanding 3.2.4

Put a check (✓) next to the correct answers in the answer column.

Question	Answer
1. What is the range of this set of numbers? $\{5, 8, 2, 11, 16, 9, 13\}$	___ 16 ___ 11 ___ 14 ___ 2
2. What is the range of this set of numbers? $\{-7, -4, -21, -19, -12\}$	___ 21 ___ -17 ___ -21 ___ 17
3. What is the range of the following amounts of money raised by six people at a sponsored walk? $15, $23, $31, $42, $19, $12	___ $30 ___ $42 ___ $31 ___ $12
4. Here are the prices of the computers Hanna has considered buying. What is the range of these prices? $1,500 $2,535 $3,950 $2,800 $1,975	___ $2,050 ___ $2,450 ___ $2,500 ___ $2,550

Topics Related to: Finding the Range

3.2.1 Finding the Average
3.2.2 Finding the Median
3.2.3 Finding the Mode

3.3 Basic Graphs

3.3.1 Reading Pictographs

A **pictograph** uses symbols (or pictures) to represent numbers. Pictographs are useful because the reader can gain an understanding of the information displayed in the graph with one quick look. There are no numbers to examine in pictographs, except in the key (or the labels on the graph).

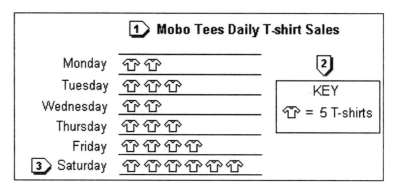

This pictograph shows the number of T-shirts sold over a period of six days at Mobo Tees T-shirt store.

Understanding the Graph

To learn more about the graph above, refer to the number labels on the graph and read the descriptions below.

1 Mobo Tees Daily T-shirt Sales

This is the title of the graph. The title is the first part of the graph that you should read. Reading the title tells you what the graph represents and makes it easier to interpret the graph.

2 KEY

A key gives you the information you need to interpret a graph. For example, in order to interpret this graph, you need to know that each T-shirt symbol represents five T-shirts.

3 Saturday

It is easy to see that the most T-shirts were sold on Saturday because it is the row with the most symbols. You can determine exactly how many T-shirts were sold on Saturday by counting the number of symbols and multiplying by 5: 6 symbols x 5 T-shirts per symbol = 30 T-shirts.

Check Your Understanding 3.3.1

Refer to the following pictograph to answer the questions below.

Mobo Tees Daily T-shirt Sales

Monday	👕 👕
Tuesday	👕 👕 👕
Wednesday	👕 👕
Thursday	👕 👕 👕
Friday	👕 👕 👕 👕
Saturday	👕 👕 👕 👕 👕 👕

KEY
👕 = 5 T-shirts

Put a check (✓) next to the correct answers in the answer column.

Question	Answer
1. How many T-shirts were sold on Thursday?	___ 3 ___ 15 ___ 30 ___ 10
2. How many T-shirt symbols would be needed to show that 35 T-shirts were sold in one day?	___ 35 ___ 6 ___ 7 ___ 5
3. Wednesday's sales total was incorrectly reported. If the total T-shirt sales for Wednesday was 20, how many T-shirt symbols should be added to the graph?	___ 1 ___ 2 ___ 3 ___ 10

Topics Related to: Reading Pictographs

3.3.9 Building Pictographs

3.3.2 Reading Bar Graphs

quantity

A quantity is an amount or number.

Bar graphs use bars to represent **quantities**. The height of a bar depends on the quantity it represents. One use for bar graphs is to compare increases and decreases in quantities over periods of time. Bar graphs can be used to quickly compare relative changes in quantity (to see that something is more or less than something else), and they can also be used to find specific quantities.

This bar graph shows the number of T-shirts sold over a six-day period at the Mobo Tees T-shirt Store.

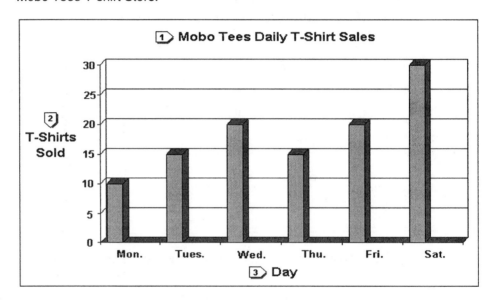

vertical axis

A vertical axis is a straight line, either imaginary or real, that runs parallel to or makes up one of the sides (usually the left side) of a graph or chart. It goes from bottom to top.

range (as a difference)

The range is the *difference* between the highest value and the lowest value in a set of data. To find the range, subtract the smallest number from the largest number.

horizontal axis

A horizontal axis is a straight line, either imaginary or real, that runs parallel to or makes up the bottom of a graph or chart. It goes from left to right.

Understanding the Graph

To learn more about the graph above, refer to the number labels on the graph and read the descriptions below.

1 Mobo Tees Daily T-Shirt Sales

This is the title of the graph. The title is the first part of the graph that you should read. Reading the title tells you what the graph represents and makes it easier to interpret the graph.

2 T-Shirts Sold

This is the label for the graph's **vertical axis**. The axis shows the **range** for the number of T-shirts sold during a six-day period. The vertical axis is read from bottom to top.

3 Day

This is the label for the graph's **horizontal axis**. The axis shows the days of the week on which T-shirts were sold. The horizontal axis is read from left to right.

Read the bar graph to find the number of T-shirts that were sold on Tuesday. Mobo Tees sold 15 T-shirts on Tuesday. To find this answer, first locate the bar that represents Tuesday. Then match the top of the bar with a number along the vertical axis (T-Shirts Sold).

 Check Your Understanding 3.3.2

Refer to the following graph to answer the questions below.

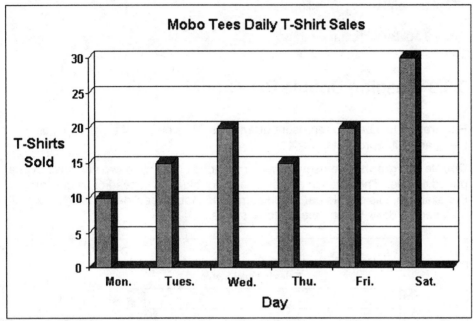

Put a check (✓) next to the correct answers in the answer column.

Question	Answer
1. On which day were fewer than 15 T-shirts sold?	___ Monday ___ Tuesday ___ Wednesday ___ Thursday
2. How many more T-shirts were sold on Friday than on Monday?	___ 15 ___ 2 ___ 5 ___ 10

3. Which day(s) had the second-highest sales?	___ Monday ___ Tuesday and Thursday ___ Wednesday and Friday ___ Thursday

Topics Related to: Reading Bar Graphs

3.3.10 Building Bar Graphs

quantity

A quantity is an amount or number.

3.3.3 Reading Double Bar Graphs

Bar graphs use bars to represent **quantities**. The height of a bar depends on the quantity it represents.

Double bar graphs are useful when comparing changes in two variables over a period of time. These types of graphs use double bars instead of single bars. For example, this double bar graph compares Mobo Tees' daily T-shirt sales with the average daily T-shirt sales in local stores.

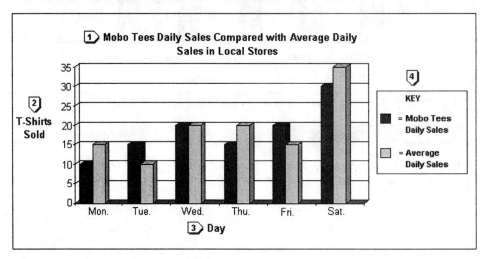

Understanding the Graph

To learn more about the graph above, refer to the number labels on the graph and read the descriptions below.

1 Mobo Tees Daily Sales . . .

This is the title of the graph. The title is the first part of the graph that you should read. Reading the title tells you what the graph represents and makes it easier to interpret the graph.

2 T-shirts Sold

This is the label for the graph's **vertical axis**. The axis shows the **range** for the number of T-shirts sold during a six-day period. The vertical axis is read from bottom to top.

3 Day

This is the label for the graph's **horizontal axis**. The axis shows the days of the week for which daily T-shirt sales and averages were recorded. The horizontal axis is read from left to right.

4 KEY

A key gives you information you need to interpret a graph. For example, in order to interpret this graph, you need to know that the dark shaded bars represent Mobo Tees' T-shirt sales and the light shaded bars represent the average T-shirt sales in local stores.

Compare the number of T-shirts sold on Saturday at Mobo Tees with the average number of T-shirts sold on Saturdays in local stores.

▶ Find the bars that represent T-shirt sales for Saturday. Use the key to determine which bar represents Mobo Tees' sales and which bar represents the daily average in local stores.

▶ The bar on the right represents an average of 35 T-shirts sold in local stores. The bar on the left represents 30 T-shirts sold at Mobo Tees. Mobo Tees' T-shirt sales were below Saturday's local average.

---

vertical axis

A vertical axis is a straight line, either imaginary or real, that runs parallel to or makes up one of the sides (usually the left side) of a graph or chart. It goes from bottom to top.

---

range (as a difference)

The range is the *difference* between the highest value and the lowest value in a set of data. To find the range, subtract the smallest number from the largest number.

---

horizontal axis

A horizontal axis is a straight line, either imaginary or real, that runs parallel to or makes up the bottom of a graph or chart. It goes from left to right.

Check Your Understanding 3.3.3

Refer to the graph below to answer the questions on the following page.

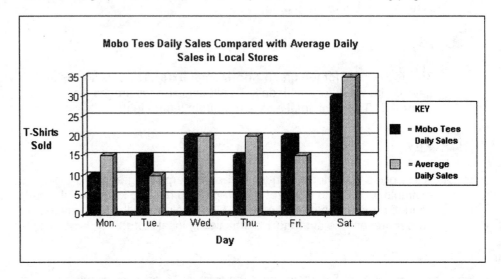

Put a check (✓) next to the correct answers in the answer column.

Question	Answer
1. On Thursday, did Mobo Tees sell more T-shirts or fewer T-shirts than the average sold in local stores?	___ Mobo Tees sold more T-shirts than the average. ___ Mobo Tees sold fewer T-shirts than the average.
2. How many more T-shirts did Mobo Tees sell on Friday compared with the average sales in local stores?	___ 20 ___ 15 ___ 10 ___ 5
3. On which days were the average daily sales in local stores lower than the daily sales at Mobo Tees?	___ Monday and Thursday ___ Tuesday and Friday ___ Tuesday and Thursday ___ Thursday and Friday

3.3.4 Reading Line Graphs

A **line graph** can be used to show changes over periods of time. It is useful because increases and decreases are easy to see. For example, this line graph shows the change in attendance at Star Theater over a period of 5 weeks.

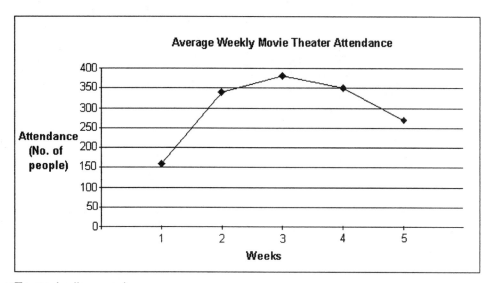

To read a line graph:

▶ Look at the title to see what the graph represents.

▶ Look at the vertical (bottom to top) and horizontal (left to right) axes. They are labeled and ordered to represent the **data** on the graph effectively (chronological, greatest to least, etc.).

▶ Points are plotted on the graph according to the horizontal and vertical axes. The lines that connect the points make the data easier to read and interpret. The average attendance for Week 4 on the line graph above is about 350.

data

Data is a collection of information such as facts or numbers. It is often used to form some sort of conclusion. For example, Company XYZ earned a profit of $5 million two years ago and $5.6 million the following year. From this data the company can conclude that during the second year its profits increased by $0.6 million.

Check Your Understanding 3.3.4

Refer to the line graph showing average weekly theater attendance to answer the questions below. Put a check (✓) next to the correct answers in the answer column.

Question	Answer
1. What is the approximate average attendance for Week 2 on the line graph?	___ 300 ___ 160 ___ 340 ___ 370
2. During which week is the average attendance about 270?	___ Week 1 ___ Week 2 ___ Week 3 ___ Week 4 ___ Week 5
3. During which week does attendance at Star Theater peak?	___ Week 1 ___ Week 2 ___ Week 3 ___ Week 4 ___ Week 5

Topics Related to: Reading Line Graphs

3.3.7   Trends in Graphs
3.3.8   Plotting Points on a Graph
3.3.11 Building Line Graphs

3.3.5 Reading Scatter Plots

data

Data is a collection of information such as facts or numbers. It is often used to form some sort of conclusion. For example, Company XYZ earned a profit of $5 million two years ago and $5.6 million the following year. From this data the company can conclude that during the second year its profits increased by $0.6 million.

A **scatter plot** is a type of graph that uses a grid and points to compare two types of **data**. For example, scatter plots can be used to compare height to weight, distance to time, perimeter to area, etc. This scatter plot compares the heights and weights of 18 men.

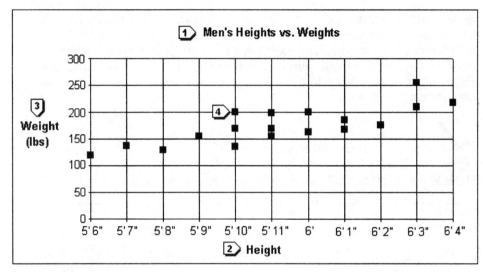

Understanding the Graph

To learn more about the graph above, refer to the number labels on the graph and read the descriptions below.

1 Men's Heights vs. Weights

This is the title of the graph. The title is the first part of a graph that you should read. Reading the title tells you what the graph represents and helps you interpret it.

horizontal axis

A horizontal axis is a straight line, either imaginary or real, that runs parallel to or makes up the bottom of a graph or chart. It goes from left to right.

2 Height

This is the label for the graph's **horizontal axis**. The axis shows the **range** of the heights of the men. A horizontal axis is read from left to right.

range (as a difference)

The range is the *difference* between the highest value and the lowest value in a set of data. To find the range, subtract the smallest number from the largest number.

3 Weight (lbs)

This is the label for the graph's **vertical axis**. The axis shows the range of the men's weight in pounds (lbs). A vertical axis is read from bottom to top.

vertical axis

A vertical axis is a straight line, either imaginary or real, that runs parallel to or makes up one of the sides (usually the left side) of a graph or chart. It goes from bottom to top.

The point that represents a man who is 5 feet 10 inches tall and weighs 200 pounds.

This point marks where the 5' 10" from the horizontal axis (height) meets the 200 from the vertical axis (weight), so it represents a man who is 5 feet 10 inches tall and weighs 200 pounds.

Scatter plots are often used to find out whether there is a relationship between the two **data** types that are plotted on it. For example, the scatter plot below shows that taller people usually weigh more. There seems to be a relationship between height and weight. However, the scatter plot also shows variations. For example, look at the 6-foot line. There are two men represented on the line; one weighs 165 pounds, and the other weighs 200 pounds.

 Check Your Understanding 3.3.5

Refer to the graph below to answer the questions that follow.

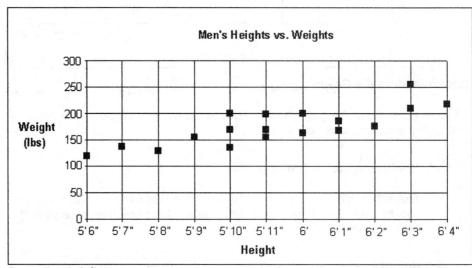

Put a check (✓) next to the correct answers in the answer column.

Question	Answer
1. According to the scatter plot above, approximately how much does the person who is 5' 9" weigh?	___ 200 lbs ___ 160 lbs ___ 190 lbs ___ 130 lbs

2. According to the scatter plot, how tall is the man who weighs 260 pounds?	___ 5' 9" ___ 6' ___ 6' 3" ___ 6' 4"
3. Based on this scatter plot, would a man who is shorter than 5 feet 10 inches be more likely to weigh	___ more than 150 pounds. ___ less than 150 pounds.

Topics Related to: Reading Scatter Plots

3.3.6   Elimination with Scatter Plots
3.3.8   Plotting Points on a Graph
3.3.12 Building Scatter Plots

3.3.6 Elimination with Scatter Plots

This *scatter plot* compares the heights and weights of 18 men. Suppose you want to find out how many men represented by this graph are *taller* than 6 feet and weigh *more than* 200 pounds. You can use a process of *elimination* to find the answer.

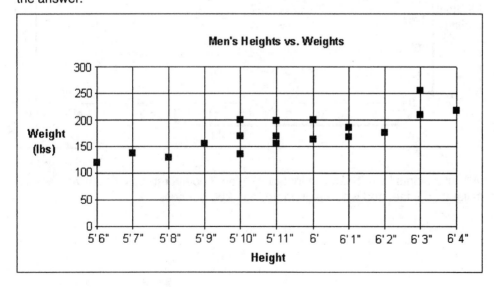

▶ First eliminate all points on the graph that represent men who are 6 feet and shorter.

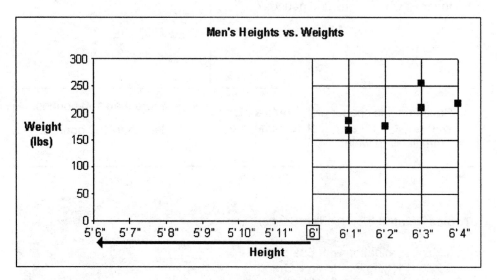

▶ Then eliminate all points on the graph that represent men who weigh 200 pounds or less.

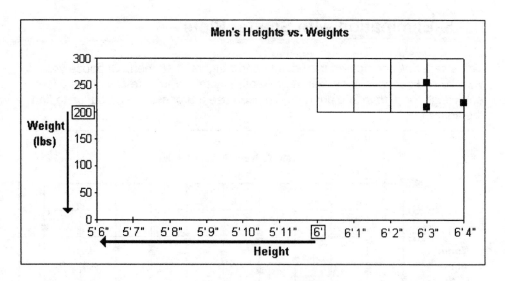

All but 3 points have been eliminated. These 3 points represent men who are taller than 6 feet and who weigh more than 200 pounds.

Check Your Understanding 3.3.6

Refer to the graph below to answer the questions that follow it.

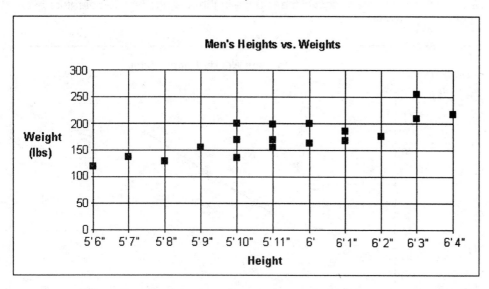

Put a check (✓) next to the correct answers in the answer column.

Question	Answer
1. According to the graph, how many men are shorter than 6 feet and weigh less than 150 pounds?	___ 3 ___ 4 ___ 5 ___ 6
2. According to the graph, how many men are taller than 5 feet 9 inches and weigh more than 100 pounds?	___ 9 ___ 10 ___ 13 ___ 14

Topics Related to: Elimination with Scatter Plots

3.3.5   Reading Scatter Plots
3.3.12 Building Scatter Plots

3.3.7 Trends in Graphs

Line graphs are commonly used to show *changes over periods of time.* For example, this line graph shows the change in the average high temperature over a period of 4 weeks.

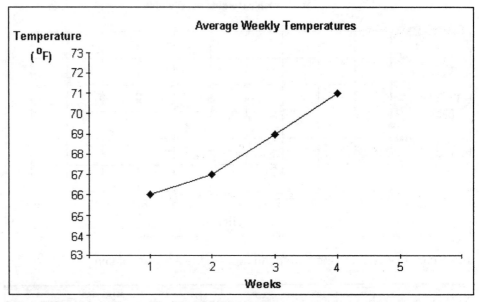

Because line graphs show changes over time, they are often used to make predictions. For example, this line graph can be used to predict the average high temperature for Week 5.

According to the graph, the average high temperature increased about 2° from Weeks 2 to 3 and from Weeks 3 to 4. If it keeps rising at this same rate (about 2° per week), you would expect the average high temperature of Week 5 to be about 73° Fahrenheit.

 Check Your Understanding 3.3.7

Put a check (✓) next to the correct answers in the answer column.

Question	Answer
1. Use the graph to predict the average temperature for the week preceding Week 1.	____ between 60° and 66° ____ between 67° and 71° ____ between 72° and 76°

2. Use the graph to predict the average temperature for Week 6.	___ between 60° and 66° ___ between 67° and 71° ___ between 73° and 77°

Topics Related to: Trends in Graphs

    3.3.4   Reading Line Graphs
    3.3.11 Building Line Graphs

3.3.8 Plotting Points on a Graph

Points are *labeled* on a graph according to their *positions*.

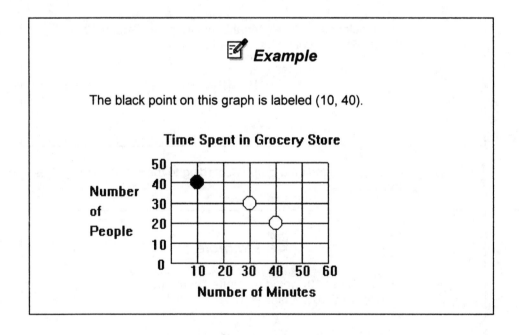

✍ *Example*

The black point on this graph is labeled (10, 40).

Time Spent in Grocery Store

▶ The first number represents the position of the point along the horizontal axis (number of minutes in the graph above). The second number represents the position of the point along the vertical axis (number of people in the graph above).

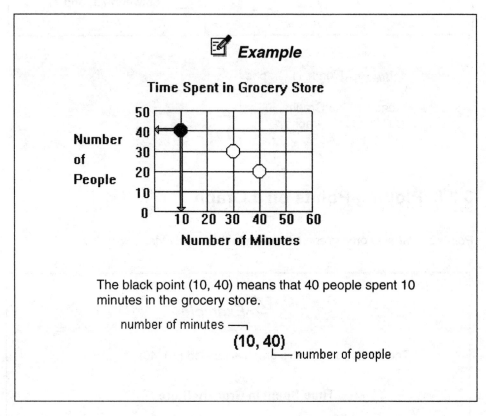

Example

The black point (10, 40) means that 40 people spent 10 minutes in the grocery store.

number of minutes ⎯⎤
(10, 40)
⎣⎯ number of people

▶ Similarly, points are *plotted* on a graph according to their relationship to the horizontal and vertical axes.

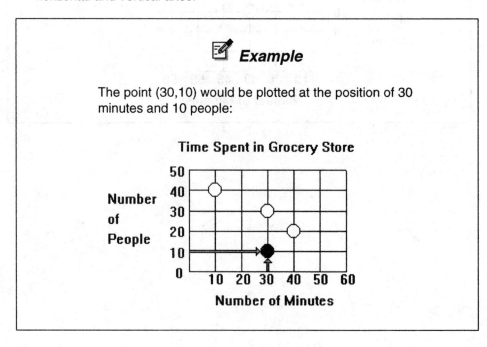

Example

The point (30,10) would be plotted at the position of 30 minutes and 10 people:

Check Your Understanding 3.3.8

Refer to the graph below to answer the questions that follow it.

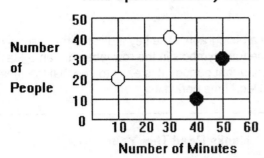

Put a check (✓) next to the correct answers in the answer column.

Question	Answer
1. What are the labels for the two black points on the graph?	____ (30,50) (10,40) ____ (40,10) (30,50) ____ (40,10) (50,30) ____ (10,40) (50,30)
2. What are the labels for the two white points on the graph?	____ (10,20) (30,40) ____ (20,10) (40,30) ____ (30,40) (20,10) ____ (40,30) (10,20)

Topics Related to: Plotting Points on a Graph

3.3.5   Reading Scatter Plots
3.3.4   Reading Line Graphs
3.3.12 Building Scatter Plots
3.3.11 Building Line Graphs

3.3.9 Building Pictographs

A *pictograph u* symbols (or pictures) to represent numbers. Pictographs are useful because the reader can gain an understanding of the information displayed in the graph with one quick look. The only numbers to examine in pictographs are in the key.

Below is an example of a pictograph. The key indicates that each symbol represents 5 books. The four symbols in the row labeled "Jan. - Mar." means that 20 books were read during that period. It is easy to see that the most books were read during the "Oct. - Dec." time period.

Books Read This Year

		KEY
Jan. - Mar.	🔲🔲🔲🔲	
Apr. - June	🔲🔲	🔲 = 5 books
July - Sept.	🔲🔲🔲	
Oct. - Dec.	🔲🔲🔲🔲🔲	

To build a pictograph, follow these steps:

1. **Make sure the data is suitable.**

   The symbols used in pictographs usually represent whole-number **quantities**, such as 10 books or 25 games. Pictographs usually are not used to represent decimal quantities, such as 4.5 pounds or 6.2 miles.

2. **Decide what symbols to use and what quantities they will represent.**

   Choose symbols that reflect the theme of the graph.

 **Example**

If you are building a pictograph to show the number of points earned in each inning of a baseball game, you might use a baseball or a bat as a symbol. You wouldn't use a football or a basketball.

---

data

Data is a collection of information such as facts or numbers. It is often used to form some sort of conclusion. For example, Company XYZ earned a profit of $5 million two years ago and $5.6 million the following year. From this data the company can conclude that during the second year its profits increased by $0.6 million.

quantity

A quantity is an amount or number.

The quantity that the symbol represents should be large or small enough to represent your **data**.

✒ *Example*

If you have data ranging from $100 to $500, you wouldn't choose a coin symbol and assign it a value of 50 cents. It would take 200 symbols just to show $100! A better quantity for the symbol to represent would be $50.

---

3. Round the numbers if necessary.

After you decide what quantity each symbol will represent, round your data to multiples of that quantity.

✒ *Example*

If you decide to use a book to represent 5 books, and a student read 13 books over the summer, then you would have to round 13 to the nearest multiple of 5, which is 15.

---

4. Make a key.

The key shows the quantity that each symbol represents.

✒ *Example*

If you are using dollar bills to represent quantities of $500,000, then the key should have a picture of a dollar bill labeled $500,000.

---

5. Find how many symbols you will need to represent each item.

Divide the quantity you wish to represent by the amount each symbol represents.

Example

On a pictograph that uses a picture of one dollar bill to represent $500,000, you would use 3 dollar bills to show $1,500,000 ($1,500,000 ÷ $500,000 = 3). To represent $3,000,000, you would use 6 dollar bills.

 Check Your Understanding 3.3.9

Put a check (✓) next to the correct answers in the answer column.

Question	Answer
1. The most appropriate symbol to represent the number of workers at different factories would be	___ a calendar. ___ a person. ___ a dollar. ___ a pen.
2. A pictograph uses a symbol of one hot dog to represent 10 hot dogs. How many hot dogs would you place on the graph to represent 110 hot dogs?	___ 10 ___ 11 ___ 12 ___ 110
3. Which set of data is best suited for a pictograph? A B C **Sunny Days in March** **U.S. Meat Consumption 1989** **Donations to Charities *** Week 1 1 Red Meat 59% Jan. 5.4 Week 2 0 Poultry 32% Feb. 2.5 Week 3 2 Seafood 9% Mar. 1.9 Week 4 3 Week 5 2 * in thousands of dollars	___ A ___ B ___ C

Topics Related to: Building Pictographs

3.3.1 Reading Pictographs

3.3.10 Building Bar Graphs

quantity

A quantity is an amount or number.

Bar graphs use bars to represent **quantities**. Bars can be oriented either vertically (as shown below) or horizontally. The height of a bar depends on the quantity it represents. Bar graphs can be used to compare discrete quantities or to show changes in a quantity over time. In the single bar graph below, the bars show changes in the numbers of T-shirts sold during a certain week. The highest bar represents the largest quantity of T-shirts sold during the week, 30.

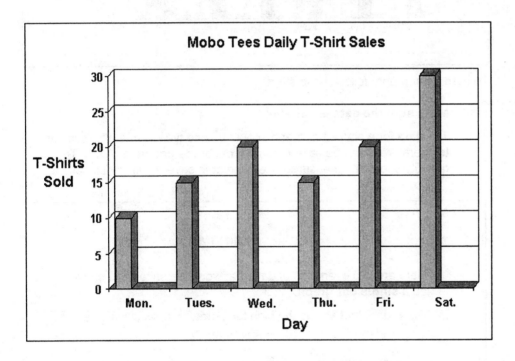

Double bar graphs are useful when comparing changes in two variables over a period of time. They use double bars instead of single bars. For example, the following double bar graph compares Mobo Tees' daily T-shirt sales with the average daily T-shirt sales in local stores.

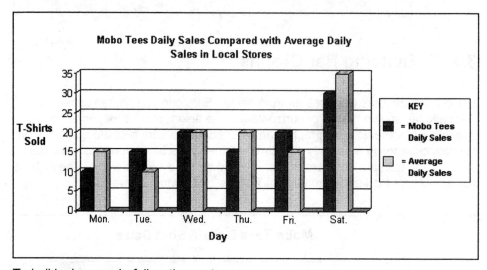

To build a bar graph, follow these steps:

1. Make sure the data is suitable.

The **data** for a single bar graph should be one type of quantity (such as temperature, average salary, number of college graduates, etc.) The quantity should be measured over time or in several different locations.

Example

Here are two examples of data that would be suitable to show on a **single bar graph**:

- data that shows the high temperature in six cities on a given day

- data that compares temperature changes in one city over a 24-hour period

A single bar graph could not be used to compare data like the average temperature and the altitude of several cities. This data would be better shown on a double bar graph, where the graph shows two types of quantity, or on a scatter plot.

---

data

Data is a collection of information such as facts or numbers. It is often used to form some sort of conclusion. For example, Company XYZ earned a profit of $5 million two years ago and $5.6 million the following year. From this data the company can conclude that during the second year its profits increased by $0.6 million.

 *Example*

Here are two examples of data that would be suitable to show on a **double bar graph**:

- data that compares the number of nurses to the number of doctors at different hospitals

- data that compares the number of viewers watching two TV channels over a four-week period

2. Organize the data.

A graph with more than 10 bars is probably too cluttered to be read easily. To avoid a cluttered graph, combine the data into 10 groups or less.

 *Example*

If you have data showing the population of all the cities in a certain state, combine the populations of some cities and show the population according to counties or regions.

3. Label the axes.

Label one axis to match the groups that the data represents, such as age groups, countries, years, etc. Label the other axis according to the quantities to be represented, such as percentages, inches, populations, etc. If you want the bars on the graph to be vertical, label the vertical axis with the quantities.

4. Create a scale.

scale

A scale is a line marked with ticks that are labeled with values. It is used to measure data.

Begin the **scale** with the lowest **data** value or with zero and end it with the highest value. Try to use no more than 10 divisions between the lowest and the highest values.

The values of the data should be close enough to make the scale reasonable. If the values of the data range between 1 and 1,000, and you need to show divisions of 5 or 10, then the data is not close enough to make a reasonable scale. On the other hand, if you only need to show divisions of 100, then the data is close enough to make the scale reasonable.

5. Create a key.

When making a double bar graph, make a key to show what the two bars represent.

6. Draw the bars to represent the quantities.

 Check Your Understanding 3.3.10

Put a check (✓) next to the correct answers in the answer column.

Question	Answer
1. Which set of data is best suited for a single bar graph? A **Weight vs. Speed in 100m dash** **(lbs) (seconds)** 180 10.9 230 11.5 170 10.2 255 12.3 165 10.0 B **Gas Prices** Orangeville $0.99 Merton $1.07 Dennington $1.01 York $0.84 Jackson City $1.10	___ A ___ B
2. What are suitable labels for the horizontal and vertical axes on a bar graph that is built to show this data? **Janton Employees,** **Various Categories** Construction 8,500 Food Services 21,200 Business 8,300 Technology 7,800 Retail Sales 17,600	___ Percentage of Employees/Job Categories ___ Number of Employees/ Occupations ___ Occupations/ Number of Unemployed

Topics Related to: Building Bar Graphs

3.3.2 Reading Bar Graphs

3.3.11 Building Line Graphs

Line graphs are commonly used to show *changes over periods of time*. For example, the line graph below shows the change in average weekly movie attendance over a period of 5 weeks.

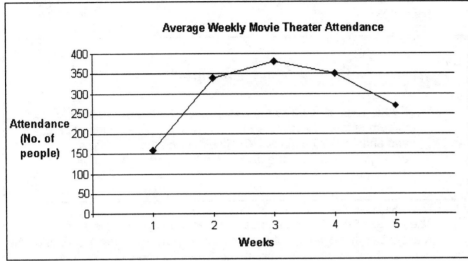

To build a line graph, follow these steps:

1. Make sure the data is suitable.

The **data** for a line graph should show **quantities** measured at specific points over a period of time. The data should measure something that changes frequently, such as the unemployment rate, inflation, or temperatures.

2. Organize the data.

A graph with more than 10 points is probably too cluttered to be read easily. To avoid a cluttered graph, combine the **data** into 10 groups or less.

 *Example*

If you have data showing the daily movie attendance over a period of 30 days, you can use the data to find the average attendance for each week. Then you make a line graph showing four average weekly attendances instead of 30 daily attendances.

---

3. Label the horizontal and vertical axes.

Label the **horizontal axis** to match the time period that the data represents, such as days, weeks, months, years, etc. Begin with the *least* recent date at the left and end with the *most* recent date at the right. Label

quantity

A quantity is an amount or number.

data

Data is a collection of information such as facts or numbers. It is often used to form some sort of conclusion. For example, Company XYZ earned a profit of $5 million two years ago and $5.6 million the following year. From this data the company can conclude that during the second year its profits increased by $0.6 million.

horizontal axis

A horizontal axis is a straight line, either imaginary or real, that runs parallel to or makes up the bottom of a graph or chart. It goes from left to right.

vertical axis

A vertical axis is a straight line, either imaginary or real, that runs parallel to or makes up one of the sides (usually the left side) of a graph or chart. It goes from bottom to top.

the **vertical axis** according to the quantities to be represented, such as feet, temperatures, costs, number of people, etc.

4. Create a scale for the vertical axis.

Begin the **scale** with the lowest value or with zero and end it with the highest. Try to use no more than 10 divisions between the lowest and highest value.

---

scale

A scale is a line marked with ticks that are labeled with values. It is used to measure data.

 Example

> If your graph is to show the weight gain of a baby from birth to three months, you could label the vertical axis beginning at zero and ending at 20 pounds. You could divide the axis into 4 equal parts and label the divisions at 5 pounds, 10 pounds, and 15 pounds.

The values of the **data** should be close enough to make the scale reasonable. If the values of the data range between 1 and 1,000, and you need to show divisions of 5 or 10, then the data is not close enough to make a reasonable scale. On the other hand, if you only needed to show divisions of 100, then the data is close enough to make the scale reasonable.

5. Plot points on the graph to represent the data.

6. Draw lines joining adjacent points.

✔ **Check Your Understanding 3.3.11**

Put a check (✓) next to the correct answers in the answer column.

Question	Answer
1. Which set of data is best suited for a line graph?	___ A ___ B ___ C

A Car Sales, Percent Change	B U.S. Meat Consumption 1989	C Rainfall (inches)
1989 6% 1990 4% 1991 -2% 1992 3% 1993 2%	Red Meat 59% Poultry 32% Seafood 9%	Orangeville 0.8 Merton 1.2 Dennington 0.9 York 0.7 Jackson City 1.1

2. This graph represents the unemployment rate over a period of eight weeks. How should the axes be labeled?

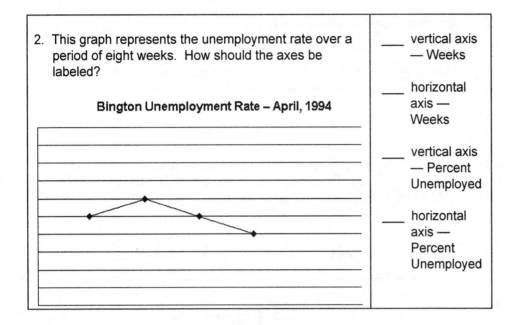

Bington Unemployment Rate – April, 1994

_____ vertical axis — Weeks

_____ horizontal axis — Weeks

_____ vertical axis — Percent Unemployed

_____ horizontal axis — Percent Unemployed

Topics Related to: Building Line Graphs

    3.3.4 Reading Line Graphs
    3.3.8 Plotting Points on a Graph

3.3.12 Building Scatter Plots

A *scatter plot* is a type of graph that uses a grid and points to compare two types of **data**. For example, a scatter plot can be used to compare height to weight, distance to time, perimeter to area, etc.

data

Data is a collection of information such as facts or numbers. It is often used to form some sort of conclusion. For example, Company XYZ earned a profit of $5 million two years ago and $5.6 million the following year. From this data the company can conclude that during the second year its profits increased by $0.6 million.

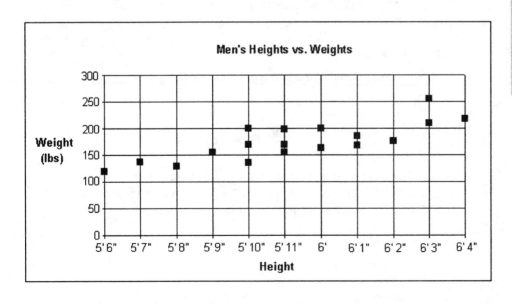

To build a scatter plot, follow these steps:

1. **Make sure the data is suitable.**

   The data for a scatter plot should give *two* measurements for each item.

   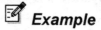
   ## Example

   When a person runs around a track, her *time* and *distance* can be measured. Or for any tree, its *age* and *height* can be measured.

   Avoid confusing measurements with groups or categories.

   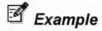
   ## Example

   If the population of a certain town is 12,300 in 1980 and 15,200 in 1990, the dates 1980 and 1990 are not measurements but categories. In this case, you have only one type of measurement, the *population*. A second measurement could be the percent of senior citizens in town.

round

Rounding is a way to write complex numbers in a simple form so that they are easier to work with. To estimate the answer to 3,983,423 x 6 = ? round the numbers to about 4,000,000 x 5. The answer is about 20,000,000.

2. **Round the data.**

   Exact values are often not necessary. Graphs are designed for quick reference and rounded numbers make graphs easier (and quicker) to read. You may want to consider **rounding** the data to whole numbers or, if the numbers have several decimal places, to numbers with fewer decimal places.

3. **Label the axis.**

   Label the axis to match the two types of measurements.

   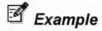
   ## Example

   If the data compares peoples' heights to their weights, then you would label one of the axes with the range in heights and the other axis with the range in weights.

4. Create a scale for each axis.

Begin the **scale** with the lowest value or with zero and end it with the highest value. Try to use no more than 15 divisions between the lowest and highest values.

scale

A scale is a line marked with ticks that are labeled with values. It is used to measure data.

✎ *Example*

If your data compares shoe sizes and heights, and the shoe sizes range from size 5 to 10, you would begin the scale at 5 and end at 10. You could divide the axis into 10 equal parts and label the divisions at size 5, 5 1/2, 6, 6 1/2, 7, etc.

The values of the data should be close enough to make the scale reasonable. If the values of the data range between 1 and 1,000, and you need to show divisions of 5 or 10, then the data is not close enough to make a reasonable scale. On the other hand, if you only needed to show divisions of 100, then the data is close enough to make the scale reasonable.

5. Plot points on the graph to represent the data.

 Check Your Understanding 3.3.12

Put a check (✓) next to the correct answers in the answer column.

Question	Answer
1. Which set of data is best suited for a scatter plot? A B C **A** — Weight vs. Speed in 100m dash (lbs) (seconds): 180 / 10.9, 230 / 11.5, 170 / 10.2, 255 / 12.3, 165 / 10.0 **B** — U.S. Meat Consumption 1989: Red Meat 59%, Poultry 32%, Seafood 9% **C** — Car Sales, Percent Change: 1989 6%, 1990 4%, 1991 -2%, 1992 3%, 1993 2%	___ A ___ B ___ C

2. Here are the axis labels for 3 graphs. Which could be a scatter plot?

       ___ A

       ___ B

       ___ C

Vertical Axis	Horizontal Axis
A. Number of Employees	Year
B. Age	Weight
C. Cars Sold (number)	Week

Topics Related to: Building Scatter Plots

    3.3.5 Reading Scatter Plots
    3.3.8 Plotting Points on a Graph

3.4 More Graphs

3.4.1 Reading Circle Graphs

A **circle graph** is a form of **data** representation that is used to show parts of a whole. There are several styles of circle graphs. On some, the sections are labeled directly; others have a **key**. These two circle graphs display the same data in different styles.

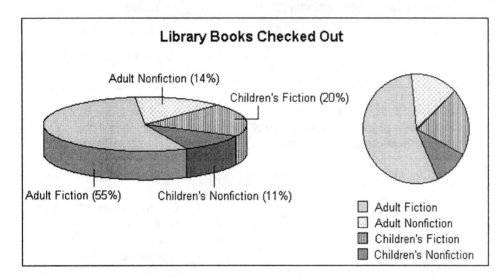

Library Books Checked Out

Adult Nonfiction (14%)
Children's Fiction (20%)
Adult Fiction (55%)
Children's Nonfiction (11%)

- Adult Fiction
- Adult Nonfiction
- Children's Fiction
- Children's Nonfiction

To decide how much of the circle each piece takes, try mentally dividing the circle into halves. Are any sections close to that size? ("Adult Fiction" is a little more than half.) Divide it into quarters. Do any sections compare? (Children's Nonfiction is a little less than a quarter.) On other graphs you may want to try dividing the circle into eighths, fifths, thirds, or sixths.

Here is some information these circle graphs tell you about the data.

▶ The majority of books checked out from the library are adult fiction.

▶ Children's fiction represents 20%, or one-fifth, of all books checked out from the library.

data

Data is a collection of information such as facts or numbers. It is often used to form some sort of conclusion. For example, Company XYZ earned a profit of $5 million two years ago and $5.6 million the following year. From this data the company can conclude that during the second year its profits increased by $0.6 million.

key

A key is a list of words, numbers, symbols, or combination of these that helps identify or give an explanation of items in a graph or chart. For example, a key for a circle graph might show what a fill pattern or color means.

Check Your Understanding 3.4.1

Refer to the circle graph on the previous page (Library Books Checked Out) to answer these questions. Put a check (✓) next to the correct answers in the answer column.

Question	Answer
1. According to the circle graph, which is the least popular book category?	____ Adult Fiction ____ Adult Nonfiction ____ Children's Fiction ____ Children's Nonfiction
2. According to the circle graph, which categories account for one-quarter of the books checked out of the library?	____ Adult Fiction and Nonfiction ____ Adult Nonfiction and Children's Fiction ____ Children's Nonfiction and Adult Nonfiction ____ Children's Fiction and Nonfiction

Topics Related to: Reading Circle Graphs

2.4.15 Percents and Circle Graphs
3.4.11 Building Circle Graphs

3.4.2 Reading Line Plots

A **line plot** is used to represent separate, related items of **data**.

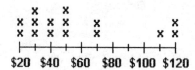

This line plot shows the prices of all the different kinds of tote bags sold in a popular mail-order catalog. Each "x" represents a kind of tote bag. The prices have been rounded. Data on a line plot is often rounded to keep the plot neat.

Can you see how many kinds of tote bags are $40? Find 40 on the scale and count the "x's." Two kinds of tote bags in the catalog are $40.

The line plot tells you the following about the prices of tote bags in the catalog:

▶   Most tote bags are in the $20 - $50 range.
▶   There are no tote bags between $80 and $100.
▶   The most expensive tote bags are $120.

Refer to the following line plot to answer the questions below.

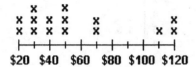

 Check Your Understanding 3.4.2

Put a check (✓) next to the correct answers in the answer column.

Question	Answer
1. Only one kind of tote bag is offered at which price?	___ $100 ___ $110 ___ $120
2. How many tote bags are offered at $50?	___ 1 ___ 2 ___ 3
3. There are no tote bags offered at	___ $90 ___ $70 ___ $50

Topics Related to: Reading Line Plots

3.4.4   Clusters
3.4.5   Gaps
3.4.6   Outliers
3.4.12 Building Line Plots

3.4.3 Reading Stem-and-Leaf Plots

data

Data is a collection of information such as facts or numbers. It is often used to form some sort of conclusion. For example, Company XYZ earned a profit of $5 million two years ago and $5.6 million the following year. From this data the company can conclude that during the second year its profits increased by $0.6 million.

Stem-and-leaf plots are used to represent separate, related pieces of **data**. They can show a high level of detail because each piece of data is plotted individually.

stem	leaves
3	6 8 8 8 8
4	2 4 4 6
5	2 6
6	
7	
8	
9	8 8 8 8
10	
11	8 8

Key
3 | 6 means 36 dollars

This stem-and-leaf plot shows the prices of all the styles of pants sold in a popular mail-order catalog. The key tells you that 3 | 6 means 36 dollars, so the stem represents the tens place and the leaves represent the ones place. The other values in the leaves row are 38, 38, 38, and 38 because 3 is in the tens place and 8 is in the ones place.

What does this stem-and-leaf plot tell you?

▶ The prices **cluster** at the low end. Most prices are between $36 and $56.

▶ Smaller clusters are at the high end. There are half a dozen prices of $98 and $118.

▶ There are no prices between $57 and $97.

cluster

A cluster is a group of values in a set of data. For example, in the set 36, 22, 23, 18, 10, the values 22 and 23 form a cluster.

✓ **Check Your Understanding 3.4.3**

Put a check (✓) next to the correct answers in the answer column.

Question	Answer
1. How many styles of pants cost $44?	___ 1 ___ 2 ___ 3 ___ 4
2. What is the price of pants costing more than $100?	___ $110 ___ $108 ___ $118

3. You want to buy a pair of pants in the $50 to $60 range. How much are the pants in this range?	___ $52 and $56 ___ $52 and $58 ___ $50 and $54

Topics Related to: Reading Stem-and-Leaf Plots

    3.4.4   Clusters
    3.4.5   Gaps
    3.4.13 Building Stem-and-Leaf Plots

3.4.4 Clusters

A **cluster** is a group of two or more values. In any set of **data** you expect the data to fall into clusters. As a matter of fact, if a plot had no clusters, you would want to ask why.

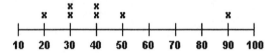

There is cluster of data between 20 and 50 on this line plot.

 Check Your Understanding 3.4.4

Put a check (✓) next to the correct answers in the answer column.

Question	Answer
1. Where is the cluster of data on this line plot? (line plot from 10 to 100 with data points clustered around 20 and 60-90)	___ 30 - 50 ___ 70 - 90 ___ 60 - 90

data

Data is a collection of information such as facts or numbers. It is often used to form some sort of conclusion. For example, Company XYZ earned a profit of $5 million two years ago and $5.6 million the following year. From this data the company can conclude that during the second year its profits increased by $0.6 million.

2. How many clusters are on this stem-and-leaf plot?

```
12 | 2
13 | 3
14 |
15 |
16 | 2
17 | 6 7
```

Key
13 | 3 means 133

___ 0

___ 1

___ 2

___ 3

Topics Related to: Clusters

3.4.2 Reading Line Plots
3.4.3 Reading Stem-and-Leaf Plots
3.4.5 Gaps

---

cluster

A cluster is a group of values in a set of data. For example, in the set 36, 22, 23, 18, 10, the values 22 and 23 form a cluster.

3.4.5 Gaps

A **gap** is the space between two **clusters** or a cluster and an **outlier**. On any kind of a plot, a gap may or may not be significant. For instance, if a very large gap exists between two clusters, you might ask yourself: Should this data be plotted on two plots instead of one?

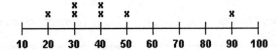

There is a gap between 50 and 90 on this line plot.

 Check Your Understanding 3.4.5

outlier

An outlier is a value that is significantly removed from other data.

Put a check (✓) next to the correct answers in the answer column.

Question	Answer
1. The gap in this line plot is between	___ 20 and 60
	___ 60 and 100
	___ 10 and 60

2. The gap in this stem-and-leaf plot is between

```
12 | 2
13 | 3
14 |
15 |
16 | 2
17 | 6 7
```

Key
13	3 means 133

___ 130 and 162

___ 140 and 150

___ 133 and 162

Topics Related to: Gaps

3.4.2 Reading Line Plots
3.4.3 Reading Stem-and-Leaf Plots
3.4.4 Clusters
3.4.6 Outliers

3.4.6 Outliers

On most plots, you expect the **data** to cluster somewhat. An **outlier** is a value that is significantly removed from a **cluster**. You might think of an outlier as an exception or something irregular or unusual. It doesn't follow the trend of the other data. These three line plots illustrate outliers.

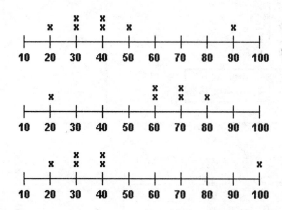

data

Data is a collection of information such as facts or numbers. It is often used to form some sort of conclusion. For example, Company XYZ earned a profit of $5 million two years ago and $5.6 million the following year. From this data the company can conclude that during the second year its profits increased by $0.6 million.

cluster

A cluster is a group of values in a set of data. For example, in the set 36, 22, 23, 18, 10, the values 22 and 23 form a cluster.

On any kind of a plot, an outlier may or may not be significant.

 Example

If you are looking at a plot of yearly salaries, most are probably between $10,000 and $100,000. A millionaire would be an outlier. Ask yourself, is this outlier significant? If you are interested in the **average**, an outlier is significant. If you are interested in the **median**, it may not be.

---

average

To find the average or "mean" of a group of numbers, first add the numbers, then divide the sum by the number of terms you added. For example, the average of 6, 7, and 2 is 5.
6 + 7 + 2 = 15 (Since you are adding 3 numbers, 3 is the number of terms.)
15 ÷ 3 = 5

✔ **Check Your Understanding 3.4.6**

Put a check (✓) next to the correct answers in the answer column.

Question	Answer
1. Does this plot have an outlier? x······x·x·x·x·x 10 20 30 40 50 60 70 80 90 100	___ Yes ___ No
2. What is the outlier on this plot? 12 | 13 | 3 14 | 15 | 16 | 2 17 | 6 7 **Key** 16 | 2 means 162	___ 3 ___ 13 ___ 133

median

The median is the middle number of a set of numbers or the average of the two middle numbers. For example, 7 is the median of 3, 4, 7, 8, 10; and 4.5 is the median of 1, 2, 4, 5, 8, 9.

Topics Related to: Outliers

3.4.2 Reading Line Plots
3.4.3 Reading Stem-and-Leaf Plots
3.4.5 Gaps

3.4.7 Reading Box-and-Whisker Plots

Box-and-whisker plots are used to show **ranges** in data rather than specific numeric values. A box-and-whisker plot consists of a lower and an upper whisker and a lower and an upper box.

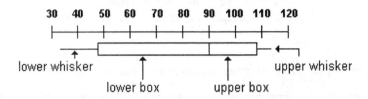

For a given set of **data**, each box and each whisker on the plot represents *one-fourth* of the values in the set. For example, this plot was based on a data set that contained 36 values. Therefore, each whisker and each box represents nine values. The lower whisker represents the nine lowest values and the upper whisker represents the nine highest values. The boxes represent the middle values.

On any box-and-whisker plot, the end of the lower whisker is called the **lower extreme**. It is the lowest value in the data set. Likewise, the end of the upper whisker is the **upper extreme**. it is the highest value in the data set. The line that separates the boxes is the **median**. It divides the data in half. The point at which a whisker meets a box is a **quartile**. The quartiles divide the data into quarters. There is both a **lower quartile** and an **upper quartile**.

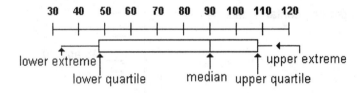

The length of each whisker and box represents the **range** of one-quarter of the data set. This is the most important information shown on a box-and-whisker plot. This box-and-whisker plot tells you the following information about these ranges.

▶ The two highest quarters (represented by the higher whisker and higher box) have a small range.

▶ The lower box has a large range.

▶ The distribution of the ranges means that half the data is tightly clustered between about 90 and 113.

Check Your Understanding 3.4.7

Refer to the following box-and-whisker plot to answer the questions below.

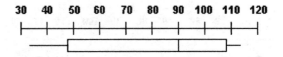

Put a check (✓) next to the correct answers in the answer column.

Question	Answer
1. In this box-and-whisker plot, which of the following has the greatest range?	___ the lower whisker ___ the lower box ___ the upper whisker ___ the upper box
2. What is the median of the data represented by the box-and-whisker plot?	___ 90 ___ 80 ___ 45
3. The upper box contains data between	___ 33 and 48. ___ 90 and 108. ___ 48 and 90. ___ 108 and 113.

Topics Related to: Reading Box-and-Whisker Plots

3.2.2   Finding the Median
3.4.8   Extremes
3.4.9   Quartiles
3.4.14 Building Box-and-Whisker Plots

3.4.8 Extremes

Extremes are the very highest or very lowest values in a set of **data**. Every set of data has both a lower extreme and an upper extreme.

data

Data is a collection of information such as facts or numbers. It is often used to form some sort of conclusion. For example, Company XYZ earned a profit of $5 million two years ago and $5.6 million the following year. From this data the company can conclude that during the second year its profits increased by $0.6 million.

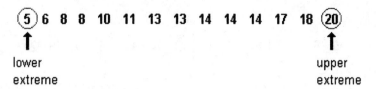

⑤ 6 8 8 10 11 13 13 14 14 14 17 18 ⑳

↑   ↑
lower   upper
extreme   extreme

Could extremes ever be equal? Yes, if all data points were the same.

 Check Your Understanding 3.4.8

Put a check (✓) next to the correct answers in the answer column.

Question	Answer
1. What are the extremes for this set of data? **29 37 47 21 27 41 23 44**	___ 29 and 44 ___ 20 and 47 ___ 21 and 47
2. What is the upper extreme of this set of data? **48 55 43 57 49 42 56 50**	___ 57 ___ 42 ___ 50

Topics Related to: Extremes

   3.4.7   Reading Box-and-Whisker Plots
   3.4.14 Building Box-and-Whisker Plots

data

Data is a collection of information such as facts or numbers. It is often used to form some sort of conclusion. For example, Company XYZ earned a profit of $5 million two years ago and $5.6 million the following year. From this data the company can conclude that during the second year its profits increased by $0.6 million.

3.4.9 Quartiles

When you see a **quartile**, think of a quarter. A quartile divides a set of **data** into quarters (four equal parts).

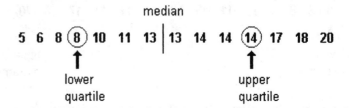

The **median** divides the data in half. The lower quartile divides the lower half of the data in half again. The upper quartile divides the upper half into half again. You find a quartile the same way you find a median; you just use half the data instead of all of it. Remember that if there is an even number of items in half the data set, you must average the two middle numbers. For example:

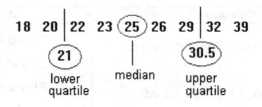

median

The median is the middle number of a set of numbers or the average of the two middle numbers. For example, 7 is the median of 3, 4, 7, 8, 10; and 4.5 is the median of 1, 2, 4, 5, 8, 9.

 Check Your Understanding 3.4.9

Put a check (✓) next to the correct answers in the answer column.

Question	Answer
1. What are the quartiles for this data? **12 13 16 18 19 21 22 25 29 31**	____ 16 and 25 ____ 13 and 25 ____ 18 and 22
2. What are the quartiles for this data? **35 36 38 42 45 47 48 51 53**	____ 37 and 51 ____ 37 and 49.5 ____ 38 and 50

Topics Related to: Quartiles

    3.2.2   Finding the Median
    3.4.7   Reading Box-and-Whisker Plots
    3.4.14 Building Box-and-Whisker Plots

3.4.10 Comparing Box-and-Whisker Plots

The primary use of a *box-and-whisker plot* is to compare two or more sets of **data**. They are useful for this purpose because you can compare data sets that are unequal in size. This data shows test scores for two different classes.

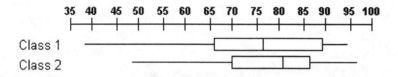

The two box-and-whisker plots highlight the differences between the classes.

▶ Class 2 has a higher **lower extreme** (compare the left ends of the lower whiskers.)

▶ Class 2 has a higher **lower quartile** (compare the left ends of the lower boxes.)

▶ Class 2 has a higher **median** (compare lines that separate the upper and lower boxes.)

▶ Class 1 has a higher **upper quartile** (compare the right end of the upper boxes.)

▶ Class 2 has a higher **upper extreme** (compare the right ends of the upper whiskers.)

Refer to the following box-and-whisker plot to answer the questions below.

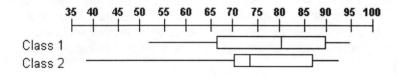

data

Data is a collection of information such as facts or numbers. It is often used to form some sort of conclusion. For example, Company XYZ earned a profit of $5 million two years ago and $5.6 million the following year. From this data the company can conclude that during the second year its profits increased by $0.6 million.

Check Your Understanding 3.4.10

Put a check (✓) next to the correct answers in the answer column.

Question	Answer
1. According to the box-and-whisker plot, which class has a higher lower quartile?	___ Class 1 ___ Class 2
2. According to the box-and-whisker plot, which class did better overall on the test?	___ Class 1 ___ Class 2

Topics Related to: Comparing Box-and-Whisker Plots

3.2.2 Finding the Median
3.4.7 Reading Box-and-Whisker Plots
3.4.8 Extremes

3.4.11 Building Circle Graphs

To build a *circle graph,* follow these steps:

1. **Make sure the data is suitable.**
   Remember that a circle graph is used to represent parts of a whole. You wouldn't use a circle graph to represent the ages of people in your mathematics class because ages make up no whole. You could, however, show what percentage of the class each of several different ages is.

2. **Organize the data.**
   You want to avoid a cluttered graph, so you may want to combine some of the data. If you want to show the electoral votes of the states, 50 divisions on a circle might not be very meaningful. Combining the data about the electoral votes of the states and listing the data in order from greatest to least is a good first step.

3. **Divide the circle.**
   This may be done by estimation or measurement. Each group of data will be represented by one section of the circle. Mentally divide the circle into halves, thirds, quarters, or whatever fraction seems appropriate. Use your mental divisions to estimate the size of each section. You could also measure the sections with a protractor.

---

data

Data is a collection of information such as facts or numbers. It is often used to form some sort of conclusion. For example, Company XYZ earned a profit of $5 million two years ago and $5.6 million the following year. From this data the company can conclude that during the second year its profits increased by $0.6 million.

4. Label the graph.

Don't forget to indicate which section of the graph represents which data. You could fill each section with a different pattern or color and create a corresponding **key**. Or you could place a label on each section.

 Check Your Understanding 3.4.11

key

A key is a list of words, numbers, symbols, or combination of these that helps identify or give an explanation of items in a graph or chart. For example, a key for a circle graph might show what a pattern or color means.

Put a check (✓) next to the correct answers in the answer column.

Question	Answer
1. Which circle graph best reflects the following data? **Museum Attendance by Age Group** Under 3 7% 3 - 12 21% Adult 42% Senior Citizen 30% A B C	___ A ___ B ___ C
2. Which data is suitable for a circle graph? A B C	___ A ___ B ___ C

Question 2 data tables:

A

Weight vs. Speed in 100m dash	
(lbs)	(seconds)
180	10.9
230	11.5
170	10.2
255	12.3
165	10.0

B

U.S. Meat Consumption 1989	
Red Meat	59%
Poultry	32%
Seafood	9%

C

Rainfall (inches)	
Orangeville	0.8
Merton	1.2
Dennington	0.9
York	0.7
Jackson City	1.1

Topics Related to: Building Circle Graphs

2.4.15 Percents and Circle Graphs
3.4.1   Reading Circle Graphs

3.4.12 Building Line Plots

To build a *line plot,* follow these steps:

data

Data is a collection of information such as facts or numbers. It is often used to form some sort of conclusion. For example, Company XYZ earned a profit of $5 million two years ago and $5.6 million the following year. From this data the company can conclude that during the second year its profits increased by $0.6 million.

1. **Make sure the data is suitable.**
   The **data** should be related. The values should be close enough to make a reasonable scale. Beware of cluttered plots. Too many values on a plot may not be as meaningful as you would like.

2. **Organize the data.**
   The data for line plots is often rounded. Consider whether **rounding** would create a better plot. You want to avoid a very long scale or a very flat plot.

3. **Create a scale.**
   Begin the **scale** with the lowest value; end it with the highest. Choose a reasonable distance for the tick marks. Common increments are 2, 5, 10, etc.

round

Rounding is a way to write complex numbers in a simple form so that they are easier to work with. To estimate the answer to 3,983,423 x 6 = ? round the numbers to about 4,000,000 x 5. The answer is about 20,000,000.

4. **Plot the data.**
   Place an "x" above the appropriate label or tick mark for each item of data. Place x's above each other where there is more than one item at a specific value. You could add interest to your plot by choosing a symbol other than an x. For instance, if you were plotting car prices, you could use a little car graphic in place of the x.

   Check Your Understanding 3.4.12

scale

A scale is a line marked with ticks that are labeled with values. It is used to measure data.

Put a check (✓) next to the correct answers in the answer column.

Question	Answer
1. Which line plot accurately reflects the following data? **150, 120, 130, 160, 120, 160, 130, 120, 160, 120** (line plots A, B, and C with scales 120 130 140 150 160)	___ A ___ B ___ C

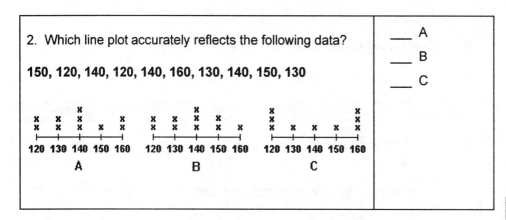

2. Which line plot accurately reflects the following data?

150, 120, 140, 120, 140, 160, 130, 140, 150, 130

_____ A

_____ B

_____ C

Topics Related to: Building Line Plots

3.4.2 Reading Line Plots

3.4.13 Building Stem-and-Leaf Plots

To build a *stem-and-leaf plot*, follow these steps:

1. **Make sure the data is suitable.**
   The **data** should be related. The values should be close enough to make a reasonable scale. Beware of cluttered plots. Too many values on a plot may not be as meaningful as you would like.

2. **Organize the data.**
   Order the data from least to greatest. Include all values. Multiple occurrences of the same value are all plotted.

3. **Create the stem.**
   The number distinguishing the magnitude or place value of the lowest item of data is the top of the **stem**.

4. Draw a line to the right of the stem to separate the **stem** from the **leaves**.

5. **Plot the leaves.**
   Use the numbers in the lowest place value for the **leaves**. Place them next to their corresponding value on the stem. Make sure you plot all values, even duplicates. List the number on each row from least to most.

6. **Add a key.**
   To make the **key**, pick any value on the plot. Show how it is plotted and say what it means. (For instance, 3|6 means 36 dollars.)

data

Data is a collection of information such as facts or numbers. It is often used to form some sort of conclusion. For example, Company XYZ earned a profit of $5 million two years ago and $5.6 million the following year. From this data the company can conclude that during the second year its profits increased by $0.6 million.

stem

The stem is the left column of numbers on a stem-and-leaf plot. It serves as a type of scale.

leaves

The leaves are the values on the right side of a stem-and-leaf plot. Each value represents an item of data.

key

A key is a list of words, numbers, symbols, or combination of these that helps identify or give an explanation of items in a graph or chart. For example, a key for a circle graph might show what a fill pattern or color means.

Check Your Understanding 3.4.13

Put a check (✓) next to the correct answers in the answer column.

Question	Answer
1. On this stem-and-leaf plot, which leaf would you put in place of the "x"? **258, 263, 266, 268, 271, 285, 292, 307** 25 | 8 26 | 3 6 x 27 | 28 | 29 | 30 | **Key** 25 | 8 means 258	___ 6 ___ 1 ___ 8
2. Which stem-and-leaf plot accurately reflects the following data? **258, 263, 266, 266, 278, 279, 280, 291, 297, 304** 25 | 8 25 | 8 25 | 8 26 | 3 6 6 26 | 3 6 6 26 | 3 6 6 27 | 8 9 27 | 8 9 27 | 8 9 28 | 28 | 0 28 | 29 | 1 1 7 29 | 1 7 29 | 1 1 7 30 | 4 30 | 4 30 | 4 [A] [B] [C] **Key** 25 | 8 means 258 feet	___ A ___ B ___ C

Topics Related to: Building Stem-and-Leaf Plots

3.4.3 Reading Stem-and-Leaf Plots

3.4.14 Building Box-and-Whisker Plots

To build a *box-and-whisker plot,* follow these steps:

1. **Make sure the data is suitable.**
   This is relatively simple since box-and-whisker plots can display very large or very small sets of data.

2. **Organize the data.**
   List the data in order from least to greatest.

3. **Find the median.**

4. **Find the quartiles**.

5. **Find the extremes.**

6. **Choose a scale.**
   Choose a value close to and less than the smallest value in the data for the low end of the scale. Choose a value close to and larger than the largest value in the data for the high end of the scale. Choose a reasonable distance for the tick marks.

7 **Draw the boxes and whisker.**
   Draw a box from the **lower quartile** to the **median**. Draw another box from the median to the **upper quartile**. Draw a whisker from the **lower extreme** to the lower quartile. Draw another whisker from the upper quartile to the **upper extreme**.

---

data

Data is a collection of information such as facts or numbers. It is often used to form some sort of conclusion. For example, Company XYZ earned a profit of $5 million two years ago and $5.6 million the following year. From this data the company can conclude that during the second year its profits increased by $0.6 million.

median

The median is the middle number of a set of numbers or the average of the two middle numbers. For example, 7 is the median of 3, 4, 7, 8, 10; and 4.5 is the median of 1, 2, 4, 5, 8, 9.

quartile

A median divides data in half; quartiles divide the halves into quarters.

extremes

Extremes are the greatest and smallest values in a set of numbers.

scale

A scale is a line marked with ticks that are labeled with values. It is used to measure data.

Check Your Understanding 3.4.14

Put a check (✓) next to the correct answers in the answer column.

<table>
<thead>
<tr><th colspan="2">Question</th><th>Answer</th></tr>
</thead>
<tbody>
<tr>
<td>1.</td>
<td>What is the median of this set of data?

     15 18 18 20 26 28 30 32 37 42</td>
<td>___ 26

___ 27

___ 28</td>
</tr>
<tr>
<td>2.</td>
<td>Which box-and-whisker plot best reflects the set of data?

     15 18 18 20 26 28 30 32 37 42

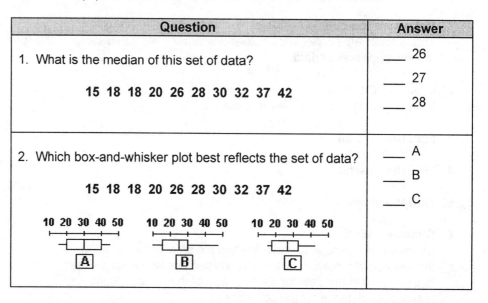</td>
<td>___ A

___ B

___ C</td>
</tr>
</tbody>
</table>

Topics Related to: Building Box-and-Whisker Plots

3.2.2 Finding the Median
3.4.7 Reading Box-and-Whisker Plots
3.4.8 Extremes
3.4.9 Quartiles

---

upper quartile

The upper quartile is the middle value in the upper half of a set of data.

lower quartile

The lower quartile is the middle value in the lower half of a set of data.

lower extreme

The lower extreme is the lowest value in a set of data.

upper extreme

The upper extreme is the highest value in a set of data.

3.5 Answers to Questions

Answers to 3.1.1

Correct Answer	Explanation
1. the winner was from the home country.	An asterisk means the winner was from the home country (where the final took place).
2. the finalists from 1978 to 1990.	The title says that this table shows the finalists (the winners and runners-up) in each final from 1978 to 1990.

Answers to 3.1.2

Correct Answer	Explanation
1. row 2	You need to look at the second row to see which restaurants received the award. Lamb's is listed twice, so they received the award twice.
2. row 3	To see the highest rating a restaurant was awarded between 1990 and 1994, you need to look at row 3. This row shows the star ratings that were awarded each restaurant. The highest rating given was five stars.

Answers to 3.1.3

Correct Answer	Explanation
1. column 2	The countries that won the World Cup are shown under column 2, which has a column heading labeled WINNERS.
2. column 5	The scores of the runners-up are listed in column 5 under the heading SCORE. This column is right of the column heading RUNNER-UP.

Answers to 3.1.4

Correct Answer	Explanation
1. West Germany	Find the column labeled RUNNER-UP. Then move down the column until you come to the row labeled 1982. The cell where the column and row meet shows the name West Germany. West Germany was the runner-up in the World Cup in 1982.
2. SITE and 1982	Find Madrid on the table. Look at the heading at the top of the column. The heading is labeled SITE. Then look along the row from Madrid and you will see the row is labeled 1982.

Answers to 3.1.5

Correct Answer	Explanation
1. $539.33	The data in the table shows a gradual increase in the average weekly salary from 1984 to 1990. This increase is less than $20 each year. It is unlikely that the average salary would go down in 1990. It is also unlikely that the average salary would go up more than $20. Therefore, the best estimate for 1991 is $539.33, which is about $13 more than the 1990 salary of $526.40.
2. 1988 and 1989	Compare the differences in the salaries for each of the years listed. You find that between 1988 and 1989 the salaries went up the most — $16.68.

Answers to 3.1.6

Correct Answer	Explanation
1. **Winner** and **Pumpkin Weight**	If you wanted a table that only represented the people that won and the size of their pumpkin, you would use **Winner** and **Pumpkin Weight** for the headers.
2. **Years** and **Pumpkin Weight**	If you wanted a table that only showed the size of the winning pumpkins between 1989 and 1994, you would use **Years** and **Pumpkin Weight** for the headers.

Answers to 3.1.7

Correct Answer	Explanation
1. heaviest to lightest	If you wanted to organize the table by winning pumpkin weight, you would order the pumpkin weights from heaviest to lightest. For example, here is part of the table. PUMPKIN WEIGHT 287 284 281 270 WINNER Wong Kleiner Polanich Gomez YEAR 1990 1994 1993 1992
2. alphabetically	If you wanted to organize the table by the names of the winners, you would order the names alphabetically. For example, here is part of the table. WINNER Gomez Johnson Kleiner Polanich PUMPKIN WEIGHT 270 265 284 281 YEAR 1992 1991 1994 1993

Answers to 3.1.8

Correct Answer	Explanation
1. $12.00	There are 6 packs of masking tape on the order form, each costing $2.00. **$2.00 x 6 = $12.00.**
2. 10	To find the quantity of invisible tape packs, you can divide the total price by the item price. **$15.00 ÷ $1.50 = 10.** This order is for 10 packs of invisible tape.

Answers to 3.2.1

Correct Answer	Explanation
1. 8	The average of this set of data is 8. The sum of the numbers in the set is 24, and there are 3 numbers in the set. $24 \div 3 = 8$
2. 9	The average of this set of data is 9. The sum of the numbers in the set is 36, and there are 4 numbers in the set. $36 \div 4 = 9$
3. 276 lbs	The average weight of the pumpkins is 276 pounds. The sum of the pumpkin weights is 1656, and there are 6 pumpkins. $1656 \div 6 = 276$

Answers to 3.2.2a

Correct Answer	Explanation
1. 6	If you order this set of numbers from smallest to largest, you can see that **6** is the middle number, or the median. Median ↓ $\{3, 4, 6, 9, 13\}$
2. 7	If you order the test scores from smallest to largest, you can see that **7** is the middle score, or the median. Median ↓ $\{1, 4, 5, 7, 9, 10, 12\}$

| 3. $6,200 | If you order the prices from smallest to largest, you can see that $6,200 is the middle score, or the median.

$1,590
$2,300
$3,100
$4,280
$6,200 ← median
$6,250
$6,590
$8,240
10,500 |

Answers to 3.2.2b

Correct Answer	Explanation
1. 8	This set of numbers ordered from smallest to largest is {5, 7, 9, 11}. The two middle numbers are 7 and 9. The average of 7 and 9 is the sum (7 + 9 = 16), divided by two (16 ÷ 2 = **8**). The median of this set is 8.
2. 30	These ages ordered from smallest to largest are {19, 24, 26, 34, 37, 41}. The two middle numbers are 26 and 34. The average of 26 and 34 is the sum (26 + 34 = 60), divided by 2 (60 ÷ 2 = **30**). The median of this set is 30.

Answers to 3.2.3a

Correct Answer	Explanation
1. 6	{3, 6, 5, 6, 3, 6, 7, 6} There are four 6s, two 3s, one 5 and one 7 in this set of numbers. The number that occurs most frequently is 6, so **6** is the mode of this set of numbers.
2. 5' 11" and 6' 1"	{6' 1", 5' 11", 5' 10", 5' 11", 6' 2", 6' 1", 6' 3"} The modes of these heights are 5' 11" and 6' 1". They both occur twice in the set, which is more frequently than any of the other numbers.

Answers to 3.2.3b

Correct Answer	Explanation
1. none	{5, 3, 8, 14, 11, 6} There is no mode in this set of numbers because each number occurs only once.
2. three	70%, 40%, 95%, 40%, 90%, 95%, 70%, 65% The modes in this set of test scores are 40%, 70%, and 95%. They all occur twice in the set, which is more frequently than any of the other numbers.

Answers to 3.2.4

Correct Answer	Explanation
1. 14	Reorder the numbers from smallest to largest. {2, 5, 8, 9, 11, 13, 16} Then subtract the smallest number in the set from the largest number. 16 - 2 = 14 The range of this data set is **14**.
2. 17	Reorder the numbers from smallest to largest. {-4, -7, -12, -19, -21} Then subtract the smallest number in the set from the largest number. (-4) - (-21) = 17 The range of this data set is **17**.

3. $30	Reorder the amounts from smallest to largest. {$12, $15, $19, $23, $31, $42} Then subtract the smallest amount from the largest amount. $42 - $12 = $30 The range of the collected amounts is **$30**.
4. $2,450	Reorder the amounts from smallest to largest. {$1,500, $1,975, $2,535, $2,800, $3,950} Then subtract the smallest amount from the largest amount. $3,950 - $1,500 = $2,450 The range of the collected amounts is **$2,450**.

Answers to 3.3.1

Correct Answer	Explanation
1. 15	There are 3 T-shirt symbols next to Thursday. Each symbol represents 5 T-shirts. $3 \times 5 = 15$ On Thursday, 15 T-shirts were sold at the store.
2. 7	Each symbol represents 5 T-shirts. $35 \div 5 = 7$ So, 7 T-shirt symbols would be needed to show that 35 T-shirts were sold in one day

| 3. 2 | Currently, there are 2 symbols next to Wednesday. This represents 10 T-shirts because each symbol represents 5 T-shirts. The total T-shirt sales for Wednesday was 20.

20 - 10 = 10

Therefore, 2 more symbols need to be added to the graph to represent the extra 10 T-shirts that were sold. |

Answers to 3.3.2

Correct Answer	Explanation
1. Monday	 To solve this problem, find 15 on the vertical axis. Draw an imaginary line across the graph from this mark, and look for any bars that fall below the imaginary line. The bar representing Monday is the only bar that falls short of this line. Only 10 T-shirts were sold on Monday.
2. 10	Mobo Tees sold 10 T-shirts on Monday and 20 T-shirts on Friday. Sales increased from 10 to 20 T-shirts — an increase of *10 T-shirts*.
3. Wednesday and Friday	You don't need to look at numbers to solve this problem. You just need to look at the height of the bars. The second-highest bars on the graph are those that show sales on Wednesday and Friday.

Answers to 3.3.3

Correct Answer	Explanation
1. Mobo Tees sold fewer T-shirts than the average.	Compare the lengths of the bars for Thursday. The bar for Mobo Tees is shorter than the bar for the average sales. So, on Thursday, Mobo Tees sold fewer T-shirts than the average.
2. 5	On Friday, the average number of T-shirt sales for local stores was 15. Mobo Tees sold 20 T-shirts that day. They sold 5 pairs more than the average.
3. Tuesday and Friday	Compare the lengths of the double bars for each day. The longest bar had the most sales. On Tuesday and Friday the Mobo Tees bar is longer than the average bar. So, on these days the average sales were lower than the sales at Mobo Tees.

Answers to 3.3.4

Correct Answer	Explanation
1. 340	To solve this problem, find the point on the graph directly above Week 2 on the horizontal axis. It is just below the line that represents 350 on the vertical axis. So, the approximate average attendance for Week 2 is 340. 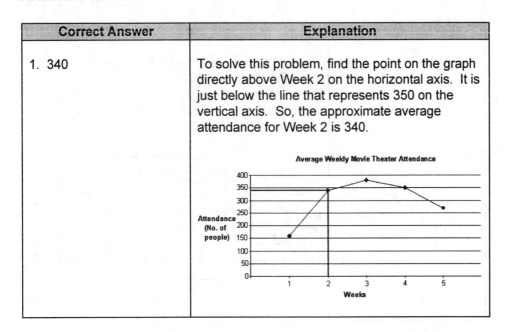

2. Week 5	Find 250 on the vertical axis. Follow the line across the graph looking for a point that is just above this line (270). The 270 point is above 5 on the horizontal axis. So, the average attendance is about 270 during Week 5. 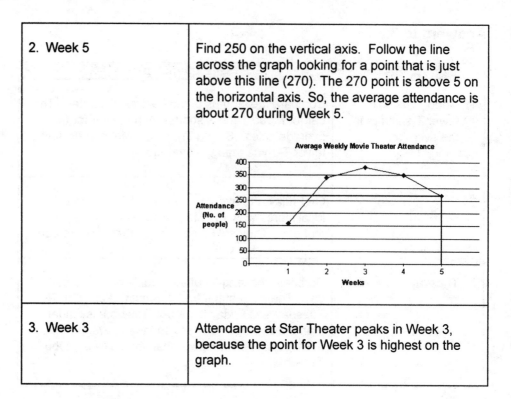
3. Week 3	Attendance at Star Theater peaks in Week 3, because the point for Week 3 is highest on the graph.

Answers to 3.3.5

Correct Answer	Explanation
1. 160 lbs	To solve this problem, find 5' 9" on the horizontal axis. Find the point that is on this line, and look to the left to find the weight on the vertical axis. The point is just above 150, so this man weighs approximately 160 pounds. 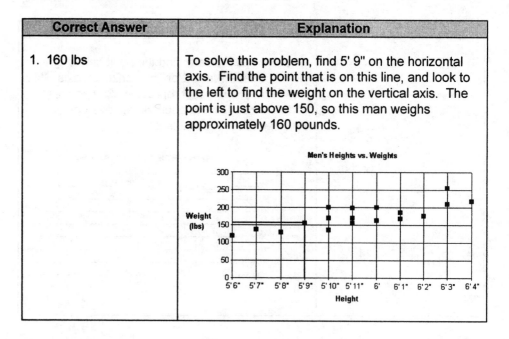

2. 6' 3"	Find 250 on the vertical axis. Follow the line across the graph looking for a point that is just above this line (260). The 260 point is above 6' 3" on the horizontal axis. So, the man who weighs 260 pounds is 6 feet 3 inches tall.

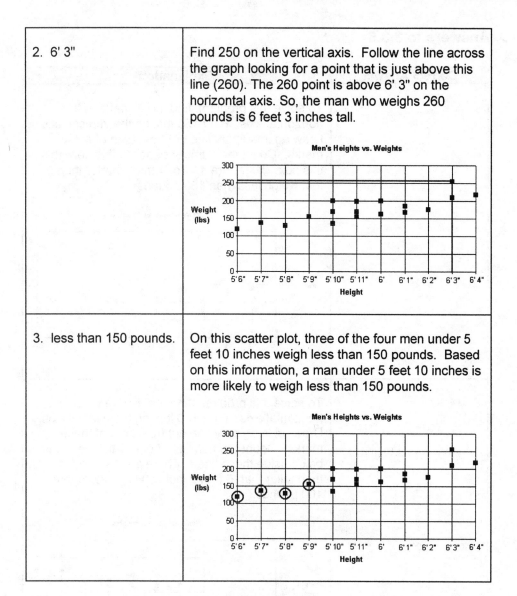

3. less than 150 pounds.	On this scatter plot, three of the four men under 5 feet 10 inches weigh less than 150 pounds. Based on this information, a man under 5 feet 10 inches is more likely to weigh less than 150 pounds.

Answers to 3.3.6

Correct Answer	Explanation
1. 4	To solve this problem, find the 6' mark on the horizontal axis. Find 150 lbs. on the vertical axis. Draw an imaginary line out from both of these marks. Count the number of points that lie within this box. There are 4. So, 4 men shorter than 6 feet weigh less than 150 pounds.
2. 14	To solve this problem, find the 5' 9" mark on the horizontal axis. Find 100 lbs. on the vertical axis. Draw an imaginary line out from both of these marks. Count the number of points that lie in the box outside these lines. There are 14. So, 14 men taller than 5 feet 9 inches weigh more than 100 pounds.

Answers to 3.3.7

Correct Answer	Explanation
1. between 60° and 66°	The average temperature was about 1° less in Week 1 than in Week 2, so the average temperature for the week preceding Week 1 was probably about 65°. This prediction assumes that there was not a dramatic rise or fall in the average temperature during the preceding week. 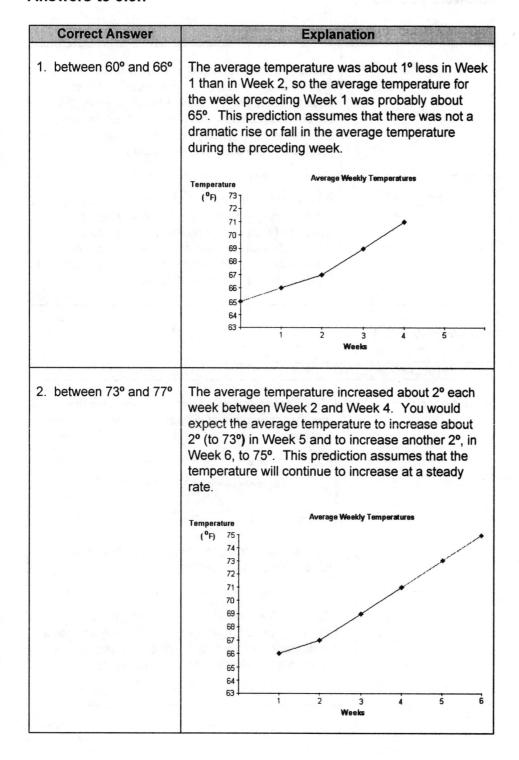
2. between 73° and 77°	The average temperature increased about 2° each week between Week 2 and Week 4. You would expect the average temperature to increase about 2° (to 73°) in Week 5 and to increase another 2°, in Week 6, to 75°. This prediction assumes that the temperature will continue to increase at a steady rate.

Answers to 3.3.8

Correct Answer	Explanation
1. (40,10) (50,30)	Points are labeled according to their relationship to the two axes. The first number represents the position of the point along the horizontal axis, and the second number represents the position along the vertical axis. Therefore, the first black point is at **(40,10)** and the second is at **(50,30).**
2. (10,20) (30,40)	Points are labeled according to their relationship to the two axes. The first number represents the position of the point along the horizontal axis, and the second number represents the position along the vertical axis. Therefore, the first white point is at **(10,20)** and the second is at **(30,40).**

Answers to 3.3.9

Correct Answer	Explanation
1. a person.	The most appropriate symbol to represent the number of workers at different factories would be a person.
2. 11	One hot dog represents 10 hot dogs. $110 \div 10 = 11$ So, you would place 11 hot dog symbols on the graph to represent 110 hot dogs.
3. A	Data set A shows whole-number quantities, which are well-suited for pictographs. One way to build a pictograph for this data would be to use a sun as the symbol and to let each symbol represent one day.

Answers to 3.3.10

Correct Answer	Explanation
1. B	The data in set A measures two types of quantity and would not be suitable for a single bar graph. The data in set B measures one type of quantity, the price of gas. The data ranges from $0.84 to $1.10, which would fit well on a scale from $0.8 to $1.1, with divisions of $0.05. Also, the data is already divided into 5 logical groups.
2. Number of Employees/ Occupations	The data shows the number of employees that work in different occupations in the city of Janton. Therefore, suitable labels for the vertical and horizontal axes are Number of Employees, and Occupations. **Number of Employees** **Occupations**

Answers to 3.3.11

Correct Answer	Explanation
1. A	The data in set A is suitable for a line graph because it shows changes over a period of time. The percent change in car sales from year to year changes continually. Notice that the data is close enough to make a reasonable scale.

2. vertical axis —
   Percent Unemployed
 	
   horizontal axis —
   Weeks
	On this line graph, the horizontal axis should be labeled "Weeks" to match the time period that the data represents. The vertical axis should be labeled "Percent Unemployed."
	
	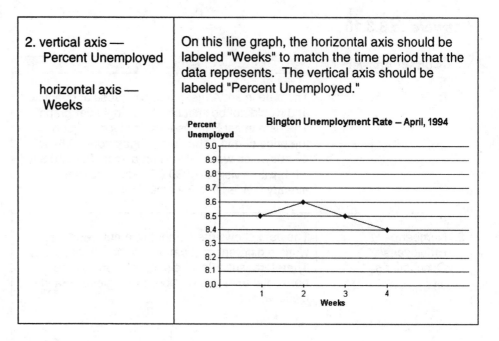

Answers to 3.3.12

Correct Answer	Explanation
1. A	The data in set A shows two measurements, weight and running speed. Since scatter plots are useful for comparing two data types, a scatter plot would be suitable for this set of data.
2. B	Axis labels **B** show two measurements, **Age** and **Weight**. Therefore, they could be shown on a scatter plot. The other two graph labels indicate that these graphs show categories (Year and Week). In these cases, there is only one type of measurement on each graph (number of employees on graph **A**, and number of cars sold on graph **C**).

Answers to 3.4.1

Correct Answer	Explanation
1. Children's Nonfiction	Children's Nonfiction is the least popular category as it is the smallest piece of the circle graph. This category accounted for only 11% of the books that were checked out from the library.
2. Adult Nonfiction and Children's Nonfiction	One-quarter is the same as 25%. Adult Nonfiction (14%) and Children's Nonfiction (11%) combined account for 25%, or one-quarter, of the books checked out of the library.

Answers to 3.4.2

Correct Answer	Explanation
1. $110	The only price with one "x" above it is $110. So, only one kind of tote bag is offered at the price of $110.
2. 3	If you look above $50 on the line plot, there are 3 x's. So, there are 3 kinds of tote bag offered at $50.
3. $90	There are no x's above $90, so you know there are no tote bags offered at this price.

Answers to 3.4.3

Correct Answer	Explanation
1. 2	Find 4 on the stem. Then count the number of leaves that are 4 at that position (in that row). There are two 4s. That means two styles of pants are $44.

2. $118	Find 10 on the stem. Then look at the leaves that are in the leaves column for the remainder of the leaf plot. There are two 8s in the leaves column next to 11 on the stem. The 11 represents $110, and the 8s in the leaves column each represent $8. Add these together and the price of pants costing more than $100 is $118.
3. $52 and $56	Find 5 and 6 on the stem. Then look at the leaves opposite these numbers. There is a 2 and 6 after the 5 stem. These numbers represent pairs of pants that cost $52 and $56. So, the pants in the $50 to $60 range cost $52 and $56.

Answers to 3.4.4

Correct Answer	Explanation
1. 60 — 90	The cluster of data on this line plot is between 60 and 90.
2. 2	There are 2 clusters on this stem-and-leaf plot.

Answers to 3.4.5

Correct Answer	Explanation
1. 20 and 60	The gap in this line plot occurs between 20 and 60.

2. 133 and 162	The gap in this stem-and-leaf plot occurs between 133 and 162. 12 | 2 13 | 3 14 | 15 | 16 | 2 17 | 6 7

Answers to 3.4.6

Correct Answer	Explanation
1. Yes	The value 20 is an outlier, as it is significantly removed from the cluster that occurs between 60 and 90.
2. 133	The value 133 is an outlier, as it is significantly removed from the cluster that occurs between 162 and 177.

Answers to 3.4.7

Correct Answer	Explanation
1. the lower box	The lower box is longer than any other box or whisker on the plot, therefore it has the largest range (about 42) 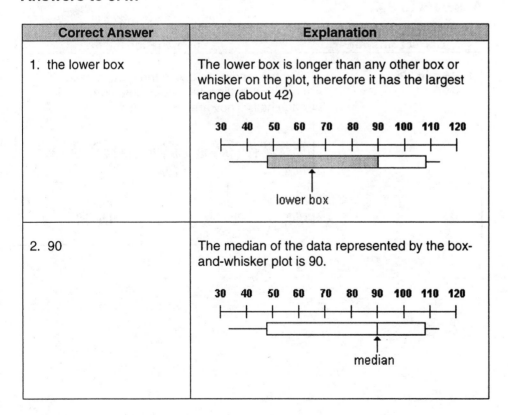 lower box
2. 90	The median of the data represented by the box-and-whisker plot is 90. median

| 3. 90 and 108 | The upper box contains data that ranges from 90 to 108. 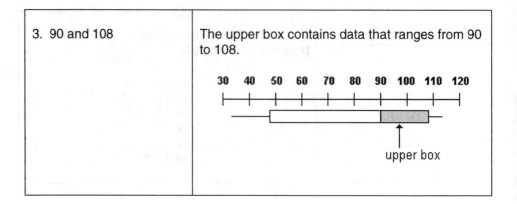 |

Answers to 3.4.8

Correct Answer	Explanation
1. 21 and 47	The extremes for this set of data are 21 and 47. They are the highest and lowest values in this set of data.
2. 57	The upper extreme is the number with the highest value. In this data set the upper extreme is 57.

Answers to 3.4.9

Correct Answer	Explanation
1. 16 and 25	Use the median to divide the data in half. Then find the quartiles, the two middle numbers in each half. They are 16 and 25.

2. 37 and 49.5	Use the median to divide the data in half. Then calculate the quartiles by finding the middle numbers in each half. You have to average the two middle numbers in the upper quartile. The lower quartile is 37 and the upper quartile is 49.5.
	35 36	38 42 (45) 47 48	51 53
	(37) lower quartile median (49.5) upper quartile

Answers to 3.4.10

Correct Answer	Explanation
1. Class 2	If you compare the left ends of the lower boxes, you will see that Class 2 has a higher lower quartile.
2. Class 1	Class 1 did better than Class 2 in all the values except the lower quartile.

Answers to 3.4.11

Correct Answer	Explanation
1. C	The Adults are slightly less than half. The Senior Citizens are close to a third, and the age 3 - 12 category is slightly less than one-quarter. The Under 3 category is slightly less than a tenth. 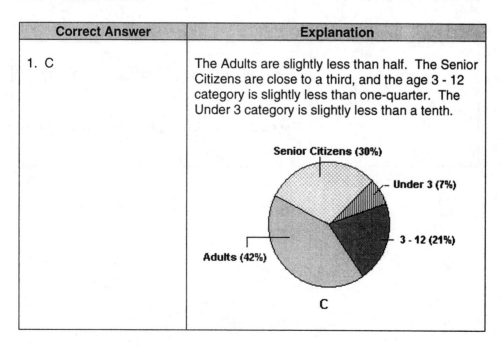

2. B	A circle graph is used to represent parts of a whole. Percentages are parts of a whole. So, the information on meat consumption (B) is suitable for a circle graph.

Answers to 3.4.12

Correct Answer	Explanation
1. C	Line plot C accurately reflects the data.
2. B	Line plot B accurately reflects the data.

Answers to 3.4.13

Correct Answer	Explanation
1. 8	The leaf represents 8 on this stem-and-leaf plot. It stands for 8 in the number 268.
2. B	Stem-and-leaf plot B reflects the data.

Answers to 3.4.14

Correct Answer	Explanation
1. 27	**15 18 18 20 26 $\mid$ 28 30 32 37 42** (27) The median, or middle number, of this data set is 27.

2. C

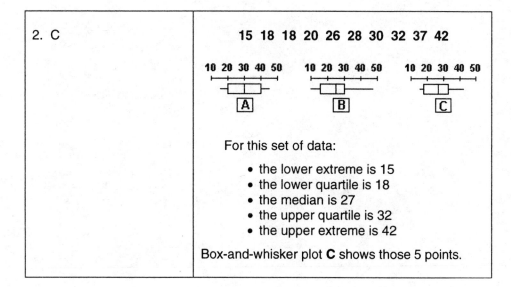

For this set of data:

- the lower extreme is 15
- the lower quartile is 18
- the median is 27
- the upper quartile is 32
- the upper extreme is 42

Box-and-whisker plot **C** shows those 5 points.

Chapter 4

Mathematical Relationships

4.1 Ratios and Proportions 265

    4.1.1   What is a Ratio? 265
    4.1.2   Ratios: Part to Part 266
    4.1.3   Part to Whole 268
    4.1.4   Three-Part Ratios 270
    4.1.5   Four-Part Ratios 271
    4.1.6   Ratios in Lowest Terms 273
    4.1.7   Equivalent Ratios 275
    4.1.8   What is a Proportion? 276
    4.1.9   Setting Up Proportions 278
    4.1.10 Scaling Up 280
    4.1.11 Scaling Down 281
    4.1.12 Cross Multiplying 283
    4.1.13 Ratios to Percents: Proportions 285
    4.1.14 Ratios to Percents: Calculator 286
    4.1.15 Percent of Increase 288

4.2 Number Patterns 290

    4.2.1   Patterns in Figures 290
    4.2.2   Patterns in Sequences 292
    4.2.3   Patterns in Tables 294

4.3 Variables, Expressions, and Equations 296

    4.3.1   Solving for Unknowns 296
    4.3.2   Evaluating Expressions 298
    4.3.3   Recognizing Equivalent Expressions 299
    4.3.4   Understanding Equations 301
    4.3.5   Manipulating Equations 303
    4.3.6   Evaluating Equations with Variables 305
    4.3.7   Exponents 307

4.4 Answers to Questions 308

Learn to understand basic
mathematical relationships by using
ratios and proportions, identifying
mathematical patterns, and exploring
variables, expressions, and equations.

4.1 Ratios and Proportions

4.1.1 What is a Ratio?

Ratios compare two or more **quantities**. They can compare parts to parts, a part to a whole, or a whole to a part.

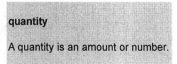

quantity

A quantity is an amount or number.

Ratios can be written three ways.

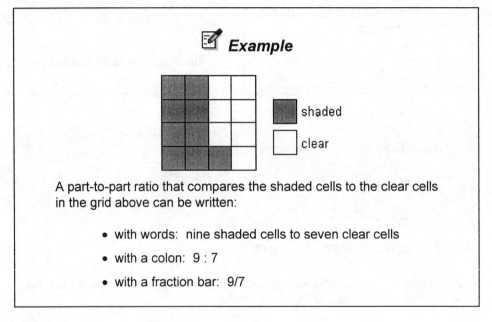

✎ *Example*

shaded

clear

A part-to-part ratio that compares the shaded cells to the clear cells in the grid above can be written:

- with words: nine shaded cells to seven clear cells
- with a colon: 9 : 7
- with a fraction bar: 9/7

 Check Your Understanding 4.1.1

Refer to the grid below to answer the following questions.

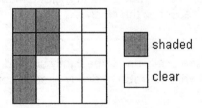

shaded

clear

Put a check (✓) next to the correct answers in the answer column.

Question	Answer
1. Which ratio represents the part-to-whole ratio of **clear** cells to **total** cells on the grid?	___ 6 : 10
	___ 10/16
	___ six clear cells to 16 total cells

2. Which ratio represents the part-to-whole ratio of **shaded** cells to **total** cells on the grid?	____ 10/16
	____ 6 : 10
	____ six shaded cells to a total of 16 cells
3. Which ratio represents the part-to-part ratio of **clear** cells to **shaded** cells on the grid?	____ 10 : 6
	____ 10/16
	____ six clear cells to 10 shaded cells

Topics Related to: What is a Ratio?

4.1.2 Ratios: Part to Part
4.1.3 Ratios: Part to Whole

4.1.2 Ratios: Part to Part

quantity

A quantity is an amount or number.

Ratios compare two or more **quantities**. A part-to-part ratio compares one part of a whole to another part of the same whole.

📝 *Example*

If there are two girls and three boys in a group music class, a part-to-part ratio that describes the class is 2 : 3.

ratio

A ratio compares two or more quantities. For example, the ratio of *shaded* squares to *clear* squares in the figure below is 2 to 6 (2:6). The ratio of *shaded* squares to *all* the squares is 2 to 8 (2:8). And the ratio of *clear* squares to *all* the squares is 6 to 8 (6:8).

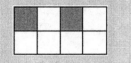

There are two darkly shaded cells and three lightly shaded cells in the grid below. There are three ways to write the **ratio** of darkly shaded cells to lightly shaded cells.

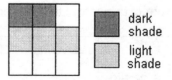

dark shade

light shade

two darkly shaded cells to three lightly shaded cells

2 : 3

2/3

Check Your Understanding 4.1.2

Put a check (✓) next to the correct answers in the answer column.

Question	Answer
1. What is the ratio of **lightly shaded** cells to **darkly shaded** cells? [grid figure] ▇ dark shade ▒ light shade	___ 3 : 6 ___ 6 : 3 ___ 6 : 16
2. What is the ratio of **lightly shaded** cells to **clear** cells? [grid figure] ☐ clear ▒ light shade	___ 3/7 ___ 6/7 ___ 7/6
2. What does the ratio 4/9 represent? [grid figure] ▇ dark shade ▒ light shade	___ darkly shaded cells to clear cells ___ clear cells to darkly shaded cells ___ darkly shaded cells to lightly shaded cells ___ lightly shaded cells to clear cells

Topics Related to: Ratios: Part to Part

    4.1.1 What is a Ratio?
    4.1.3 Ratios: Part to Whole

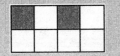

quantity

A quantity is an amount or number.

ratio

A ratio compares two or more quantities. For example, the ratio of *shaded* squares to *clear* squares in the figure below is 2 to 6 (2:6). The ratio of *shaded* squares to *all* the squares is 2 to 8 (2:8). And the ratio of *clear* squares to *all* the squares is 6 to 8 (6:8).

4.1.3 Part to Whole

Ratios compare two or more **quantities**. A part-to-whole ratio compares one part of a whole to the whole.

✏️ *Example*

If there are two girls and three boys in a group music class, a part-to-whole ratio that describes the number of girls in the class is 2 : 5.

There are two darkly shaded cells, three lightly shaded cells and four clear cells in this grid. There are three ways to write the **ratio** of darkly shaded cells to total cells.

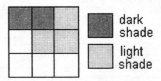

two darkly shaded cells to nine total cells

2 : 9

2/9

 Check Your Understanding 4.1.3

Put a check (✓) next to the correct answers in the answer column.

Question	Answer
1. What is the ratio of **lightly shaded** cells to **total** cells?	___ 4/9
	___ 3/9
	___ 9/4
	___ 9/2

2. What does the ratio 2/9 represent? dark shade ■ light shade ▨	____ clear cells to darkly shaded cells ____ darkly shaded cells to lightly shaded cells ____ darkly shaded cells to total cells ____ lightly shaded cells to total cells
3 What is the ratio of darkly shaded cells to total cells? dark shade ■ light shade ▨	____ 3 : 4 ____ 2 : 9 ____ 3 : 9 ____ 4 : 9
4. What does the ratio 5 : 9 represent? dark shade ■ light shade ▨	____ clear cells to darkly shaded cells ____ darkly shaded cells to lightly shaded cells ____ darkly shaded cells to total cells ____ lightly shaded cells to total cells

Topics Related to: Ratios: Part to Whole

    4.1.1 What is a Ratio?
    4.1.2 Ratios: Part to Part

4.1.4 Three-Part Ratios

Three-part ratios are used to compare three related **quantities**. For example, a three-part ratio could be used to compare the population of three different cities. This 16-cell grid has three kinds of cells that are each shaded differently.

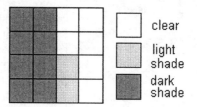

One way to write a three-part **ratio** that compares **clear** cells to **lightly shaded** cells to **darkly shaded** cells is: **6 : 2 : 8**.

 Check Your Understanding 4.1.4

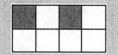
Put a check (✓) next to the correct answers in the answer column.

Question	Answer
1. What is the ratio of **clear** cells to **lightly shaded** cells to **darkly shaded** cells on this grid?	___ 8 : 5 : 3 ___ 3 : 8 : 5 ___ 5 : 3 : 8
2. What does the ratio 4 : 5 : 7 represent?	___ darkly shaded cells to clear cells to lightly shaded cells ___ clear cells to darkly shaded cells to lightly shaded cells ___ clear cells to darkly shaded cells to total cells ___ clear cells to lightly shaded cells to darkly shaded cells

3. What is the ratio of **hammers** to **scissors** to **tape measures**? (scissors, tape measures, hammers figures)	___ 2 : 3 : 4 ___ 4 : 3 : 2 ___ 3 : 4 : 2 ___ 3 : 2 : 4
4. In this pattern, what is the ratio of **circles** to **squares** to **triangles**? 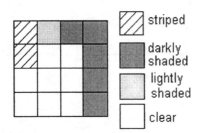	___ 1 : 2 : 4 ___ 1 : 4 : 2 ___ 2 : 4 : 1 ___ 4 : 1 : 2

Topics Related to: Three-Part Ratios

4.1.1 What is a Ratio?
4.1.2 Ratios: Part to Part
4.1.5 Four-Part Ratios

4.1.5 Four-Part Ratios

Four-part ratios are used to compare four related **quantities**. For example, a four-part ratio could be used to compare the starting salaries of four different jobs.

This 16-cell grid has three shades of cells.

(16-cell grid figure)

▨ striped

▪ darkly shaded

▫ lightly shaded

□ clear

One way to write a **ratio** that compares **striped** cells to **lightly shaded** cells to **clear** cells to **darkly shaded** cells is: **2 : 1 : 8 : 5**

quantity

A quantity is an amount or number.

ratio

A ratio compares two or more quantities. For example, the ratio of *shaded* squares to *clear* squares in the figure below is 2 to 6 (2:6). The ratio of *shaded* squares to *all* the squares is 2 to 8 (2:8). And the ratio of *clear* squares to *all* the squares is 6 to 8 (6:8).

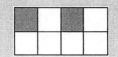

Check Your Understanding 4.1.5

Put a check (✓) next to the correct answers in the answer column.

Question	Answer
1. What is the ratio of **striped** cells to **lightly shaded** cells to **darkly shaded** cells to **clear** cells in this grid? striped darkly shaded lightly shaded clear	___ 5 : 1 : 7 : 3 ___ 3 : 1 : 5 : 7 ___ 1 : 3 : 7 : 5 ___ 1 : 7 : 3 : 5
2. What does the ratio 1 : 6 : 3 : 2 represent? striped darkly shaded lightly shaded clear	___ striped cells to lightly shaded cells to darkly shaded cells to clear cells ___ striped cells to darkly shaded cells to lightly shaded cells to clear cells ___ striped cells to clear cells to darkly shaded cells to lightly shaded cells
3. What is the ratio of **hammers** to **scissors** to **tape measures** to **brushes**?	___ 3 : 1 : 4 : 2 ___ 4 : 3 : 1 : 2 ___ 4 : 1 : 3 : 2 ___ 3 : 4 : 2 : 1

4. In this pattern, what does the ratio 3 : 2 : 1 : 4 represent?

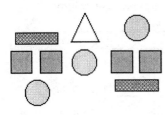

___ triangles to squares to circles to rectangles

___ circles to squares to triangles to rectangles

___ squares to rectangles to triangles to circles

___ circles to rectangles to triangles to squares

Topics Related to: Four-Part Ratios

4.1.1 What is a Ratio?
4.1.2 Ratios: Part to Part
4.1.4 Three-Part Ratios

ratio

A ratio compares two or more quantities. For example, the ratio of *shaded* squares to *clear* squares in the figure below is 2 to 6 (2:6). The ratio of *shaded* squares to *all* the squares is 2 to 8 (2:8). And the ratio of *clear* squares to *all* the squares is 6 to 8 (6:8).

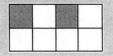

4.1.6 Ratios in Lowest Terms

A **ratio** is in **lowest terms** when the **greatest common factor (GCF)** of all the **terms** in the ratio is 1.

▶ To write a ratio in lowest terms:

- Find the common **factors** of all the terms in the ratio.
- Determine the greatest common factor (GCF) of the terms.
- Divide each term by the GCF. The result will be the ratio in lowest terms.

greatest common factor (GCF)

The greatest common factor is the largest factor that two or more numbers have in common. For example, the common factors of 36 and 42 are 2, 3, and 6. Six is the greatest common factor.

✏️ *Example*

To write the ratio 6:18:12 in lowest terms:

- Find the common factors — 1, 2, 3, and 6.
- Determine the greatest common factor — 6.
- Divide each term in the ratio by 6.
- The result is 1:3:2, a ratio in lowest terms.

---

terms

The terms of a ratio or fraction are the numbers being compared. For example, the terms of the ratio 5:3 are 5 and 3. The terms of the fraction 4/7 are 4 and 7.

Check Your Understanding 4.1.6

Put a check (✓) next to the correct answers in the answer column.

factor

A factor is an integer that divides another integer evenly, with no remainder. For example, 3 and 7 are factors of 21. One (1) is a factor of every number.

Question	Answer
1. What are the common factors of the ratio 8 : 16 : 24?	____ 1, 2, and 4 ____ 1, 2, 4, and 8 ____ 1, 2, 3, 4, and 8
2. What is the greatest common factor of the ratio 8 : 16 : 24?	____ 1 ____ 2 ____ 3 ____ 4 ____ 8 ____ 12
3. How would you write the ratio 8 : 16 : 24 in lowest terms?	____ 1 : 2 : 3 ____ 2 : 4 : 6 ____ 1 : 2 : 4
4. How would you write the ratio 12 : 20 : 46 in lowest terms?	____ 6 : 12 : 23 ____ 10 : 6 : 23 ____ 6 : 10 : 23
5. How would you write the ratio 420 : 70 : 350 in lowest terms?	____ 6 : 1 : 5 ____ 60 : 10 : 50 ____ 42 : 7 : 35

Topics Related to: Ratios in Lowest Terms

4.1.1   What is a Ratio?
4.1.7   Equivalent Ratios
4.1.11 Scaling Down

4.1.7 Equivalent Ratios

An **equivalent ratio** is found by multiplying or dividing all of the **terms** of a **ratio** by the same number.

 **Example**

If both terms of the ratio 3 : 4 are multiplied by 5, the result is an equivalent ratio of 15 : 20.

$$\frac{3 \times 5}{4 \times 5} = \frac{15}{20}$$

 Check Your Understanding 4.1.7a

Put a check (✓) next to the correct answers in the answer column.

Question	Answer
1. Each term of the ratio 4:7 was multiplied by what number to get the equivalent ratio 28 : 49?	___ 6 ___ 7 ___ 8
2. What is the equivalent ratio if you multiply each term of the ratio 3 : 4 by 9?	___ 36 : 27 ___ 21 : 28 ___ 27 : 36
3. Each term of the ratio 5 : 8 was multiplied by what number to get the equivalent ratio 60 : 96?	___ 11 ___ 12 ___ 13
4. What is the equivalent ratio if you multiply each term of the ratio 8 : 7 by 5?	___ 35 : 40 ___ 40 : 35 ___ 48 : 42

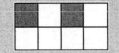

Check Your Understanding 4.1.7b

Draw a line to connect each item in the match column with the correct answer in the answer column.

Question	Match	Answer
1. Which ratios are equivalent to these ratios?	3 : 5 : 12 7 : 10 : 2 15 : 4 : 5	56 : 80 : 16 30 : 8 : 10 30 : 16 : 10 12 : 20 : 48
2. Which ratios are equivalent to these ratios?	48 : 72 : 30 250 : 400 : 600 490 : 630 : 420	7 : 9 : 6 5 : 8 : 12 8 : 12 : 5 8 : 12 : 9

Topics Related to: Equivalent Ratios

    4.1.1 What is a Ratio?
    4.1.8 What is a Proportion?
    4.1.10 Scaling Up
    4.1.11 Scaling Down

4.1.8 What is a Proportion?

A **proportion** is a statement of equality between two **ratios.** You can multiply or divide to show that the ratios used in a proportion are equivalent.

---

ratio

A ratio compares two or more quantities. For example, the ratio of *shaded* squares to *clear* squares in the figure below is 2 to 6 (2:6). The ratio of *shaded* squares to *all* the squares is 2 to 8 (2:8). And the ratio of *clear* squares to *all* the squares is 6 to 8 (6:8).

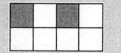

 Example

$$\frac{4}{2} = \frac{8}{4} \quad \text{is a proportion because}$$

$$\frac{4 \times 2}{2 \times 2} = \frac{8}{4} \quad \text{and}$$

$$\frac{4}{2} = \frac{8 \div 2}{4 \div 2}$$

Check Your Understanding 4.1.8

Put a check (✓) next to the correct answers in the answer column.

Question	Answer
1. Which of these is a proportion?	___ 4/9 ___ 2/7 = 8/28 ___ 12 : 15 ___ 3/5 = 6/9
2. Which of these is a proportion?	___ 15/17 ___ 5/7 = 20/35 ___ 3/8 = 15/40 ___ 14 : 9
3. Which of these is <u>not</u> a proportion?	___ 12/5 = 36/15 ___ 45/60 = 9/12 ___ 54/72 = 6/8 ___ 125/250 = 5/6
4. Which of these is <u>not</u> a proportion?	___ 15/6 = 300/120 ___ 6/8 = 36/48 ___ 7/5 = 49/40 ___ 3/7 = 210/490

Topics Related to: What is a Proportion?

4.1.1   What is a Ratio?
4.1.7   Equivalent Ratios
4.1.9   Setting up Proportions
4.1.10 Scaling Up
4.1.11 Scaling Down

proportion

A proportion is a statement of equality between two ratios. For example, 3/5 = 9/15 is a proportion.

quantity

A quantity is an amount or number.

ratio

A ratio compares two or more quantities. For example, the ratio of *shaded* squares to *clear* squares in the figure below is 2 to 6 (2:6). The ratio of *shaded* squares to *all* the squares is 2 to 8 (2:8). And the ratio of *clear* squares to *all* the squares is 6 to 8 (6:8).

4.1.9 Setting Up Proportions

You can set up a **proportion** to solve problems like this one:

If a bicyclist can ride 2 miles in 5 minutes, how long will it take her to ride 22 miles if she maintains the same speed?

1. Using two known **quantities**, write a **ratio**:

$$\frac{2 \text{ miles}}{5 \text{ minutes}}$$

2. Using the third known quantity and a (?), write a similar ratio:

$$\frac{22 \text{ miles}}{? \text{ minutes}}$$

(Note that both ratios compare miles to minutes, with miles on the top and minutes on the bottom.)

3. To complete the proportion, set the two ratios equal to each other:

$$\frac{2 \text{ miles}}{5 \text{ minutes}} = \frac{22 \text{ miles}}{? \text{ minutes}}$$

For help in solving the proportion, see the Handbook topics on scaling up and down and on cross multiplying.

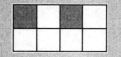 **Check Your Understanding 4.1.9**

Put a check (✓) next to the correct answers in the answer column.

Question	Answer
1. A book costs $5. How much will 7 copies of the same book cost? Choose the proportion that is correctly set up to solve the problem. A $\quad \dfrac{\$5}{1 \text{ book}} = \dfrac{\$?}{7 \text{ books}}$ B $\quad \dfrac{\$?}{\$5} = \dfrac{1 \text{ book}}{7 \text{ books}}$ C $\quad \dfrac{\$5}{7 \text{ books}} = \dfrac{\$?}{1 \text{ book}}$	___ A ___ B ___ C

2. A student can walk 4 miles per hour. How long will it take her to walk 10 miles if she maintains the same speed? Choose the proportion that is correctly set up to solve the problem.

       _____ A
       _____ B
       _____ C

   A $\quad \dfrac{4 \text{ miles}}{10 \text{ miles}} = \dfrac{? \text{ hours}}{1 \text{ hour}}$

   B $\quad \dfrac{4 \text{ miles}}{? \text{ hours}} = \dfrac{10 \text{ miles}}{1 \text{ hour}}$

   C $\quad \dfrac{4 \text{ miles}}{1 \text{ hour}} = \dfrac{10 \text{ miles}}{? \text{ hours}}$

3. If Monte can plant 2 rows of corn in 10 minutes, how long will it take him to plant 15 rows if he plants at the same rate? Choose the proportion that is correctly set up to solve the problem.

       _____ A
       _____ B
       _____ C

   A $\quad \dfrac{2 \text{ rows}}{15 \text{ rows}} = \dfrac{? \text{ minutes}}{10 \text{ minutes}}$

   B $\quad \dfrac{15 \text{ rows}}{2 \text{ rows}} = \dfrac{? \text{ minutes}}{10 \text{ minutes}}$

   C $\quad \dfrac{15 \text{ rows}}{10 \text{ minutes}} = \dfrac{2 \text{ rows}}{? \text{ minutes}}$

4. Rachel can buy 3 boxes of *Mac's Snacks* for $1.24. How much will 25 boxes cost her? Choose the proportion that is correctly set up to solve the problem.

       _____ A
       _____ B
       _____ C

   A $\quad \dfrac{3 \text{ boxes}}{\$1.24} = \dfrac{25 \text{ boxes}}{? \$}$

   B $\quad \dfrac{\$1.24}{? \$} = \dfrac{25 \text{ boxes}}{3 \text{ boxes}}$

   C $\quad \dfrac{\$1.24}{25 \text{ boxes}} = \dfrac{? \$}{3 \text{ boxes}}$

Topics Related to: Setting Up Proportions

4.1.1 What is a Proportion?
4.1.7 Equivalent Ratios
4.1.10 Scaling Up
4.1.11 Scaling Down
4.1.12 Cross-Multiplying

4.1.10 Scaling Up

ratio

A ratio compares two or more quantities. For example, the ratio of *shaded* squares to *clear* squares in the figure below is 2 to 6 (2:6). The ratio of *shaded* squares to *all* the squares is 2 to 8 (2:8). And the ratio of *clear* squares to *all* the squares is 6 to 8 (6:8).

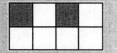

Scaling up means to multiply *both* terms in a **ratio** by the same number.

 **Example**

You can scale up the ratio 1/3 by multiplying both terms by 2:

$$\frac{1}{3} = \frac{1 \times 2}{3 \times 2} = \frac{2}{6}$$

The ratio 1/3 is equivalent to 2/6.

proportion

A proportion is a statement of equality between two ratios. For example, 3/5 = 9/15 is a proportion.

Scale up to solve **proportions** such as:

$$\frac{7}{10} = \frac{?}{30}$$

▶ Ask yourself, "10 times *what* equals 30?"

▶ Then multiply 7 by the number you are thinking of.

Since 10 x 3 = 30, you should multiply 7 by 3 to get **21**.

 Check Your Understanding 4.1.10

Put a check (✓) next to the correct answers in the answer column.

Question	Answer
1. What is the solution to this problem? $\frac{4}{7} = \frac{?}{42}$	___ 6 ___ 24 ___ 28

2. What is the solution to this problem? $\dfrac{2}{9} = \dfrac{?}{63}$	___ 14 ___ 7 ___ 18
3. What is the solution to this problem? $\dfrac{3 \text{ miles}}{20 \text{ minutes}} = \dfrac{18 \text{ miles}}{? \text{ minutes}}$	___ 30 minutes ___ 54 minutes ___ 60 minutes ___ 120 minutes
4. What is the solution to this problem? $\dfrac{5 \text{ boxes}}{\$1.30} = \dfrac{20 \text{ boxes}}{?\$}$	___ \$2.60 ___ \$5.20 ___ \$6.50 ___ \$10.00

Topics Related to: Scaling Up

4.1.1   What is a Proportion?
4.1.7   Equivalent Ratios
4.1.9   Setting Up Proportions
4.1.11 Scaling Down

4.1.11 Scaling Down

Scaling down means to divide *both* terms in a ratio by the same number.

✐ *Example*

You can scale down the ratio 6/9 by dividing both terms by 3:

$$\frac{6}{9} = \frac{6 \div 3}{9 \div 3} = \frac{2}{3}$$

The ratio 6/9 is equivalent to 2/3.

---

proportion

A proportion is a statement of equality between two ratios. For example, 3/5 = 9/15 is a proportion.

Scale down to solve **proportions** such as:

$$\frac{14}{10} = \frac{?}{5}$$

▶ Ask yourself, "10 divided by *what* equals 5?"

▶ Then divide 14 by the number you are thinking of.

10 ÷ 2 = 5, so you should divide 14 by 2 to get **7**.

 Check Your Understanding 4.1.11

Put a check (✓) next to the correct answers in the answer column.

Question	Answer
1. What is the solution to this problem? $\frac{20}{35} = \frac{?}{7}$	___ 5 ___ 7 ___ 4
2. What is the solution to this problem? $\frac{44}{55} = \frac{?}{5}$	___ 4 ___ 11 ___ 5
3. What is the solution to this problem? $\frac{120 \text{ pages}}{180 \text{ minutes}} = \frac{2 \text{ pages}}{? \text{ minutes}}$	___ 2 minutes ___ 3 minutes ___ 30 minutes
4. What is the solution to this problem? $\frac{550 \text{ gallons}}{250 \text{ days}} = \frac{11 \text{ gallons}}{? \text{ days}}$	___ 2 days ___ 5 days ___ 50 days

Topics Related to: Scaling Down

4.1.1   What is a Proportion?
4.1.7   Equivalent Ratios
4.1.9   Setting Up Proportions
4.1.10 Scaling Up

4.1.12 Cross Multiplying

Proportions such as this one can't readily be solved by scaling. To solve them, you can *cross multiply*.

$$\frac{4}{5} = \frac{?}{8}$$

Cross multiply means to multiply the **numerator** of one ratio by the **denominator** of the other ratio.

> **numerator**
>
> The numerator is the number in a fraction that represents part of a whole. For example, in the fraction 7/13, the numerator is 7.

▶ Think of the equal (=) sign as a cross: (✕) .

$$\frac{4}{5} = \frac{?}{8} \quad \rightarrow \quad \frac{4}{5} \, ✕ \, \frac{?}{8}$$

▶ Multiply the numbers at the ends of the cross:

$$4 \times 8 = 5 \times ?$$
$$\text{or} \quad 32 = 5 \times ?$$

> **denominator**
>
> The denominator is the number in a fraction that represents the number of parts that make a whole. For example, in the fraction 7/13, the denominator is 13.

▶ Use division and a calculator to solve the equation:

$$\frac{32}{5} = ?$$

$$32 \div 5 = \textbf{6.4}, \quad \text{so} \quad \frac{4}{5} = \frac{\textbf{6.4}}{8}$$

 Check Your Understanding 4.1.12

Put a check (✓) next to the correct answers in the answer column.

Question	Answer
1. What is the solution to this proportion? $\dfrac{11}{8} = \dfrac{?}{5}$	____ 6.875 ____ 7.725 ____ 6.5
2. What is the solution to this proportion? $\dfrac{4}{5} = \dfrac{?}{7}$	____ 7.4 ____ 6.25 ____ 5.6

3. What is the solution to this proportion? $$\frac{3}{4} = \frac{?}{9}$$	___ 0.08 ___ 1.33 ___ 6.75
4. What is the solution to this proportion? $$\frac{2}{3} = \frac{5}{?}$$	___ 0.13 ___ 7.5 ___ 15.2
5. What is the solution to this proportion? $$\frac{5}{6} = \frac{7}{?}$$	___ 0.12 ___ 5.83 ___ 8.4
6. What is the solution to this proportion? $$\frac{23}{5} = \frac{15}{?}$$	___ 0.31 ___ 3.26 ___ 4.6

Topics Related to: Cross Multiplying

4.1.1   What is a Proportion?
4.1.7   Equivalent Ratios
4.1.9   Setting Up Proportions
4.1.10 Scaling Up
4.1.11 Scaling Down

4.1.13 Ratios to Percents: Proportions

A *percent* is a special kind of **ratio**. It compares a **quantity** to 100. For example, 55/100 = 55%.

When the **denominator** of a ratio is a **factor** of 100 exactly, you can use a **proportion** to write the ratio as a percent.

 ***Example***

1. Set the **ratio** equal to ?/100.

$$\frac{3}{10} = \frac{?}{100}$$

2. Solve the proportion by scaling.

$$\frac{3 \times 10}{10 \times 10} = \frac{30}{100}$$

3. Write the second ratio as a percent.

$$\frac{30}{100} = \mathbf{30\%}$$

 Check Your Understanding 4.1.13

Draw a line to connect each item in the match column with the correct answer in the answer column.

Question	Match	Answer
1. Which percent is equivalent to each of these ratios?	3/5	20%
	1/4	25%
	7/20	35%
	1/2	50%
		60%

quantity

A quantity is an amount or number.

denominator

The denominator is the number in a fraction that represents the number of parts that make a whole. For example, in the fraction 7/13, the denominator is 13.

factor

A factor is an integer that divides another integer evenly, with no remainder. For example, 3 and 7 are factors of 21. One (1) is a factor of every number.

proportion

A proportion is a statement of equality between two ratios. For example, 3/5 = 9/15 is a proportion.

ratio

A ratio compares two or more quantities. For example, the ratio of *shaded* squares to *clear* squares in the figure below is 2 to 6 (2:6). The ratio of *shaded* squares to *all* the squares is 2 to 8 (2:8). And the ratio of *clear* squares to *all* the squares is 6 to 8 (6:8).

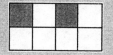

2. Which ratio is equivalent to each of these percents?	8%	2/5
	10 %	4/5
	40%	3/4
	75 %	1/10
		2/25

ratio

A ratio compares two or more quantities. For example, the ratio of *shaded* squares to *clear* squares in the figure below is 2 to 6 (2:6). The ratio of *shaded* squares to *all* the squares is 2 to 8 (2:8). And the ratio of *clear* squares to *all* the squares is 6 to 8 (6:8).

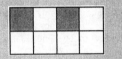

Topics Related to: Ratios to Percents: Proportions

2.4   Percents
4.1.9   Setting Up Proportions
4.1.10 Scaling Up
4.1.11 Scaling Down
4.1.12 Cross Multiplying
4.1.14 Ratios to Percents: Calculator

4.1.14 Ratios to Percents: Calculator

A *percent* is a special kind of **ratio**. It compares a quantity to 100. For example, 55/100 = 55%.

If the **denominator** of a ratio is not a **factor** of 100, you can use the calculator to write the ratio as a percent.

factor

A factor is an integer that divides another integer evenly, with no remainder. For example, 3 and 7 are factors of 21. One (1) is a factor of every number.

📝 *Example*

The denominator of 4/16 is not a factor of 100, because 16 does not evenly divide 100: 100 ÷ 16 = 6, remainder 4. To find a percent that is equivalent to 4/16:

▶ Divide the **numerator** by the **denominator**.

$$\frac{4}{16} \;\rightarrow\; 4 \div 16 \;\rightarrow\; 0.25$$

▶ Multiply the answer by 100 to find the **percent**:

$$0.25 \times 100 = \mathbf{25\%}$$

---

numerator

The numerator is the number in a fraction that represents part of a whole. For example, in the fraction 7/13, the numerator is 7.

denominator

The denominator is the number in a fraction that represents the number of parts that make a whole. For example, in the fraction 7/13, the denominator is 13.

Check Your Understanding 4.1.14

Draw a line to connect each item in the match column with the correct answer in the answer column.

Question	Match	Answer
1. Which percents are equivalent to each of these ratios (rounded to the nearest tenth)?	2/3 13/15 25/26 11/12	33.4% 66.7% 74.3% 86.7% 96.2%
2. Which ratios (rounded to the nearest tenth) are equivalent to each of these percents?	5/16 3/7 1/3 4/9	26.4% 31.3% 42.9% 44.4% 56.2%

Topics Related to: Ratios to Percents: Calculator

2.4   Percents
4.1.10 Scaling Up
4.1.11 Scaling Down
4.1.12 Cross Multiplying
4.1.13 Ratios to Percents: Proportions

percent

A percent (%) is a special kind of ratio. It compares a quantity to 100. The word percent means "per one hundred".

4.1.15 Percent of Increase

Percent of increase means, "By what **percent** has the original amount increased?"

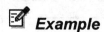 *Example*

If you have $10 and someone gives you $5 more, the amount of money you have has increased by 50%.

To find the percent of increase:

1. Write the **ratio**

$$\frac{\text{amount } \textbf{of} \text{ increase}}{\text{amount } \textbf{before} \text{ increase}}$$

For example: $\dfrac{\$5}{\$10}$

ratio

A ratio compares two or more quantities. For example, the ratio of *shaded* squares to *clear* squares in the figure below is 2 to 6 (2:6). The ratio of *shaded* squares to *all* the squares is 2 to 8 (2:8). And the ratio of *clear* squares to *all* the squares is 6 to 8 (6:8).

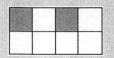

2. Set up the **proportion**

$$\frac{\text{amount of increase}}{\text{amount before increase}} = \frac{?}{100}$$

For example: $\dfrac{\$5}{\$10} = \dfrac{?}{100}$

3. Solve the proportion for (?):

$$\frac{\$5}{\$10} = \frac{50}{100}$$

Percent of increase = 50%

proportion

A proportion is a statement of equality between two ratios. For example, 3/5 = 9/15 is a proportion.

Check Your Understanding 4.1.15

Put a check (✓) next to the correct answers in the answer column.

Question	Answer
1. There are 25 cabbages in the produce section of a grocery store. Ten more are added. What is the percent of increase?	___ 31% ___ 35% ___ 40% ___ 45%
2. You have $500 in the bank. At the end of the year, $20 interest was added to this amount. What is the percent of increase?	___ 4% ___ 5% ___ 8% ___ 40%
3. Tanner was 30 inches tall last year. He grew 3 inches this year. What is the percent of increase?	___ 5% ___ 10% ___ 15% ___ 20%
4. The local "Help a Friend See" drive collected 650 used glasses frames last year. This year they collected 325 more than the previous year. What is the percent of increase?	___ 25% ___ 45% ___ 50% ___ 200%

Topics Related to: Percent of Increase

2.4 Percents
4.1.9 Setting Up Proportions
4.1.10 Scaling Up
4.1.11 Scaling Down
4.1.12 Cross Multiplying

4.2 Number Patterns

4.2.1 Patterns in Figures

Almost anywhere you look, you can find *patterns*. For example, there are patterns in nature, in numbers, and in music. Sometimes figures in a group follow a pattern.

▶ Here are some hints on how to find a pattern among a group of figures. Refer to the following figures.

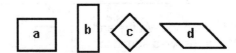

1. Choose two figures to compare. Then ask yourself, "How are these two figures related?"

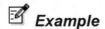 **Example**

Compare figures **a** and **b**. The angles of figure **a** are equal to the angles of figure **b**.

---

2. Choose two other figures and see if they have the same relationship.

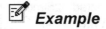 **Example**

Compare figures **c** and **d**. Are the angles of figure **c** equal to the angles of figure **d**? No.

---

3. If they don't have the same relationship, repeat steps 1 and 2.

4. Keep going until you find a relationship that matches all of the figures or until you cannot think of any more relationships.

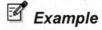 **Example**

Compare figures **a** and **b** again. Another way figures **a** and **b** are related is that they both have opposite sides that are parallel. Figures **c** and **d** also have opposite sides that are parallel.

Check Your Understanding 4.2.1

Put a check (✓) next to the correct answers in the answer column.

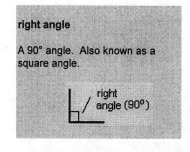
Question	Answer
1. How are these figures related? □ Y ∀ L	___ Each figure has four corners. ___ Each figure has four line segments, or sides. ___ Each figure has at least one right angle (90°).
2. How are these figures related? ⋈ ⅄ M ▯	___ Each figure has four corners. ___ Each figure has four line segments, or sides. ___ Each figure has at least one right angle (90°).
3. How are these figures not related? ▽ △ △ N	___ Each figure has three line segments, or sides. ___ Each figure forms at least two corners or angles where lines intersect. ___ Each figure has all sides connected.
4. How are these figures not related? □ ▱ ▱ ▱	___ Each figure has four sides. ___ Each figure is skewed (has no right angles). ___ Each figure has four corners.

product

The result of multiplying numbers.

difference

The result of subtraction. For example, the difference of 8 - 5 is 3.

sum

A sum is the result of the addition of two or more numbers or quantities. For example, the sum of 3 and 5 is 8.

adjacent

Two objects that are adjacent are next each other. For example, in a group of three dots (. . .), the first and second dots are adjacent, and the second and third dots are adjacent. However, the first and third dots are *not* adjacent.

4.2.2 Patterns in Sequences

Sometimes a series or a group of numbers follows a pattern.

To find a pattern in a *number sequence,* look for relationships involving **sums, differences,** or **products** between **adjacent** numbers.

▶ For example, this pattern involves **sums.** Try adding 3 to each number in the sequence.

$$2, \ 5, \ 8, \ 11, \ \ldots$$
$$+3 \ +3 \ +3$$

What do you think the next number in this sequence is?

11 + 3 = 14, so **14** should be the next number in the sequence.

▶ This pattern involves **differences.** Try subtracting 10 from the first number in the sequence, 9 from the second number, 8 from the third number, etc.

$$40, \ 30, \ 21, \ 13, \ \ldots$$
$$-10 \ -9 \ -8$$

What do you think the next number in this sequence is?

13 - 7 = 6, so **6** should be the next number in the sequence.

▶ This pattern involves **products.** Try multiplying **adjacent** numbers together.

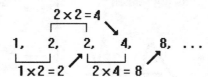

What do you think the next number in this sequence should be?

4 x 8 = 32, so **32** should be the next number in the sequence.

Check Your Understanding 4.2.2

Put a check (✓) next to the correct answers in the answer column.

Question	Answer
1. What is the pattern in this number sequence? **6, 13, 20, 27, ...**	____ Add 7 to any number in the sequence to get the next number. ____ Multiply any number in the sequence by 2 to get the next number. ____ Add 2 adjacent numbers to get the next number.
2. What is the pattern in this number sequence? **1, 3, 7, 15, 31...**	____ Multiply each number by itself and add 2 to get the next number. ____ Multiply each number by itself and add 1 to get the next number. ____ Multiply each number by 2 and add 1 to get the next number.
3. What is the pattern in this number sequence? **2, 8, 26, 80...**	____ Add 1 x 6 to the first number. Add 2 x 6 to the second number. Add 3 x 6 to the third number. Continue this pattern through the sequence. ____ Multiply any number by 3 then add 2 to get the next number in the sequence. ____ Multiply any number by 4 to get the following number in the sequence.

Topics Related to: Patterns in Sequences

4.2.1 Patterns in Figures
4.2.3 Patterns in Tables

4.2.3 Patterns in Tables

Sometimes numbers follow a pattern when they are shown in a table.

▶ Here are some hints on how to find a relationship among pairs of numbers in a *table*.

- Choose two corresponding numbers from one row in the table below: 2 and 4.

- Compare the two numbers and find one way that they are related: 4 is twice as large as 2, for example.

2	4
5	7
1	3

- Choose a different pair of numbers and see if they have a similar relationship: Is 7 twice as large as 5? No.

- If they don't have a similar relationship, then find how they *are* related and see if the other pairs of numbers have a similar relationship.

  Seven is *not* twice as large as 5, but 7 *is* 2 greater than 5. Similarly, 3 is 2 greater than 1 and 4 is 2 greater than 2.

  Each number in the second column of the table is 2 more than the number in the first column:

  $$2 + 2 = 4$$
  $$5 + 2 = 7$$
  $$1 + 2 = 3$$

Check Your Understanding 4.2.3

Put a check (✓) next to the correct answers in the answer column.

Question	Answer
1. Which relationship between 3 and 7 matches the relationship between the other pairs of numbers in the table? $\begin{array}{\|c\|c\|}\hline 3 & 7 \\\hline 5 & 11 \\\hline 9 & 19 \\\hline\end{array}$	____ 3 plus 4 is 7 ____ 3 times itself minus 2 is 7 ____ 3 times 2 plus 1 is 7
2. Which relationship between 14 and 9 matches the relationship between the other pairs of numbers in the table? $\begin{array}{\|c\|c\|}\hline 14 & 9 \\\hline 28 & 23 \\\hline 52 & 47 \\\hline\end{array}$	____ 14 times 2 minus 19 is 9 ____ 14 minus 5 is 9 ____ 14 plus 4 divided by 2 is 9
3. Which relationship between 7 and 19 matches the relationship between the other pairs of numbers in the table? $\begin{array}{\|c\|c\|}\hline 7 & 19 \\\hline 11 & 27 \\\hline 15 & 35 \\\hline\end{array}$	____ 7 times itself minus 30 is 19 ____ 2 times 7 plus 5 is 19 ____ 3 times 7 minus 2 is 19
4. Which relationship between 60 and 25 does **not** match the relationship between the other pairs of numbers in the table? $\begin{array}{\|c\|c\|}\hline 60 & 25 \\\hline 14 & 2 \\\hline 48 & 19 \\\hline\end{array}$	____ 60 divided by 2 minus 5 is 25 ____ 2 times 60 divided by 6 plus 5 is 25 ____ .5 times 60 minus 5 is 25

Topics Related to: Patterns in Tables

    4.2.1 Patterns in Figures
    4.2.2 Patterns in Sequences

4.3 Variables, Expressions, and Equations

4.3.1 Solving for Unknowns

When an **equation** has only one letter representing an *unknown value,* you can solve the equation for the unknown value. In order to solve equations for unknown values, you need to remember these important concepts:

▶ Addition and subtraction are **inverse operations**. Similarly, multiplication and division are inverse operations. In other words, subtraction undoes addition and division undoes multiplication.

▶ When you perform an operation such as addition, subtraction, multiplication, or division, be careful to preserve equality.

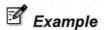 *Example*

In the equation $3 + 7 = 10$, if you subtract 7 from only the left side of the equation, the equality is destroyed. However, if you subtract 7 from *both* sides of the equation, the equality is preserved.

Destroys equality	**Preserves equality**
$3 + 7 = 10$	$3 + 7 = 10$
$3 + 7 - 7 = 10$	$3 + 7 - 7 = 10 - 7$
$3 \neq 10$	$3 = 3$

▶ Inverse operations can sometimes help solve for an unknown value.

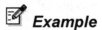 *Example*

To solve for the unknown value represented by the letter y in the equation $y \div 9 = 27$, follow these steps:

$$y \div 9 = 27$$

$$(y \div 9) \times 9 = 27 \times 9$$

inverse operations

The solution to the equation is: $y = 243$

Check Your Understanding 4.3.1

Put a check (✓) next to the correct answers in the answer column.

Question	Answer
1. Which number is the solution to the equation y + 27 = 48?	___ 21 ___ 31 ___ 75
2. Which number is the solution to the equation y - 16 = 92?	___ 76 ___ 86 ___ 108
3. Which number is the solution to the equation t x 12 = 480?	___ 40 ___ 60 ___ 5,760
4. Which number is the solution to the equation t ÷ 8 = 8?	___ 1 ___ 16 ___ 64
5. Which number is the solution to the equation z ÷ 250 = 100?	___ 2.5 ___ 2,500 ___ 25,000
6. Which number is the solution to the equation z x 6 = 420?	___ 0.014 ___ 70 ___ 700

Topics Related to: Solving for Unknowns

4.3.5 Manipulating Equations

4.3.2 Evaluating Expressions

A mathematical **expression** is a combination of letters, symbols, and numbers. For example, 3n + 9, $n^2 \div 5$ and 3(a + b) are expressions. When you **evaluate** an expression, you replace the letters in the expression with given numbers. The expression then has a numerical value.

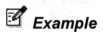 **Example**

To evaluate the expression K - 5 when K = 12, simply replace **K** with **12**.

$$\mathbf{K} - 5 = \mathbf{12} - 5 = 7$$

The value of the expression K - 5, when K = 12, is 7.

 Check Your Understanding 4.3.2

Put a check (✓) next to the correct answers in the answer column.

Question	Answer
1. What is the value of the expression 4T + 7 when T = 3?	___ 8 ___ 12 ___ 14 ___ 19
2. What is the value of the expression 6N ÷ 3 when N = 8?	___ 4 ___ 16 ___ 24 ___ 48
3. What is the value of the expression 20z - 5 when z = 7?	___ 105 ___ 135 ___ 140 ___ 145

4. What is the value of the expression 8d x 4 when d = 25?	___ 6.25 ___ 32 ___ 200 ___ 800

Topics Related to: Evaluating Expressions

4.3.6 Evaluating Equations with Variables

4.3.3 Recognizing Equivalent Expressions

At first glance, two **expressions** may not appear *equivalent* when they really are. Here are some hints to remember when trying to recognize equivalent expressions:

▶ The order in which numbers are added can always be reversed:

$$4 + 2 = 2 + 4.$$

The order in which numbers are subtracted *cannot* be reversed:

$$6 - 5 \neq 5 - 6.$$

▶ The order in which numbers are multiplied can always be reversed:

$$5 \times 6 = 6 \times 5.$$

The order in which numbers are divided *cannot* be reversed:

$$9 \div 3 \neq 3 \div 9.$$

▶ Repeated addition is the same as multiplication:

$$a + a + a = 3 \times a = 3a.$$

Similarly, multiplication is the same as repeated addition:

$$3(a + b) = (a + b) + (a + b) + (a + b) = 3a + 3b.$$

▶ Be careful: $n \times n = n^2$, and $n \times n \times n = n^3$.

But n^2 in general does *not* equal 2n and n^3 does *not* equal 3n.

▶ If you are ever in doubt, try replacing the letters with numbers.

expression

An expression is a combination of numbers and symbols. For example, 5n + 3, (b + a), and 7 - y are expressions.

Example

To check that 5(y + z) is the same as 5y + 5z, **replace y with 1 and z with 2.**

$$5(y + z) = 5(1 + 2) = 5(3) = 15$$
and
$$5y + 5z = 5(1) + 5(2) = 5 + 10 = 15$$

Both expressions equal 15, so when x is 1 and y is 2, 5(y + z) equals 5y + 5z.

▶ If you find that any numbers in expressions you are comparing are not equal, then you know that the expressions are not equivalent.

✓ **Check Your Understanding 4.3.3**

Put a check (✓) next to the correct answers in the answer column.

Question	Answer
1. Which expressions are equivalent? (Mark all that apply.)	___ 7(y + z) and 7y + 7z ___ c + c and 2c ___ d(4 - 2) and 3d
2. Which expressions are equivalent? (Mark all that apply.)	___ m^3 + 4t and m x m + 4t ___ 9 ÷ 6f and 3(2f) ÷ 9 ___ 7(2p + 9p) and 77p
3. Which of these expressions are **not** equivalent? (Mark all that apply.)	___ 4y + 4z and 4 (y + z) ___ 6p and 5p + 1p ___ 5z - 2z and 2z - 5z
4. Which of these expressions are **not** equivalent? (Mark all that apply.)	___ 12a + 15b and 3(4a + 5b) ___ c^2 + 4d and 2c + 2d + 2d ___ 7y - 7z and 7(y - z)

Topics Related to: Recognizing Equivalent Expressions

4.3.6 Evaluating Equations with Variables

4.3.4 Understanding Equations

An **equation** uses an equal (=) sign to equate two **expressions**. Many equations use letters to represent one or more unknown values. The letters can be on either side of the equal sign. Some examples of equations are:

$n = 3 + b$
$6 = 24 - t$
$6s - 2 = 2 \times (3s - 1)$.

Equations that use letters to represent unknown values can be either true or false, depending on the values assigned to the letters.

▶ Some equations are *true* only for certain values of the unknown.

📝 *Example*

The equation $6 = 24 - t$ is *true* only when $t = 18$.

$6 = 24 - t$
$6 = 24 - 18$
$6 = 6$

If t equals any number other than 18, the equation is *false*.

▶ Some equations are *true* for any value of an unknown because the expressions on both sides of the equal sign are equivalent.

📝 *Example*

The equation $6s - 2 = 2 \times (3s - 1)$ is *true* for any value of s.

$6s - 2 = 2 \times (3s - 1)$
$6s - 2 = (2 \times 3s) - (2 \times 1)$
$6s - 2 = 6s - 2$

▶ Some equations are *true* for any value of an unknown because the value of one unknown depends on the value of another unknown in the same equation.

equation

An equation is a statement of equality between two expressions. For example, $2b + 4 = 2 \times (b + 2)$ is an equation. It is understood as meaning: $2b + 4$ *is equal to* $2 \times (b + 2)$.

expression

An expression is a combination of numbers and symbols. For example, $5n + 3$, $(b + a)$, and $7 - y$ are expressions.

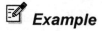 ***Example***

n = 3 + b is true for any value of b.

$$n = 3 + b$$
$$\text{if } b = 1, \ n = 4$$
$$\text{if } b = 2, \ n = 5, \text{ and so on.}$$

 Check Your Understanding 4.3.4

Put a check (✓) next to the correct answers in the answer column.

Question	Answer
1. Which equation is *true* only when a = 4?	___ 11 = 3 + 3a ___ 5a - 7 = 13 ___ a - 2 = 2a
2. Which equation is *true* for any value?	___ 8t - 4 = 2(4t - 2) ___ 3(4t -3) = 7t ___ 38 = 9t + 2
3. Which equation is *true* only when p = 2?	___ 2p x 4 = 2 ___ 4 - p = 2 (p - 1) ___ 6p - 4 = 8
4. Which equation is *true* for any value?	___ 14z - 12 = 6 ___ 2a + 4 = z ___ 5(z + 1) = 4z -12

Topics Related to: Understanding Equations

4.3.5 Manipulating Equations
4.3.6 Evaluating Equations with Variables

4.3.5 Manipulating Equations

equation

An equation is a statement of equality between two expressions. For example, $2b + 4 = 2 \times (b + 2)$ is an equation. It is understood as meaning: $2b + 4$ *is equal to* $2 \times (b + 2)$.

At first glance, two **equations** may appear different, when they are really the same.

✍ *Example*

The equations

$$9 \div r = 3 \quad \text{and} \quad 9 = 3 \times r$$

appear to be different, but actually they are the same or equivalent.

▶ You might wonder: "How can you tell when two equations are equivalent?" The answer is to manipulate one of the equations to make it look like the other equation.

▶ When you manipulate equations, you must perform the same operation to both sides of the equation in order to preserve the equality.

✍ *Example*

In the equation $3 + 7 = 10$, if you subtract 7 from only the left side of the equation, the equality is destroyed. However, if you subtract 7 from *both* sides of the equation, the equality is preserved.

Destroys equality	Preserves equality
$3 + 7 = 10$	$3 + 7 = 10$
$3 + 7 - 7 = 10$	$3 + 7 - 7 = 10 - 7$
$3 \neq 10$	$3 = 3$

▶ To make $9 \div r = 3$ look like $9 = 3 \times r$, first multiply both sides of the equation by r. Then, since multiplying by r is opposite to dividing by r, you can simplify.

$$(9 \div r) \times r = 3 \times r.$$
$$9 = 3 \times r.$$

Check Your Understanding 4.3.5

Put a check (✓) next to the correct answers in the answer column.

Question	Answer
1. Which of these steps will transform the equation $5 = (7 \div t)$ to $5 \times t = 7$?	____ Subtract 7 from both sides of the equation. ____ Add t to both sides of the equation. ____ Multiply both sides of the equation by t.
2. Which of these steps will transform the equation $4 - p = 23$ to $4 = 23 + p$?	____ Add p to both sides of the equation. ____ Subtract p from both sides of the equation. ____ Multiply both sides of the equation by p.
3. Which of these steps will transform the equation $a \times 13 = 36$ to $a = 36 \div 13$?	____ Multiply both sides of the equation by 13. ____ Divide both sides of the equation by 13. ____ Divide both sides of the equation by a.
4. Which of these steps will transform the equation $y + 52 = 12$ to $12 - y = 52$?	____ Subtract y from both sides of the equation ____ Add 12 to both sides of the equation ____ Add y to both sides of the equation

Topics Related to: Manipulating Equations

4.3.1 Solving for Unknowns

4.3.6 Evaluating Equations with Variables

Some **equations** contain two or more **variables**. To solve these equations you must have values to replace all but one variable — the variable you wish to find. One useful example is the equation to find the **interest** on money borrowed.

$$I = p \, r \, t$$

I represents the interest that must be paid on the money borrowed.

p represents the principle, the amount of money borrowed.

r represents the interest rate. It is expressed as a percent.

t represents time (the time for which the money is borrowed). It is expressed in years.

> **variable**
>
> In algebra, a variable is a letter which represents any number from a specific set of numbers. For example, the variable c in $2 \times c < 5$ can represent any number from the set $\{0,1,2\}$.

✏️ *Example*

A person needs to borrow $300 for 6 months. The bank offers an annual interest rate of 6%.

To determine the interest that will be paid on this loan, replace the variables p, r, and t with the values given in the problem text. Solve using a calculator.

> I = prt, where p = $300, **r** = 6%, and **t** = 6 months or 0.5 year
> I = $300 x 6% x 0.5 = $300 x 0.06 x 0.5
> **I = $9**

 Check Your Understanding 4.3.6

Put a check (✓) next to the correct answers in the answer column.

> **equation**
>
> An equation is a statement of equality between two expressions. For example, $2b + 4 = 2 \times (b + 2)$ is an equation. It is understood as meaning: $2b + 4$ *is equal to* $2 \times (b + 2)$.

Question	Answer
1. Use the equation **I = prt** to calculate the interest on $1,750 borrowed at a rate of 9% per year over a 3-year period.	—— $4,725 ___ $52.50 ___ $472.50 ___ $525.50

2. Use the equation **I = prt** to calculate the interest on $25,000 borrowed at a rate of 12% per year over a 15-year period.	___ $450 ___ $4,500 ___ $45,000 ___ $450,000
3. Use the equation **I = prt** to solve this problem: Shandra needs a $10,000 loan for a car. At 8% interest, how much more will a 5-year loan cost her in interest than a 3-year loan?	___ $800 ___ $1,600 ___ $2,400 ___ $4,000
4. Use the equation **I = prt** to solve this problem: Jason has a $50,000, 30-year home loan. He will end up paying $150,000 interest on the loan over the 30 years. What is the interest rate on the loan?	___ 8% ___ 9 % ___ 10% ___ 15%

Topics Related to: Evaluating Equations with Variables

2.4.5 Decimal Percent Equivalence
2.4.10 Calculations Using Percents
4.3.2 Evaluating Expressions
4.3.4 Understanding Equations

4.3.7 Exponents

An **exponent** is a number that is written superscript. This means it appears above another number or expression. The value of the exponent tells how many times the number should be multiplied by itself.

 Example

In the expression 5^2 the **exponent** is ^{2}. The ^{2} signifies that 5 appears as a factor two times. In other words, $5^2 = 5 \times 5$. Similarly, the expression $2^3 = 2 \times 2 \times 2$.

 Check Your Understanding 4.3.7

Draw a line to connect each item in the match column with the correct answer in the answer column.

Question	Match	Answer
1. What is the value of each of these expressions?	2^6	9
	3^3	25
	5^2	27
	10^4	64
	10^6	10,000
		100,000
		1,000,000
		10,000,000
2. Which expression corresponds with each of these values?	16	2^2
	36	2^4
	49	6^2
	1,000	7^2
		10^3
		10^4

4.4 Answers to Questions

Answers to 4.1.1

Correct Answer	Explanation
1. 10/16	This ratio compares a part to a whole. It compares 10 clear cells to 16 total cells in the grid.
2. six shaded cells to a total of 16 cells	This ratio compares a part to a whole. It compare the shaded cells (6) to all the cells in the grid (16).
3. 10 : 6	This ratio compares a part to a part. It compares 10 clear cells to 6 shaded cells in the grid.

Answers to 4.1.2

Correct Answer	Explanation
1. 6 : 3	This ratio compares 6 lightly shaded cells to 3 darkly shaded cells.
2. 7/6	There are 7 lightly shaded cells in the grid and 6 clear cells. So this ratio is 7/6.
3. darkly shaded cells to lightly shaded cells	On this grid, the ratio 4/9 compares 4 darkly shaded cells to 9 lightly shaded cells.

Answers to 4.1.3

Correct Answer	Explanation
1. 4/9	You are comparing 4 lightly shaded cells to 9 total cells.
2. darkly shaded cells to total cells	On this grid, the ratio 2/9 compares 2 darkly shaded cells to 9 total cells.

3. 3 : 9	This grid has 3 darkly shaded cells and 9 cells total. So the ration is 3 : 9.
4. lightly shaded cells to total cells	On this grid, the ration 5 : 9 compares the 5 lightly shaded cells to the 9 total cells.

Answers to 4.1.4

Correct Answer	Explanation
1. 3 : 8 : 5	This ratio compares 3 clear cells to 8 lightly shaded cells to 5 darkly shaded cells.
2. clear cells to darkly shaded cells to lightly shaded cells	The ratio 4 : 5 : 7 compares 4 clear cells to 5 darkly shaded cells to 7 lightly shaded cells.
3. 3 : 4 : 2	The ratio 3 : 4 : 2 compares the 3 hammers to the 4 scissors to the 3 tape measures.
4. 1 : 4 : 2	The ratio 1 : 4 : 2 compares the 1 circle to the 4 squares to the 2 triangles.

Answers to 4.1.5

Correct Answer	Explanation
1. 1 : 7 : 3 : 5	Ask yourself: In what order are the quantities being compared? This ratio compares striped cells to lightly shaded cells to darkly shaded cells to clear cells.
2. striped cells to darkly shaded cells to lightly shaded cells to clear cells	Ask yourself: In what order are the quantities being compared? The ratio 1 : 5 : 3 : 2 compares striped cells to darkly shaded cells to lightly shaded cells to clear cells.
3. 4 : 3 : 1 : 2	The ratio 4 : 3 : 1 : 2 compares the 4 hammers to the 3 scissors to the 1 tape measure to the 2 brushes. This is the order specified in the question.

| 4. circles to rectangles to triangles to squares | Look at the numbers in the ratio and see which figures each represents. Compare the order to the order shown in the answers. |

Answers to 4.1.6

Correct Answer	Explanation
1. 1, 2, 4, and 8	Each term in the ratio 8 : 16 : 24 can be divided by the factors 1, 2, 4, and 8.
2. 8	The number 8 is the largest common factor of 8, 16, and 24.
3. 1 : 2 : 3	Reduce the ratio by dividing each term by the GCF (8) for a ratio in lowest terms. $8 : 16 : 24 \Rightarrow 8 \div 8 : 16 \div 8 : 24 \div 8 \Rightarrow 1 : 2 : 3$
4. 6 : 10 : 23	Reduce the ratio by dividing each term by the GCF (2) for a ratio in lowest terms.
5. 6 : 1 : 5	Reduce the ratio by dividing each term by the GCF (70) for a ratio in lowest terms.

Answers to 4.1.7a

Correct Answer	Explanation
1. 7	Each term of the ratio 4 : 7 was multiplied by 7 to get the equivalent ratio 28 : 49. $\dfrac{4 \times 7}{7 \times 7} = \dfrac{28}{49}$
2. 27 : 36	If you multiply each term of the ratio 3 : 4 by 9, you get the equivalent ratio 27 : 36. $\dfrac{3 \times 9}{4 \times 9} = \dfrac{27}{36}$

3. 12	If you multiply each term of the ratio 5 : 8 by 12, you get the equivalent ratio 60/96. $$\frac{5 \times 12}{8 \times 12} = \frac{60}{96}$$
4. 40 : 35	If you multiply each term of the ratio 8 : 7 by 5, you get the equivalent ratio 40/35. $$\frac{8 \times 5}{7 \times 5} = \frac{40}{35}$$

Answers to 4.1.7b

Correct Answer	Explanation

1. 3 : 5 : 12 --- 12 : 20 : 48
  7 : 10 : 2 --- 56 : 80 : 16
  15 : 4 : 5 --- 30 : 8 : 10
	If you multiply each term of the ratio 3 : 5 : 12 by 4, you get the equivalent ratio 12 : 20 : 48. If you multiply each term of the ratio 7 : 10 : 2 by 8, you get the equivalent ratio 56 : 80 : 16. Finally, if you multiply each term of the ratio 15 : 4 : 5 by 2, you get the equivalent ratio 30 : 8 : 10.

2. 48 : 72 : 30 --- 8 : 12 : 5
  250 : 400 : 600 --- 5 : 8 : 12
  490 : 630 : 420 --- 7 : 9 : 6
	If you divide each term of the ratio 48 : 72 : 30 by 6, you get the equivalent ratio 8 : 12 : 5. If you divide each term of the ratio 250 : 400 : 600 by 50, you get the equivalent ratio 5 : 8 : 12. Finally, if you divide each term of the ratio 490 : 630 : 420 by 70, you get the equivalent ratio 7 : 9 : 6.

Answers to 4.1.8

Correct Answer	Explanation
1. 2/7 = 8/28	Two equivalent ratios make a proportion. $$\frac{2}{7} = \frac{8}{28} \quad \text{because} \quad \frac{2 \times 4}{7 \times 4} = \frac{8}{28}$$

2. 3/8 = 15/40	Two equivalent ratios make a proportion. $$\frac{3}{8} = \frac{15}{40} \quad \text{because} \quad \frac{3 \times 5}{8 \times 5} = \frac{15}{40}$$
3. 125/250 = 5/6	This is not a proportion. $$\frac{125}{250} \neq \frac{5}{6} \quad \text{because} \quad \frac{125 \div 25}{250 \div 25} = \frac{5}{10}$$
4. 7/5 = 79/40	This is not a proportion. $$\frac{7}{5} \neq \frac{49}{40} \quad \text{because} \quad \frac{7 \times 7}{5 \times 7} = \frac{49}{35}$$

Answers to 4.1.9

Correct Answer	Explanation
1. A	Five dollars is to 1 book as (?) dollars is to 7 books. Another correct way to write the proportion is $$\frac{1 \text{ book}}{7 \text{ books}} = \frac{\$5}{\$?}$$
2. C	Four miles is to 1 hour as 10 miles is to (?) hours. Another correct way to write the proportion is $$\frac{4 \text{ miles}}{10 \text{ miles}} = \frac{1 \text{ hour}}{? \text{ hours}}$$
3. B	Fifteen rows is to 2 rows as (?) minutes is to 10 minutes. Another correct way to write the proportion is $$\frac{2 \text{ rows}}{10 \text{ minutes}} = \frac{15 \text{ rows}}{? \text{ minutes}}$$

4. A	Three boxes is to $1.24 as 25 boxes is to (?) dollars. Another correct way to write the proportion is $$\frac{3 \text{ boxes}}{25 \text{ boxes}} = \frac{\$1.24}{? \ \$}$$

Answers to 4.1.10

Correct Answer	Explanation
1. 24	Ask yourself, "7 times *what* equals 42?" The answer is 6. Multiply 4 by 6. $$\frac{4 \times 6}{7 \times 6} = \frac{\textbf{24}}{42}$$
2. 14	Ask yourself, "9 times *what* equals 63?" The answer is 7. Multiply 2 by 7. $$\frac{2 \times 7}{9 \times 7} = \frac{\textbf{14}}{63}$$
3. 120 minutes	Ask yourself, "3 times *what* equals 18?" The answer is 6. Multiply 20 by 6. $$\frac{3 \text{ miles} \quad \times 6}{20 \text{ minutes} \ \times 6} = \frac{18 \text{ miles}}{\textbf{120} \text{ minutes}}$$
4. $5.20	Ask yourself, "5 times *what* equals 20?" The answer is 4. Multiply 1.30 by 4. $$\frac{5 \text{ boxes} \times 4}{\$1.30 \quad \times 4} = \frac{20 \text{ boxes}}{\textbf{\$5.20}}$$

Answers to 4.1.11

Correct Answer	Explanation
1. 4	Ask yourself, "35 divided by *what* equals 7?" The answer is 5. Divide 20 by 5. $$\frac{20}{35} = \frac{20 \div 5}{35 \div 5} = \frac{4}{7}$$
2. 4	Ask yourself, "55 divided by *what* equals 5?" The answer is 11. Divide 44 by 11. $$\frac{44}{55} = \frac{44 \div 11}{55 \div 11} = \frac{4}{5}$$
3. 3 minutes	Ask yourself, "120 divided by *what* equals 2 ?" The answer is 60. Divide 180 by 60. $$\frac{120 \text{ pages}}{180 \text{ minutes}} = \frac{120 \text{ pages} \div 60}{180 \text{ minutes} \div 60} = \frac{2 \text{ pages}}{3 \text{ minutes}}$$
4. 50 days	Ask yourself, "550 divided by *what* equals 11?" The answer is 5. Divide 250 by 5. $$\frac{550 \text{ gallons}}{250 \text{ days}} = \frac{550 \text{ gallons} \div 5}{250 \text{ days} \div 5} = \frac{11 \text{ gallons}}{5 \text{ days}}$$

Answers to 4.1.12

Correct Answer	Explanation
1. 6.875	$$\frac{11}{8} = \frac{?}{5} \rightarrow \frac{11}{8} \bowtie \frac{?}{5}$$ $$11 \times 5 = 8 \times ?$$ $$55 = 8 \times ?$$ $$55 \div 8 = ?$$ $$6.875 = ?$$ $$\frac{11}{8} = \frac{6.875}{5}$$

2. 5.6	$$\frac{4}{5} = \frac{?}{7} \rightarrow \frac{4}{5} \bowtie \frac{?}{7}$$ $$4 \times 7 = 5 \times ?$$ $$28 = 5 \times ?$$ $$28 \div 5 = ?$$ $$5.6 = ?$$ $$\frac{4}{5} = \frac{\mathbf{5.6}}{7}$$
3. 6.75	$$\frac{3}{4} = \frac{?}{9} \rightarrow \frac{3}{4} \bowtie \frac{?}{9}$$ $$3 \times 9 = 4 \times ?$$ $$27 = 4 \times ?$$ $$27 \div 4 = ?$$ $$6.75 = ?$$ $$\frac{3}{4} = \frac{\mathbf{6.75}}{9}$$
4. 7.5	$$\frac{2}{3} = \frac{5}{?} \rightarrow \frac{2}{3} \bowtie \frac{5}{?}$$ $$2 \times ? = 3 \times 5$$ $$2 \times ? = 15$$ $$? = 15 \div 2$$ $$? = 7.5$$ $$\frac{2}{3} = \frac{5}{\mathbf{7.5}}$$
5. 8.4	$$\frac{5}{6} = \frac{7}{?} \rightarrow \frac{5}{6} \bowtie \frac{7}{?}$$ $$5 \times ? = 6 \times 7$$ $$5 \times ? = 42$$ $$? = 42 \div 5$$ $$? = 8.4$$ $$\frac{5}{6} = \frac{7}{\mathbf{8.4}}$$

6. 3.26	
	$$\frac{23}{5} = \frac{15}{?} \rightarrow \frac{23}{5} \bowtie \frac{15}{?}$$ $$23 \times ? = 15 \times 5$$ $$23 \times ? = 75$$ $$? = 75 \div 23$$ $$? = 3.26$$ $$\frac{23}{5} = \frac{15}{\mathbf{3.26}}$$

Answers to 4.1.13

Correct Answer	Explanation
1. 3/5 ------ 60% 1/4 ------ 25% 7/20 ---- 35% 1/2 ---- 50%	In each case, set the ratio and then solve the proportion by scaling up, like this: $$\frac{1 \times 20}{5 \times 20} = \frac{20}{100} = \mathbf{20\%}$$
2. 8% ----- 2/25 10% ---- 1/10 40% ---- 2/5 75% ---- 3/4	In each case, set the ratio and then solve the proportion by scaling down, like this: $$40\% = \frac{40 \div 20}{100 \div 20} = \frac{2}{5}$$

Answers to 4.1.14

Correct Answer	Explanation
1. 2/3 --------- 66.7% 13/15 ------ 86.7% 25/26 ------ 96.2% 11/12 ------ 91.7%	Divide the numerator by the denominator and then multiply the answer by 100 to get a percent. Round your answers to the nearest tenth of a percent. Here's an example: 2/3 = 0.66666.... = **0.667** .67 x 100 = **66.7%**

2. 5/16 --------- 31.3% 3/7 ---------- 42.9% 1/3 ---------- 33.3% 4/9 ---------- 44.4%	Divide the numerator by the denominator and then multiply the answer by 100 to get a percent. Round your answers to the nearest tenth of a percent. Here's an example: 5/16 = 0.3125.... = **0.313** 0.313 x 100 **= 31.3%**

Answers to 4.1.15

Correct Answer	Explanation
1. 40%	10/25 = 40/100 = **40%** 10 is **40%** of 25
2. 4%	20/500 = 4/100 = **4%** 20 is **4%** of 500
3. 10%	3/30 = 1/10 = **10%** 3 is **10%** of 30
4. 50%	325/650 = 1/2 = **50%** 325 is **50%** of 650

Answers to 4.2.1

Correct Answer	Explanation
1. Each figure has at least one right angle (90°).	Each figure has at least one right angle (90°).

2. Each figure has four line segments, or sides.	Each figure has 4 line segments, or sides.
3. Each figure has all sides connected.	This is <u>not</u> how these figures are related. Only one figure has all its sides connected.
4. Each figure is skewed (has no right angles).	This is <u>not</u> how these figures are related. One of the figures has right angles.

Answers to 4.2.2

Correct Answer	Explanation
1. Add 7 to any number in the sequence to get the next number.	6 + 7 = 13 and 13 + 7 = 20 and 20 + 7 = 27.
2. Multiply each number by 2 and add 1 to get the next number.	(2 x 1) + 1 = 3 (2 x 3) + 1 = 7 (2 x 7) + 1 = 15 (2 x 15) + 1 = 31
3. Multiply any number by 3 and add 2 to get the next number in the sequence.	(2 x 3) + 2 = 8 (8 x 3) + 2 = 26 (26 x 3) + 2 = 80

Answers to 4.2.3

Correct Answer	Explanation
1. 3 times 2, plus 1 is 7	$(3 \times 2) + 1 = 6 + 1 = 7$ $(5 \times 2) + 1 = 10 + 1 = 11$ $(9 \times 2) + 1 = 18 + 1 = 19$
2. 14 minus 5 is 9	$14 - 5 = 9$ $28 - 5 = 23$ $52 - 5 = 47$
3. 2 times 7 plus 5 is 19	$(2 \times 7) + 5 = 19$ $(2 \times 11) + 5 = 27$ $(2 \times 15) + 5 = 35$
4. 2 times 60 divided by 6 plus 5 is 25	This is **not** a relationship that works for the other numbers. $((2 \times 60) \div 6) + 5 = 25$ $((2 \times 14) \div 6) + 5 = 9.67$ — should be 2

Answers to 4.3.1

Correct Answer	Explanation
1. 21	Addition and subtraction are inverse operations, so you can subtract both sides of the equation by 27 in order to solve it. $y + 27 - 27 = 48 - 27$ $y = 21$
2. 108	Addition and subtraction are inverse operations, so you can subtract both sides of the equation by 27 in order to solve it. $y - 16 + 16 = 92 + 16$ $y = 108$

3. 40	Division and multiplication are inverse operations, so you can divide both sides of the equation by 12 in order to solve it. (t x 12) ÷ 12 = 480 ÷ 12 t = 40
4. 64	Division and multiplication are inverse operations, so you can multiply both sides of the equation by 8 in order to solve it. (t ÷ 8) x 8 = 8 x 8 t = 64
5. 25,000	Multiply both sides of the equation by 250 to solve it. (z ÷ 250) x 250 = 100 x 250 z = 25,000
6. 70	Divide each side of the equation by 6 to solve it. (z x 6) ÷ 6 = 420 ÷ 6 z = 70

Answers to 4.3.2

Correct Answer	Explanation
1. 19	When T = 3, the expression becomes 4(3) + 7 or 12 + 7 = 19.
2. 16	When N = 8, the expression becomes 6(8) ÷ 3 or 48 ÷ 3 = 16.
3. 135	When z = 7, the expression becomes 20(7) -5 or 140 - 5 = 135
4. 800	When d = 25, the expression becomes 8(25) x 4 or 200 x 4 = 800.

Answers to 4.3.3

Correct Answer	Explanation
1. 7(y + z) and 7y + 7z c + c and 2c	Both addition and multiplication are reversible. So, 7(y + z) = 7y + 7z. Repeated addition is the same as multiplication, so c + c =2c.
2. 7(2p + 9p) and 77p	Both addition and multiplication are reversible. So, 7(2p + 9p) = 7(11p) = 77p.
3. 5z - 2z and 2z - 5z	The order in which numbers are subtracted cannot be reversed. So these expressions are **not** equivalent.
4. c^2 + 4d and 2c + 2d + 2d	The expression c^2 is most often not equal to 2c. So these expressions are **not** equivalent.

Answers to 4.3.4

Correct Answer	Explanation
1. 5a - 7 = 13	When a = 4, the equation becomes: 5(4) - 7 = 13 20 - 7 = 13 13 = 13, which is true.
2. 8t - 4 = 2(4t - 2)	The equation 8t - 4 = 2(4t - 2) is true for any value of t. 8t - 4 = 2(4t - 2) 8t - 4 = (2 x 4t) - (2 x 2) 8t - 4 = 8t - 4
3. 6p - 4 = 8	When p = 2, the equation becomes: 6(2) - 4 = 8 12 - 4 = 8 8 = 8, which is true.

| 4. $2a + 4 = z$ | The equation $2a + 4 = z$ is true for any value of an unknown because if the value of *a* changes so does the value of z. For instance,

if a = 2, z = 8
if a = 3, z = 10
if a = 4, z = 12, and so on. |

Answers to 4.3.5

Correct Answer	Explanation
1. Multiply both sides of the equation by t.	If you multiply both sides of the equation by t you get: $5 \times t = (7 \div t) \times t$ which simplifies to: $5 \times t = 7$
2. Add p to both sides of the equation.	If you add p to both sides of the equation, you get: $4 - p + p = 23 + p$ which simplifies to: $4 = 23 + p$
3. Divide both sides of the equation by 13.	If you divide both sides of the equation by 13, you get: $(a \times 13) \div 13 = 36 \div 13$ which simplifies to $a = 36 \div 13$
4. Subtract y from both sides of the equation.	If you subtract y from both sides of the equation, you get: $y + 52 - y = 12 - y$ which simplifies to $52 = 12 - y$

Answers to 4.3.6

Correct Answer	Explanation
1. $472.50	If you replace all of the variables in the equation with the values given in the problem, the interest is **$472.50**. I = prt, where p = $1,750, r = 9%, t = 3 I = 1750 x .09 x 3 = $472.50
2. $45,000	If you replace all of the variables in the equation with the values given in the problem, the interest is **$45,000**. I = prt, where p = $25,000, r = 12%, t = 15 I = 25,000 x 0.12 x 15 = $45,000
3. $1,600	To solve this problem, you need to figure the interest twice, substituting a different pay period in each equation. Then you should subtract the interest you calculated for the two different equations to find the difference. I = prt, where **p** = $10,000, **r** = 8% and **t** = 5 years I = 10,000 x 0.08 x 5 = $4,000 **t** = 3 years I = 10,000 x .08 x 3 = $2,400 So, $4,000 - $2,400 = $1,600

| 4. 10% | To solve this problem, substitute the known values in the equation and then manipulate the equation to solve for the unknown.

I = prt, where **I** = $150,000, **p** = $50,000, **t** = 30

150,000 = 50,000 x r x 30
150,000 = (50,000 x 30) x r

150,000 ÷ 1,500,000 = (1,500,000 x r) ÷ 1,500,000

.10 = r
10% = **r** |

Answers to 4.3.7

Correct Answer	Explanation
1. 2^6 ------------ 64 3^3 -------------- 27 5^2 ------------ 25 10^4 ----------10,000 10^6 --------1,000,000	The exponent in each number signifies how many times the number appears as a factor. For instance, 2^6 = 2 x 2 x 2 x 2 x 2 x 2 = 64
2. 16 ------------ 2^4 36 ------------ 6^2 49 ------------ 7^2 1,000 --------- 10^3	Ask yourself, "What number times itself one or more times would equal this number?" Look at the possibilities and try them out.

Chapter 5
Geometry and Measurement

5.1 Lines and Angles 327

    5.1.1   Measuring Angles 327
    5.1.2   Classifying Angles 329
    5.1.3   Angle Relationships 331
    5.1.4   Familiar Angles 335
    5.1.5   Estimating Angles 337
    5.1.6   Classifying Triangles 339

5.2 Two-Dimensional and Three-Dimensional
    Figures 342

    5.2.1   Polygons 342
    5.2.2   What is a Cone? 350
    5.2.3   What is a Cylinder? 351
    5.2.4   What is a Prism? 352
    5.2.5   What is a Pyramid? 353
    5.2.6   What is a Transformation? 354

5.3 Measurement and Perimeter 358

    5.3.1   Units of Measure 358
    5.3.2   Standard Units of Measure 359
    5.3.3   Metric Units of Measure 361
    5.3.4   Converting Measures 363
    5.3.5   Perimeter 364
    5.3.6   Circumference 366
    5.3.7   Understanding Scale Factors 367

5.4 Area, Volume, and Surface Area 369

    5.4.1   Square Units (unit2) 369
    5.4.2   Understanding Area 370
    5.4.3   Area of a Rectangle 371
    5.4.4   Area of a Square 372
    5.4.5   Area of a Triangle.. 373
    5.4.6   Area of a Circle 374
    5.4.7   Understanding Surface Area 375
    5.4.8   Surface Area of a Rectangular Prism............... 376
    5.4.9   Surface Area of a Triangular Prism................... 378
    5.4.10 Surface Area of a Cylinder 379
    5.4.11 Cubic Units (units3)... 381
    5.4.12 Understanding Volume...................................... 382
    5.4.13 Volume of a Rectangular Prism 383

5.4.14   Volume of a Triangular Prism.. 386

5.4.15   Volume of a Cylinder.. 388

5.5 Answers to Questions 390

Learn principles of geometry relating to lines, angles, and two-dimensional and three-dimensional figures. Also, learn about measuring perimeter, area, volume, and surface area

5.1 Lines and Angles

5.1.1 Measuring Angles

Angles are measured using a **protractor** like the one illustrated here. The unit of measure used for *measuring angles* is the **degree**. There are 360 degrees in a circle. Most protractors are half-circles with two scales from 0° to 180°. On this protractor, the inside scale reads counterclockwise, and the outside scale reads clockwise.

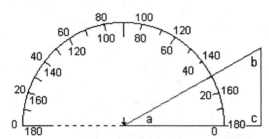

To measure an angle using a protractor:

▶ Place the **base of the protractor** on one side of the angle with the center mark exactly on the **vertex** of the angle.

▶ Decide whether to use the inside or the outside scale of the protractor. In the example above, you would use the inside scale, because the 0 on the inside scale lines up with one edge of the angle.

▶ Determine where the other side of the angle crosses the protractor scale. In the example above, it crosses the inside scale of the protractor halfway between the 20 and the 40 degree marks. Thus, the measure of angle *a* is 30°, which is written as: m ∠ *a* = 30°.

▶ If it is not possible to place the base of the on-line protractor along one side of the angle, you will need to find the difference in degrees between the two sides of the angle.

---

protractor

A protractor is used to measure angles. The scale of a protractor is marked in degrees.

---

degree

The degree is a unit of angular measure. There are 360 degrees in a full circle. The raised circle (°) means *degrees*.

For example, m ∠ *a* = 40° is read, "The measure of angle *a* equals 40 degrees."

---

base of the protractor

The base of the protractor is the straight line at the bottom of the protractor. A small arrow marks the center of the base.

---

vertex

A vertex of an angle is the point at which its sides meet.

Check Your Understanding 5.1.1

Put a check (✓) next to the correct answers in the answer column.

Question	Answer
1. What is the measure of angle *a*?	___ 65° ___ 70° ___ 110°
2. What is the measure of angle *a*?	___ 50° ___ 125° ___ 130°
3. What is the measure of angle *d*?	___ 30° ___ 40° ___ 70°

4. What is the measure of angle *x*?

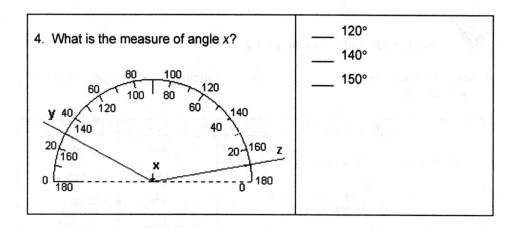

_____ 120°

_____ 140°

_____ 150°

Topics Related to: Measuring Angles

> 5.1.4 Familiar Angles
> 5.1.5 Estimating Angles

5.1.2 Classifying Angles

An *angle* can be *classified* as acute, right, obtuse, or straight, depending on its measure.

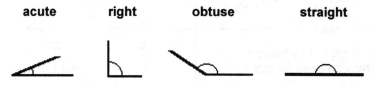

| acute | right | obtuse | straight |

▶ An **acute** angle is an angle that measures less than 90°.

▶ A **right** angle is an angle that measures exactly 90°.

▶ An **obtuse** angle is an angle that measures greater than 90° but less than 180°.

▶ A **straight** angle is an angle that measures exactly 180°, which is a straight line.

Check Your Understanding 5.1.2

Draw a line to connect each item in the match column with the correct answer in the answer column.

Question	Match	Answer
1. Identify each of the angles below: a. A————B————C b. E F D c. I G————H d. K L J	a. ∠ ABC b. ∠ DEF c. ∠ GHI d. ∠ JKL	acute right obtuse straight cannot say
2. Identify each angle of this triangle. (An answer may be used for more than one angle.) E F————G	e. ∠ E f. ∠ F g. ∠ G	acute right obtuse cannot say

Topics Related to: Classifying Angles

5.1.1 Measuring Angles
5.1.4 Familiar Angles
5.1.5 Estimating Angles

5.1.3 Angle Relationships

Knowing the *relationships* of *angles* in lines and figures may help you find the measure of an angle without using a protractor. Consider the following examples:

▶ Using the diagram below, determine the measure of angle EBC without using a protractor.

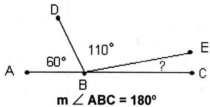

$$m \angle ABC = 180°$$

$m \angle ABC = 180°$
"$m \angle ABC = 180°$" is read "*the measure of angle ABC equals 180 degrees.*"

- Angle ABC is a straight line, so the sum of the angles that form $\angle$ ABC must be 180° (the measure of a straight angle).

$$m \angle ABD + m \angle DBE + m \angle EBC = 180°$$

- Add the measures of the known angles and subtract the sum from 180°.

$$m \angle EBC = 180° - (60° + 110°) = 10°$$

▶ The sum of the angle measures in a parallelogram is always 360°. Angles that are opposite each other diagonally (e.g., angles 1 and 4) have equal measures.

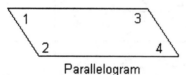

Parallelogram

You would only have to know one angle measure in a parallelogram to find the others. For example, if $m \angle 1 = 55°$, then $m \angle 4$ must also be 55°. These sum to 110°, and 360° - 110° = 240°, so the other two angle measures would each be half of 240°, or 120°.

Check Your Understanding 5.1.3

Write the correct answers in the answer column.

Question	Answer
1. C 60° 90° A B E D m ∠ DBE = ___?___	m ∠ DBE = _____
2. X Y 50° 95° V W Z m ∠ XWY = ___?___	m ∠ XWY = _____
3. H 20° I 15° F G J m ∠ FGH = ___?___	m ∠ FGH = _____
4. N O 135° 45° M P m ∠ MPO = ___?___	m ∠ MPO = _____

Topics Related to: Angle Relationships

5.1.3.1 Vertical Angles
5.1.4 Familiar Angles
5.1.5 Estimating Angles

5.1.3.1 Vertical Angles

Angles formed by intersecting lines have certain relationships. Here are some examples:

▶ When two straight lines cross, as in the diagram below, they form two pairs of opposite or **vertical angles**. In this diagram, angles 1 and 3 are vertical angles. Angles 4 and 2 are also a pair of vertical angles.

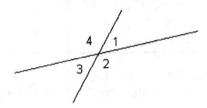

The measures of vertical angles are equal.

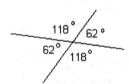

The sum of the measures of all the angles formed by two intersecting lines is always 360°.

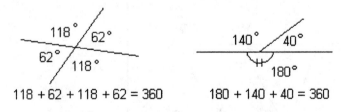

$$118 + 62 + 118 + 62 = 360 \qquad 180 + 140 + 40 = 360$$

▶ If two parallel lines, l_1 and l_2, are crossed by another line, the vertical angles formed at each intersection have equal measures. This means that angles a, b, c, and d have equal measures, as do angles 1, 2, 3, and 4.

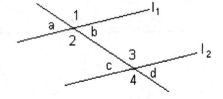

Check Your Understanding 5.1.3.1

Put a check (✓) next to the correct answers in the answer column.

Question	Answer
1. Lines l_1 and l_2 are parallel. If ∠ b = 90°, what are the measures of angles f and g?	m ∠ f = _____ m ∠ g = _____
2. Lines l_1 and l_2 are parallel. If ∠ h = 150° what are the measures of angles a and b?	m ∠ a = _____ m ∠ b = _____
3. Lines l_1 and l_2 are parallel. If ∠ f = 45°, what are the measures of angles c and d?	m ∠ c = _____ m ∠ d = _____

Topics Related to: Angle Relationships

5.1.3   Angle Relationships
5.1.4   Familiar Angles

5.1.4 Familiar Angles

Some angles are seen more often than other angles. For example, angles that measure in factors of 360 are *familiar,* because there are 360° in a circle. Angles that you see every day, or angles that have special relationships, are easier to estimate than less familiar angles. Several examples of familiar angles are shown here.

 *Example*

Group 1: 90° angles

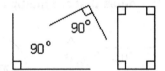

A 90° angle is called a right angle. Right angles are found in squares and rectangles and are used everywhere — in homes, furniture, appliances, etc. Right angles are probably the most easily recognized.

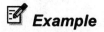

Example

Group 2: 45° angles

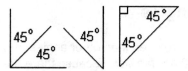

A 45° angle is easy to recognize because it is half of a right angle. A triangle that has two 45° angles and a right angle also has two sides of equal length.

Example

Group 3: Angles that are multiples of 30°

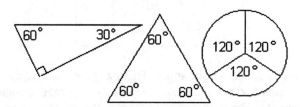

Other familiar angles are multiples of 30°. Many drawing sets include a 30°, 60° and 90° triangle template. The familiar equilateral triangle has three 60° angles.

Check Your Understanding 5.1.4

Draw a line to connect each item in the match column with the correct answer in the answer column.

Question	Match	Answer
1. Identify these familiar angles.	m ∠ a	30°
	m ∠ b	45°
	m ∠ c	60°
	m ∠ d	90°

Topics Related to: Familiar Angles

5.1.2 Classifying Angles
5.1.5 Estimating Angles

5.1.5 Estimating Angles

There are techniques to use when *estimating* the measure of an angle.

▶ One technique is to compare the angle with a familiar angle.

It is usually easy to tell if an angle is more or less than 90° (a **right angle**), especially if the sides are vertical and horizontal. To be more exact, hold a corner of a piece of paper next to the angle.

If an angle is smaller than a right angle, what part of a right angle is it? If it divides the right angle into two even parts, it is about 45°. If three of the smaller angles could go into the right angle, it is about 30°, and so on.

right angle

A right angle measures 90° and is indicated by a small square in the corner.

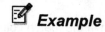

Example

This angle is about 1/4 or 1/5 of a right angle,

so it is between 18° and 22°.

▶ Another technique is to create a familiar setting.

Example

Imagine placing the angle on a clock face. There are 12 hour marks, so each hour represents 1/12 of 360, or 30°.

You can also hold a straight edge to one side of the angle to make a right angle, then compare the angle with the right angle as described above.

Check Your Understanding 5.1.5

Write the correct answers in the answer column.

Question	Answer
1. Estimate the measure of each angle.	∠ d = _____ ∠ e = _____ ∠ f = _____ ∠ p = _____ ∠ q = _____ ∠ r = _____ ∠ s = _____ ∠ t = _____

Topics Related to: Estimating Angles

5.1.1 Measuring Angles
5.1.2 Classifying Angles
5.1.3 Angle Relationships
5.1.4 Familiar Angles

5.1.6 Classifying Triangles

A *triangle* can be *classified* according to the measures of its angles. Four classifications of triangles are shown below.

acute

An acute angle is an angle whose measure is less than 90°. An acute triangle is a triangle that has only acute angles.

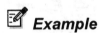 *Example*

Equilateral

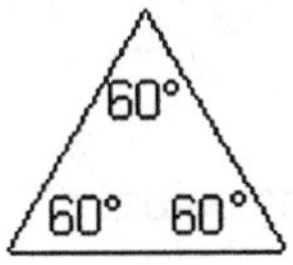

In an equilateral triangle, all three sides are the same length, and all three angles have the same measure.

 *Example*

Right

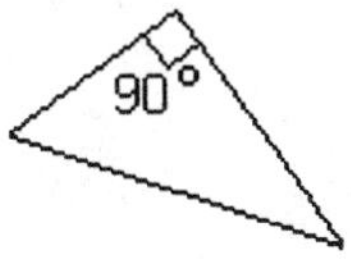

A right triangle has one right (90°) angle and two acute angles.

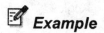

Isosceles

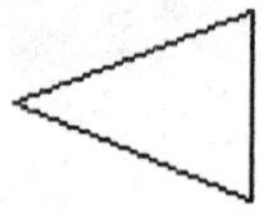

An isosceles triangle has at least two angles that have the same measure and two sides that are the same length.

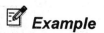

Scalene

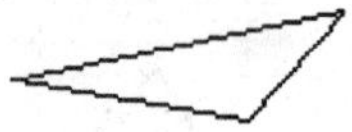

A scalene triangle has no angles equal in measure and no sides equal in length.

All triangles that are not right triangles are either **acute** or **obtuse**. In an acute triangle, all angles are smaller than a right angle. An obtuse triangle has one angle that measures greater than 90°. The equilateral and isosceles triangles shown above are acute, while the scalene triangle is obtuse.

obtuse

An obtuse angle measures greater than 90°. An obtuse triangle contains an obtuse angle.

Topics Related to: Classifying Triangles

5.1.2 Classifying Angles

Check Your Understanding 5.1.6

Put a check (✓) next to the best choice in the answer column.

Question	Answer
1. Classify the triangle below. A	___ right ___ scalene ___ isosceles ___ equilateral
2. Classify the triangle below. B	___ right ___ scalene ___ isosceles ___ equilateral
3. Classify the triangle below. C	___ right ___ scalene ___ isosceles ___ equilateral
4. Classify the triangle below. D	___ right ___ scalene ___ isosceles ___ equilateral
5. Triangle B above is obtuse.	___ true ___ false
6. Triangle D above is obtuse.	___ true ___ false

5.2 Two-Dimensional and Three-Dimensional Figures

5.2.1 Polygons

A **polygon** is a figure with three or more straight sides (or edges) that meet at the end points. A polygon always has the same number of vertices (or corners) as it does sides.

The diagram below illustrates that quadrilaterals are one type of polygon. Parallelograms and trapezoids are special kinds of quadrilaterals. Rectangles and rhombuses are special kinds of parallelograms. A square is a special kind of rectangle or rhombus.

To learn more about the polygons in this diagram, refer to the number labels on the diagram and read the descriptions below.

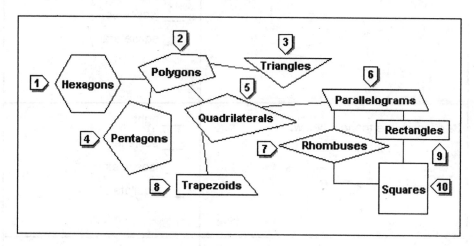

1 ▷ Hexagons

A hexagon is a polygon with exactly six sides.

2 ▷ Polygons

A polygon is a closed two-dimensional figure with three or more straight sides (or edges). A polygon always has the same number of vertices (or corners) as it does sides. For example, these figures are polygons:

3 ▷ Triangles

A triangle is a polygon with exactly three sides.

4 Pentagons

A pentagon is a polygon with exactly five sides.

5 Quadrilaterals

A quadrilateral is a polygon with exactly four sides.

6 Parallelograms

A parallelogram is a quadrilateral with two sets of opposite sides that are parallel.

7 Rhombuses

A rhombus is a quadrilateral with exactly four equal sides.

8 Trapezoids

A trapezoid is a quadrilateral with four sides and one pair of opposite sides that are parallel. The parallel sides of a trapezoid are not the same length. For example, these figures are trapezoids.

9 Rectangles

A rectangle is a quadrilateral with exactly four sides and four right angles. The lengths of the opposite sides of a rectangle are always equal.

10 Squares

A square is a quadrilateral with exactly four sides of equal length and four right angles.

Check Your Understanding 5.2.1

Put a check (✓) next to the correct answers in the answer column.
Refer to the chart above for help in answering the questions below.

Question	Answer
1. A quadrilateral is a four-sided polygon.	___ true ___ false
2. All polygons are quadrilaterals.	___ true ___ false
3. A trapezoid is a parallelogram.	___ true ___ false
4. A rhombus has four equal sides and four equal angles.	___ true ___ false
5. Squares, rectangles, and rhombuses are types of parallelograms.	___ true ___ false

Topics Related to: Polygons

5.2.1.1 What is a Square?
5.2.1.2 What is a Rectangle?
5.2.1.3 What is a Rhombus?
5.2.1.4 What is a Trapezoid?
5.2.1.5 What is a Parallelogram?

5.2.1.1 What is a Square?

A square is a **polygon** with exactly four equal sides and exactly four **right angles**. These figures are squares.

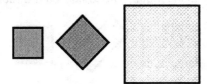

 Check Your Understanding 5.2.1.1

Put a check (✓) next to the best choices in the answer column.

Question	Answer
1. Which figures below are squares? a b c d	___ a ___ b ___ c ___ d
2. Which statements are true about squares?	___ All squares are polygons. ___ All quadrilaterals are squares. ___ All squares are rhombuses. ___ All squares are rectangles.

polygon

A polygon is a closed two-dimensional figure with three or more straight sides (or edges). A polygon always has the same number of vertices (or corners) as it does sides.

right angle

A right angle measures 90° and is indicated by a small square in the corner.

345

polygon

A polygon is a closed two-dimensional figure with three or more straight sides (or edges). A polygon always has the same number of vertices (or corners) as it does sides.

right angle

A right angle measures 90° and is indicated by a small square in the corner.

5.2.1.2 What is a Rectangle?

A rectangle is a **polygon** with exactly four **right angles**. The opposite sides of a rectangle are always equal in length. These figures are rectangles.

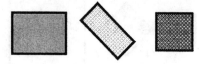

A **square** is a rectangle because it has four right angles and its opposite sides are equal in length. But not all rectangles are squares.

 Check Your Understanding 5.2.1.2

Put a check (✓) next to the best choices in the answer column.

Question	Answer
1. Identify the rectangles below. e f g h	___ e ___ f ___ g ___ h
2. Which of the following statements are true?	___ All rectangles are squares. ___ All rectangles are trapezoids. ___ All rectangles are parallelograms. ___ All quadrilaterals are rectangles.

5.2.1.3 What is a Rhombus?

A rhombus is a **polygon** with exactly four sides that are equal in length. These figures are rhombuses.

A **square** is a rhombus because it has four equal sides, but not all rhombuses are squares.

 Check Your Understanding 5.2.1.3

Put a check (✓) next to the best choices in the answer column.

Question	Answer
1. Identify the rhombuses below. j k l m	___ j ___ k ___ l ___ m
2. Which of the following statements are true?	___ All rhombuses are quadrilaterals. ___ All rectangles are rhombuses. ___ All angles of a rhombus are equal. ___ All rhombuses are parallelograms.

polygon

A polygon is a closed two-dimensional figure with three or more straight sides (or edges). A polygon always has the same number of vertices (or corners) as it does sides.

parallel lines

When two lines are parallel, they remain a constant distance apart.

For example, these lines are

parallel:

These lines are *not* parallel:

5.2.1.4 What is a Trapezoid?

A trapezoid is a **polygon** with exactly two sides that are **parallel**. The parallel sides are not the same length. These figures are trapezoids.

 Check Your Understanding 5.2.1.4

Put a check (✓) next to the best choices in the answer column.

Question	Answer
1. Which of the figures below are trapezoids? n o p q	___ n ___ o ___ p ___ q
2. Which of the following statements are true about trapezoids?	___ Trapezoids have two sides that are equal in length and parallel. ___ Trapezoids are quadrilaterals. ___ Parallelograms are trapezoids.

5.2.1.5 What is a Parallelogram?

A parallelogram is a **polygon** with two sets of opposite sides that are **parallel**. These figures are parallelograms.

Squares, **rectangles** and **rhombuses** are parallelograms because they all have two pairs of opposite sides that are parallel.

 Check Your Understanding 5.2.1.5

Put a check (✓) next to the best choices in the answer column.

Question	Answer
1. Identify the parallelograms below. r　s　t　u	＿＿ r ＿＿ s ＿＿ t ＿＿ u
2. Which of the following statements about parallelograms are true?	＿＿ Squares, rectangles, and rhombuses are parallelograms. ＿＿ All quadrilaterals are parallelograms. ＿＿ All trapezoids are parallelograms.

square

A square is a polygon with exactly four sides of equal length and four right angles.

rectangle

A rectangle is a polygon with exactly four sides and four right angles. The lengths of the opposite sides of a rectangle are always equal.

rhombus

A rhombus is a polygon with exactly four equal sides.

solid

A solid is a three-dimensional object that occupies space.

5.2.2 What is a Cone?

A cone is a **solid** that has exactly one circular base and one vertex. These figures are cones.

 Check Your Understanding 5.2.2

Put a check (✓) next to the correct answers in the answer column.

Question	Answer
1. Identify the figures below that are cones. a b c d	____ a ____ b ____ c ____ d
2. The base of a cone must be circular.	____ true ____ false
3. A cone can have more than one vertex.	____ true ____ false

5.2.3 What is a Cylinder?

A cylinder is a **solid** that has two identical circular bases. The bases are in **parallel planes**. These figures are cylinders.

parallel planes

When two planes are parallel, they are a constant distance apart.

 Check Your Understanding 5.2.3

Put a check (✓) next to the best choices in the answer column.

Question	Answer
1. Identify those figures below that are cylinders. 	___ e ___ f ___ g ___ h
2. A cylinder has two vertices.	___ true ___ false
3. The bases of a cylinder are parallel.	___ true ___ false

polygon

A polygon is a closed two-dimensional figure with three or more straight sides (or edges). A polygon always has the same number of vertices (or corners) as it does sides.

parallelogram

A parallelogram is a polygon with two sets of opposite sides that are parallel.

5.2.4 What is a Prism?

The bases of a prism are **polygons** that are in **parallel planes**. The sides of a prism are **parallelograms**. Arrows point to the parallel bases of these prisms. These figures are prisms.

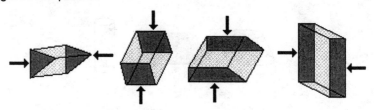

 Check Your Understanding 5.2.4

Put a check (✓) next to the correct answers in the answer column.

Question	Answer
1. Which of the figures below are prisms? *(figures labeled i, j, k, l)*	___ i ___ j ___ k ___ l
2. The bases of a prism are always quadrilaterals.	___ true ___ false
3. The sides of a prism are always rectangles.	___ true ___ false

Topics Related to: What is a Prism?

    5.2.1   Polygons
    5.2.1.5 What is a Parallelogram?

5.2.5 What is a Pyramid?

A pyramid is a **solid** with a **polygon** for a base. Pyramids have triangular sides. All the sides of a pyramid share exactly one vertex. An arrow points to the vertex of each pyramid. These figures are pyramids.

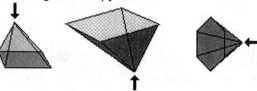

Pyramids are named for the type of polygon that forms the base. There are triangular pyramids, square pyramids, rectangular pyramids, pentagonal pyramids, etc. The Egyptian pyramids are square pyramids.

 Check Your Understanding 5.2.5

Put a check (✓) next to the correct answers in the answer column.

Question	Answer
1. Which of the figures below are pyramids?	___ m ___ n ___ o ___ p
2. Pyramids have only triangular sides.	___ true ___ false
3. A pyramid has a polygon for a base.	___ true ___ false

Topics Related to: What is a Pyramid?

   5.2.1 Polygons

solid	A solid is a three-dimensional object that occupies space.
polygon	A polygon is a closed two-dimensional figure with three or more straight sides (or edges). A polygon always has the same number of vertices (or corners) as it does sides.

5.2.6 What is a Transformation?

A transformation occurs when a geometric figure changes its position. These figures illustrate transformations.

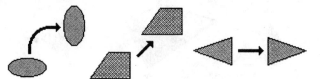

 Check Your Understanding 5.2.6

Put a check (✓) next to the correct answers in the answer column.

Question	Answer
1, Which of these figures show a transformation that preserves shape?	___ q ___ r ___ s
2. In a transformation, the figure's shape is changed.	___ true ___ false
3. When a geometric figure changes its position, a transformation has occurred.	___ true ___ false

Topics Related to: What is a Transformation?

5.2.6.1 Rotations
5.2.6.2 Reflections
5.2.6.3 Slides

5.2.6.1 Rotations

A rotation is a **transformation** in which a figure is rotated about a fixed point.

To imagine a rotation, first think of the figure drawn on a piece of paper. Then imagine tacking the paper down with a thumbtack and turning the paper around the thumbtack (the fixed point).

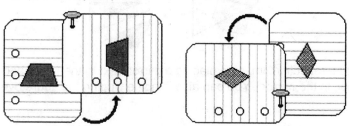

Each vertex (or corner) of a figure is the same distance from the thumbtack (fixed point) before and after the rotation.

 Check Your Understanding 5.2.6.1

Put a check (✓) next to the correct answers in the answer column.

Question	Answer
1. Which of the transformations below is a rotation? t u v	___ t ___ u ___ v
2. A transformation is a type of rotation.	___ true ___ false
3. If a figure is rotated to a new position, each vertex of the figure in its new position is the same distance from the point of rotation as it was in its original position.	___ true ___ false

transformation

A transformation occurs when a geometric figure changes its position.

5.2.6.2 Reflections

A reflection is a **transformation** in which the mirror image of a figure is produced.

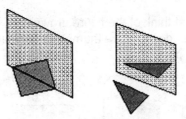

To visualize a reflection, imagine placing a mirror next to the figure and looking at the reflection in the mirror. You can also imagine flipping the figure over a line.

 Check Your Understanding 5.2.6.2

Put a check (✓) next to the correct answers in the answer column.

Question	Answer
1. Which of the figures are reflections? x y z	___ x ___ y ___ z
2. A reflection produces a mirror image of a figure.	___ true ___ false
3. A reflection is a transformation.	___ true ___ false

5.2.6.3 Slides

A slide is a **transformation** in which a figure slides along a straight line.

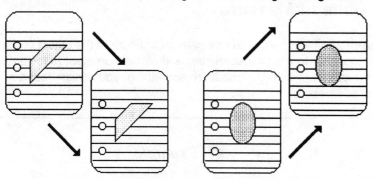

To imagine a slide, first think of the figure drawn on a piece of paper. Then imagine sliding the paper in one direction (or along a straight line).

 Check Your Understanding 5.2.6.3

Put a check (✓) next to the correct answers in the answer column.

Question	Answer
1. Which of the following are slides? a b c	___ a ___ b ___ c
2. Slides, reflections, and rotations are all types of transformations.	___ true ___ false
3. A transformation in which a figure slides along a curved path is a slide.	___ true ___ false

5.3 Measurement and Perimeter

5.3.1 Units of Measure

U.S. Customary System

The U.S. Customary System of measurement is used in the United States and is similar to measurement systems used in most English-speaking countries.

To **measure** an object means to compare an attribute of the object (such as length or capacity) to a widely used standard of measurement (such as an inch, a meter, or a gallon). When you measure something, you assign both a *number* and a *unit* of measure.

✍ *Example*

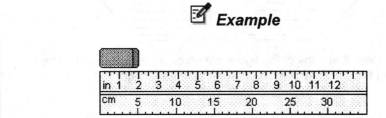

To measure the length of this eraser, compare it with the ruler. The ruler is divided into inches on one side **(U.S. Customary System)** and centimeters on the other side **(metric system)**.

The eraser is *2 inches* in length using the U.S. Customary System. It is about *5 centimeters* in length using the metric system.

---

metric system

The metric system of measurement is used for nearly all scientific measurement. The metric system uses measures such as centimeters, grams, and liters. In the metric system, all units of measure are related to each other by powers of 10.

 Check Your Understanding 5.3.1

Write the correct answers in the answer column.

Question	Answer
1. What is the length in inches of the pencil (A)? What is the length of the staple (B) in centimeters? ![pencil and ruler diagram with A pointing to pencil, in 1–12, cm 5–30, and B below]	length of A = _____ inches length of B = _____ cm

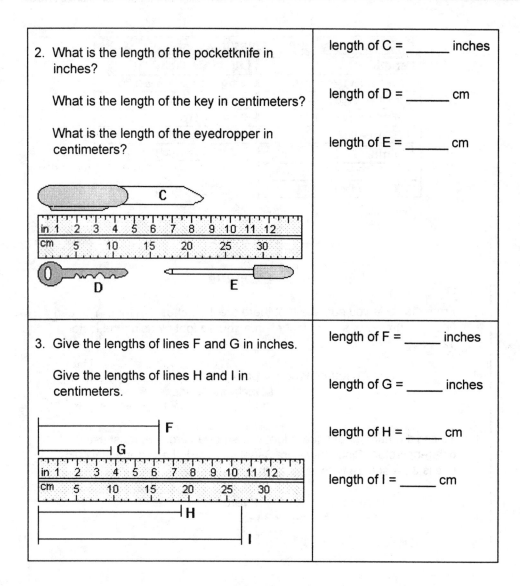

2. What is the length of the pocketknife in inches?

   What is the length of the key in centimeters?

   What is the length of the eyedropper in centimeters?

length of C = _____ inches

length of D = _____ cm

length of E = _____ cm

3. Give the lengths of lines F and G in inches.

   Give the lengths of lines H and I in centimeters.

length of F = _____ inches

length of G = _____ inches

length of H = _____ cm

length of I = _____ cm

5.3.2 Standard Units of Measure

The **standard units of measure** used in the United States are called the **U.S. Customary System**. The U.S. Customary System includes measures such as inches, cups, and pounds. These are probably the units of measure you are most familiar with.

The U.S. Customary System does not use a common factor or set of factors to convert from one unit of measure to another, so it is important to know the relationship between the units of measure. The table below shows the relationships.

U.S. Customary Units of Measure...	
Length	**Liquid Capacity**
12 inches (in) = 1 foot (ft)	2 tbsp = 1 fluid ounce (fl oz)
3 ft = 1 yard (yd)	8 fl oz = 1 cup (c)
5,280 ft = 1 mile (mi)	2 c = 1 pint (pt)
1,760 yd = 1 mi	2 pt = 1 quart (qt)
Weight	4 qt = 1 gallon (gal)
16 ounces (oz) = 1 pound (lb)	
2,000 lb = 1 ton (T)	

✎ *Example*

From the table you can see that there are 12 inches in a foot. You can find the number of square inches in a square foot by using the factor 12.

$$1 \text{ square foot} = 1 \text{ foot} \times 1 \text{ foot}$$
$$= 12 \text{ inches} \times 12 \text{ inches}$$
$$= 144 \text{ square inches (inches}^2)$$

To find the number of square feet in a square yard, you must use a different factor. Since there are 3 feet in 1 yard, the factor you would use is **3**. A square yard is equal to 9 square feet.

$$1 \text{ square yard} = 1 \text{ yard} \times 1 \text{ yard}$$
$$= 3 \text{ feet} \times 3 \text{ feet}$$
$$= 9 \text{ square feet}$$

Check Your Understanding 5.3.2

Put a check (✓) next to the correct answers in the answer column.

Question	Answer	
1. Which factor and unit would you use to find the number of pounds in a three-ton steel beam?	___ 200 ___ 16 ___ 2,000	___ ounces ___ pounds ___ tons
2. Which factor and unit is used to find the number of miles in a hiking trail that is 10,000 feet long?	___ 12 ___ 5,280 ___ 1,760	___ feet ___ yards ___ miles
3. Which factor and unit is used to find the number of ounces in 2.5 pounds?	___ 8 ___ 2,000 ___ 16	___ ounces ___ pounds
4. Which factor and unit is used to find the number of quarts in seven gallons of water?	___ 2 ___ 8 ___ 4	___ ounces ___ quarts ___ gallons

5.3.3 Metric Units of Measure

The **metric system** is used for nearly all scientific measurement. It uses *units of measure* such as centimeters, grams, and liters.

In the metric system, all units of measure are related to each other by powers of 10. The use of factors of 10 makes it easy to convert between units of measure.

Use these tables to help you visualize the metric system's units of measure.

Metric Units of Length...	
diameter of a nickel	about 2 cm
new pencil's length	about 20 centimeters or 200 millimeters
1 walking stride	about 1 meter
1 mile	about 1.5 kilometers

Metric Units of Liquid Capacity...	
1 teaspoon	about 5 milliliters
1 ounce	about 30 milliliters
quart of milk	about 1 liter or 100 centiliters

Metric Units of Mass...	
quarter (coin)	about 25 grams
200-pound man	about 90 kilograms
car (2 tons)	about 2 metric tons

 Check Your Understanding 5.3.3

Put a check (✓) next to the correct answers in the answer column.

Question	Answer
1. What metric unit would be used to measure the distance between two cities?	___ kilometer ___ meter ___ centimeter
2. What metric unit would you use to measure the amount of contact lens solution needed to cover one lens?	___ liter ___ teaspoon ___ milliliter
3. To measure the weight of a letter in a standard-size envelope, what metric unit would be used?	___ pound ___ kilogram ___ gram
4. What metric unit would be used to measure the length of an eyelash?	___ centimeter ___ meter ___ inch

5.3.4 Converting Measures

When changing from one system of measurement to another, such as from U.S. Customary System units of measure to *metric,* you need to use a table or to perform a mathematical operation, such as multiplying or dividing by some number. The number you use to multiply, divide, add, or subtract is a **constant**.

 *Example*

1 inch = 2.54 centimeters. The constant 2.54 is the number you always multiply by to change from inches to centimeters. It does not change.

▶ Here are more examples of lengths measured in inches and their **equivalent** measures in centimeters:

Inches	Multiply by 2.54	Centimeters
10	x 2.54	25.4
12	x 2.54	30.48
36	x 2.54	91.44

 Check Your Understanding 5.3.4

Put a check (✓) next to the correct answers in the answer column.

Question	Answer
1. A spectator watching an international track meet wonders whether the 100-meter dash is shorter or longer than the 100-yard dash. What would you say? 1 yard = .9144 meter	___ shorter ___ longer ___ same length
2. Jason is moving to London. The airline he is flying on has a maximum weight limit of 50 kilograms for luggage. Jason's luggage weighs 130 pounds. Will he be OK? 2.2 pounds = 1 kilogram	___ Yes, his luggage weighs less than 50 kilograms. ___ No, it weighs more than 50 kilograms. ___ Yes, 130 pounds = 50 kg.

3. Maria's gas tank holds 12 gallons of gasoline. When she drives to her sister's home in Canada, she will have to fill up her tank. Gasoline in Canada is sold by the liter. Assuming her tank is empty, about how many liters will she need to purchase?

1 gallon = 3.785 liters

_____ 50 liters

_____ 45 liters

_____ 38 liters

Topics Related to: Converting Measures

2.3.6 Multiplying Decimals

---

closed two-dimensional figure

A closed figure has no endpoints. Figure A is an example of a closed two-dimensional figure. Figures B is a two-dimensional figure that is not closed.

A B

---

sum

A sum is the result of the addition of two or more numbers or quantities. For example, the sum of 3 and 5 is 8.

5.3.5 Perimeter

Perimeter is the distance around a **closed two-dimensional figure**, or the **sum** of the lengths of all the sides of the figure.

📝 *Example*

▶ The perimeter of Figure A is found by adding the lengths of the sides:

13 in + 11 in + 6 in + 9 in + 7 in + 20 in = 66 in

▶ The perimeter of Figure B is similarly found:

13 in + 22 in + 13 in + 22 in = 70 in

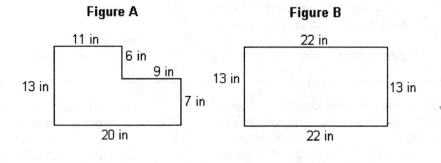

Figure A

11 in
6 in
9 in
13 in
7 in
20 in

Figure B

22 in
13 in
13 in
22 in

Check Your Understanding 5.3.5

Put a check (✓) next to the best choice in the answer column.

Question	Answer
1. What is the perimeter of this figure? 10 cm 6 cm 6 cm 2 cm 3 cm	___ 34 cm ___ 36 cm ___ 38 cm
2. Find the perimeter of isosceles triangle ABC. A 8 in B C 4 in	___ 20 in ___ 16 in ___ 12 in
3. The Changs recently bought a small farm in the country. They plan to put up a fence around their property. What will the total length of the fence be? 250 ft 110 ft 75.5 ft 260 ft 123 ft 240 ft	___ 1,004.5 feet ___ 978.5 feet ___ 1,058.5 feet

5.3.6 Circumference

Circumference is the distance around a circle (its **perimeter**). Circumference can be found without measuring the distance around the circle if the length of the **diameter** or of the **radius** is known.

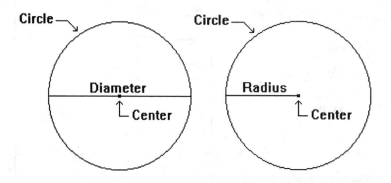

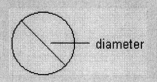

▶ The formula for finding the circumference of a circle is

C = πd

d = length of the diameter

π **(Pi)** = ratio of the circumference to the length of the diameter

The approximate decimal value of π is **3.14**.

📝 *Example*

If the diameter of a circle is 3 inches, its circumference is

$$C = \pi d$$
$$= 3.14 \times 3 \text{ inches}$$
$$= 9.42 \text{ inches}$$

This diagram shows the length of a piece of string that was wrapped around the circle and then measured. It has the same measure as the circumference of the circle

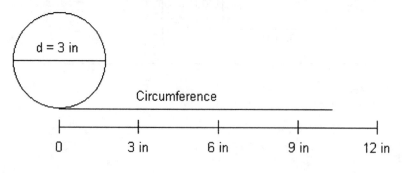

▶ If only the length of the radius of a circle is known, the formula for finding the circumference is C = 2πr, since the length of the diameter is twice the length of the radius.

 Check Your Understanding 5.3.6

Write the correct answers in the answer column.

Question	Answer
1. To the nearest foot, what is the circumference of a round swimming pool that is 32 feet in diameter?	1. _____
2. A car tire with a 14-inch radius has a circumference of about how many inches?	2. _____
3. A large oak tree measures 3 feet in diameter. About what is its circumference?	3. _____

radius

The radius of a circle is a line segment from the center of a circle to a point on the circle.

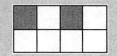

radius

5.3.7 Understanding Scale Factors

A **scale factor** is a **ratio** of the actual size of something to its size in a drawing or model.

$$\text{scale factor} = \text{actual size} : \text{model size}$$

Architects *scale down* drawings to show the dimensions of a structure. Small scientific instruments are *scaled up* so that they can be easily viewed in diagrams.

ratio

A ratio compares two or more quantities. For example, the ratio of *shaded* squares to *clear* squares in the figure below is 2 to 6 (2:6). The ratio of *shaded* squares to *all* the squares is 2 to 8 (2:8). And the ratio of *clear* squares to *all* the squares is 6 to 8 (6:8).

📝 *Example*

An architect's drawing is scaled so that one inch represents every 12 feet of an office building's floor plan. To find the actual dimensions of a conference room that is 1.5 inches by 2 inches in the drawing, scale up each dimension by a factor of 12.

$$1.5\,\text{in} \times \frac{12\,\text{ft}}{\text{in}} = 18\,\text{ft} \qquad 2\,\text{in} \times \frac{12\,\text{ft}}{\text{in}} = 24\,\text{ft}$$

The actual dimensions of the conference room are 18 feet by 24 feet.

Check Your Understanding 5.3.7

Put a check (✓) next to the correct answers in the answer column.

Question	Answer
1. A model race car measures 2 feet in length. The actual race car it is modeled after is 20 feet long. What is the scale-down factor?	___ 2 ___ 10 ___ 20
2. A photographer wants to make a copy of an 8-by-12-inch photograph that will fit in a 4-by-6-inch frame. What scale-down factor must he use?	___ .5 ___ 2 ___ 4
3. A house plan is drawn at a scale where 1/4 inch equals 1 foot. If the bathroom measures 1 1/4 inches by 2 inches on the floor plan, what is its actual size?	___ 10 feet by 16 feet ___ 5 feet by 8 feet ___ 6 feet by 12 feet

Topics Related to: Understanding Scale Factors

4.1.10 Scaling Up
4.1.11 Scaling Down

5.4 Area, Volume, and Surface Area

5.4.1 Square Units (unit²)

Units of measure such as an inch, a foot, or a centimeter are *linear units*; they are used to measure length. **Square units**, such as a square inch or a square mile, are used to measure **area**.

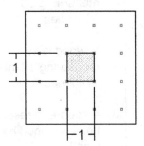

▶ To understand square units, think of a square that measures one unit along each side. The area inside the square is a *square unit (unit²)*.

✎ *Example*

A square that measures one inch along each side is a square inch. If four one-inch squares are placed side by side, the area inside the resulting figure is *four square inches (in²)*.

▶ The area of any two-dimensional figure (such as a triangle, square, or circle) is measured in square units. The **surface area** of any three-dimensional figure (such as a prism, cone, or sphere) is also measured in square units.

Check Your Understanding 5.4.1

Draw a line to connect each item in the match column with the correct answer in the answer column.

Question	Match	Answer
What is the unit of measure for the following?	1. Carpet is sold in units measuring 36 inches by 36 inches 2. Plywood is sold in units measuring 12 inches by 12 inches 3. A square measured in units one inch by one inch? 4. A large forest measured in units one mile by one mile.	square miles square inches linear feet square feet square yards cubic feet

5.4.2 Understanding Area

The **area** of a closed two-dimensional figure is the measure of the region that is within the figure.

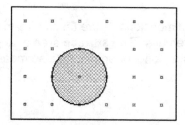

For example, the interior of this circle is shaded. The area is the number of square units that are shaded.

Check Your Understanding 5.4.2

Put a check (✓) next to the correct answers in the answer column.

Question	Answer
The area of a closed two-dimensional figure is _____	____ the distance around the figure. ____ the distance across the object. ____ measured in square units.

5.4.3 Area of a Rectangle

The **area** of a **rectangle** is found by multiplying the **length** of the rectangle by the **width** of the rectangle. The area is expressed in **square units**.

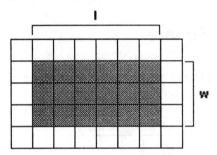

▶ The formula used to calculate the area of a rectangle is:

Area of a Rectangle = l x w
l is the length (the measure of the longer side of the rectangle)
w is the width (the measure of the shorter side of the rectangle)

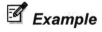 *Example*

The shaded rectangle is 6 units long and 3 units wide. To find the area:

$$l \times w = 6 \text{ units} \times 3 \text{ units} = 18 \text{ unit}^2$$

Glossary

area

Area is the measure of the region within a closed two-dimensional figure.

rectangle

A rectangle is a polygon with exactly four sides and four right angles. The lengths of the opposite sides of a rectangle are always equal.

length (l)

Length is the measure of the longest side of a two-dimensional figure, or the measure of the longest side of the base of a three-dimensional figure.

width (w)

Width is the shorter or shortest dimension of a figure, or the number that measures this dimension.

square units

A square unit is the unit of measure for the area of a two-dimensional figure. For example, the area of a square that measures one inch along each side is a square inch (1 in^2).

Check Your Understanding 5.4.3

Write the correct answers in the answer column.

Question	Answer
What is the area of the following rectangles? 1. A sheet of paper 12 inches by 4 inches	1. _____ inches²
2. A sheet of plywood 6 feet by 2 feet	2. _____ feet²
3. A field 100 yards by 30 yards	3. _____ yards²
4. A stamp 1.5 cm by 2.5 cm	4. _____ cm²

square

A square is a polygon with exactly 4 sides of equal length and 4 right angles.

5.4.4 Area of a Square

The **area** of a **square** is found by multiplying the lengths of two sides of the square. The area is expressed in **square units**.

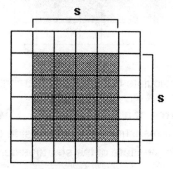

▶ The formula used to calculate the area of a square is:

$$\text{Area of a square} = s \times s = s^2$$

s represents the length of any side of the square.

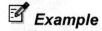 *Example*

The length of a side of the shaded square is 4 units. The area is:

$$s \times s = 4 \text{ units} \times 4 \text{ units} = 16 \text{ square units (unit}^2)$$

Check Your Understanding 5.4.4

Write the correct answers in the answer column.

Question	Answer
1. What is the area of a square with a 3.5-inch side?	1. _____
2. What is the area of the shaded region? (Both figures are squares.) 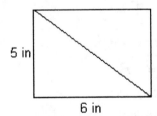	2. _____

5.4.5 Area of a Triangle

If you form two **triangles** from a **rectangle**, the **area** of the triangle is half the area of the rectangle.

Area of a rectangle = **b** x **h**

Area of a triangle = ½(b x h)
b is the **base of a triangle**
h is the **height of a triangle**

📝 *Example*

The above triangle has a base of 6 and a height of 5. To find the area:

½ **(b x h)** = ½(6 units x 5 units) = 15 units squared

---

triangle

A triangle is a polygon with exactly three sides.

rectangle

A rectangle is a polygon with exactly four sides and four right angles. The lengths of the opposite sides of a rectangle are always equal.

area

Area is the measure of the region within a closed two-dimensional figure.

base (b) of a triangle

The base (b) of a triangle is any one of its three sides. Every triangle, therefore, has three bases.

height (h) of a triangle

The height (h) of a triangle is the perpendicular measure from one of the three points of the triangle to the opposite base. Every triangle, therefore, has three heights, one for each base.

radius

The radius of a circle is a line segment from the center of a circle to a point on the circle.

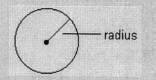
radius

square units

A square unit is the unit of measure for the area of a two-dimensional figure. For example, the area of a square that measures one inch along each side is a square inch (1 in^2).

☑ **Check Your Understanding 5.4.5**

Write the correct answers in the answer column.

Question	Answer
1. What is the area of a triangle with a base of 2 inches and a height of 7 inches?	1. _____
2. What is the area of a triangle with a base of 6 cm and a height of 18 cm?	2. _____

5.4.6 Area of a Circle

The **area** of a *circle* can be found by multiplying **pi (π)** times the **radius** squared. The area is expressed in **square units**.

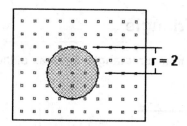

▶ The formula used to calculate the area of a circle is

Area of a circle $= \pi r^2$

π (*pi*) is approximately 3.14

r is the radius of the circle

 *Example*

The radius of the above circle is 2. The area is:

$$\pi r^2 = 3.14(2 \text{ units})^2 = 3.14 \,(2 \text{ units} \times 2 \text{ units}) = 12.56 \text{ unit}^2$$

Check Your Understanding 5.4.6

Put a check (✓) next to the correct answers in the answer column.

Question	Answer
1. A circle has a radius of 3 meters. Which equation would you use to find its area?	___ 3.14 x 3 x 2 ___ 3.14 x 3² ___ (3.14 x 3)²
2. A circle has a radius of 10 inches. What is its area?	___ 314 sq in ___ 62.8 sq in ___ 1,256 sq in
3. A circle has a diameter of 6 centimeters. What is its area?	___ 88.73 cm² ___ 28.26 cm² ___ 113.04 cm²

5.4.7 Understanding Surface Area

Imagine that you have flattened out a box. The **surface area** of the box is the **sum** of the **areas** of the six **faces**.

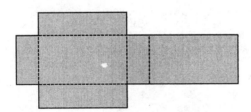

For example, this diagram shows an unfolded cereal box. The surface area of the box is the combined areas of the front, back, sides, top, and bottom of the box. Surface area is expressed in **square units**.

sum

A sum is the result of the addition of two or more numbers or quantities. For example, the sum of 3 and 5 is 8.

area

Area is the measure of the region within a closed two-dimensional figure.

face

A face is any of the flat surfaces of a three-dimensional figure or a solid. For example, a box has six flat sides. Each of these sides is a face of the box.

square units

A square unit is the unit of measure for the area of a two-dimensional figure. For example, the area of a square that measures one inch along each side is a square inch (1 in^2).

Check Your Understanding 5.4.7

Put a check (✓) next to the correct answers in the answer column.

Question	Answer
1. Surface area is measured in square units.	____ true ____ false
2. Surface area = length x width x height.	____ true ____ false
3. Surface area is the same as the perimeter of an object.	____ true ____ false
4. Surface area is the sum of the areas of each face of the object.	____ true ____ false

rectangular prism

A rectangular prism is a closed three-dimensional figure with six rectangular faces. A cereal box is an example of a rectangular prism.

rectangle

A rectangle is a polygon with exactly four sides and four right angles. The lengths of the opposite sides of a rectangle are always equal.

prism

A prism is a solid with two bases that are polygons. The bases are in parallel planes. The sides of the prism are parallelograms.

surface area

Surface area is the total area of all outside surfaces of a three-dimensional object. For example, a box has six outside surfaces. They are the sides, or faces, of the box. To find the surface area, you must find the area of each face, and then add the areas together.

5.4.8 Surface Area of a Rectangular Prism

A **rectangular prism** has six **faces**. Each face is a **rectangle**. The **surface area** of the **prism** is found by adding together the **areas** of the six faces.

Rectangular Prism

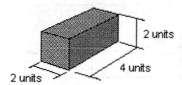

Area of a Square Face = side x side
Area of a Rectangular Face = length x width

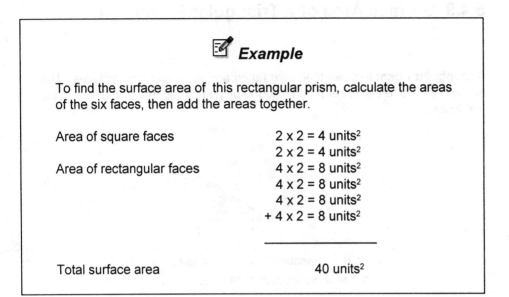

Example

To find the surface area of this rectangular prism, calculate the areas of the six faces, then add the areas together.

Area of square faces $2 \times 2 = 4$ units^2
                               $2 \times 2 = 4$ units^2
Area of rectangular faces $4 \times 2 = 8$ units^2
                               $4 \times 2 = 8$ units^2
                               $4 \times 2 = 8$ units^2
                               $+\ 4 \times 2 = 8$ units^2
                               _____

Total surface area 40 units^2

Check Your Understanding 5.4.8

Put a check (✓) next to the correct answers in the answer column.

Question	Answer
1. What is the surface area of the rectangular prism below? 7mm 10mm 3mm	___ 121 sq millimeters ___ 242 sq millimeters ___ 210 sq millimeters
2. What is the surface area of the rectangular prism below? 2 feet 3 feet 5 feet	___ 31 sq feet ___ 31 cu feet ___ 62 sq feet

5.4.9 Surface Area of a Triangular Prism

triangular prism

A triangular prism is a prism with two triangular faces as the bases and three rectangular faces as the sides.

area

Area is the measure of the region within a closed two-dimensional figure.

face

A face is any of the flat surfaces of a three-dimensional figure or a solid. For example, a box has six flat sides. Each of these sides is a face of the box.

A **triangular prism** has two triangular **faces** and three rectangular faces. The **surface area** of a triangular prism is found by adding together the **areas** of the five faces.

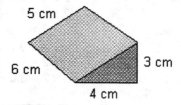

Area of a triangular face = ½(base x height)
Area of a rectangular face = length x width

 Example

To find the surface area of this triangular prism, calculate the areas of the 5 faces, then add the areas together.

Area of 2 triangular faces:	½(4 x 3) =	6 cm²
	½(4 x 3) =	6 cm²
Area of 3 rectangular faces:	4 x 6 =	24 cm²
	5 x 6 =	30 cm²
	+ 3 x 6 =	18 cm²
		_____
Total surface area:		84 cm²

---

surface area

Surface area is the total area of all outside surfaces of three-dimensional objects. For example, a box has six outside surfaces. They are the sides, or faces, of the box. To find the surface area, you must find the area of each face, then add them.

✓ **Check Your Understanding 5.4.9**

Put a check (✓) next to the correct answers in the answer column.

Question	Answer
1. A triangular prism has three triangular faces and two rectangular faces.	____ true ____ false
2. The surface area of a triangular prism is equal to the sum of the areas of the six faces.	____ true ____ false

3. Find the surface area of the triangular prism.

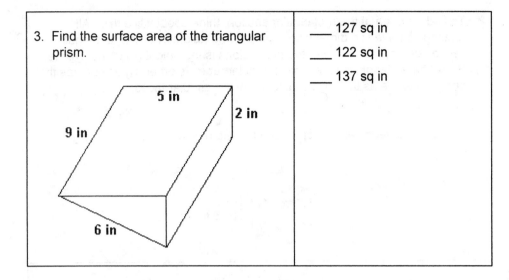

___ 127 sq in

___ 122 sq in

___ 137 sq in

5.4.10 Surface Area of a Cylinder

A **cylinder** is made of two circular bases and one rectangular section. The rectangular section is rolled into a tube and the circular faces cap the ends of the tube. An example of a cylinder is a juice can.

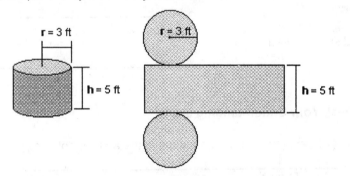

Area of a circular base = πr^2

Area of the rectangular section = length x width = $2\pi r$ x **h**

▶ The **surface area** of a cylinder is found by adding together the **areas** of the two circular bases and the **area** of the rectangular section.

area

Area is the measure of the region within a closed two-dimensional figure.

▶ To find the area of the rectangular section, think about it like this: All rectangles have two dimensions: length and height. For the rectangular section of a cylinder, one of the dimensions is the height (h) of the cylinder. Since the rectangle is rolled into a circular tube, its other dimension has the same measure as the **circumference** of the circular faces.

area of rectangular section = length x width = circumference x height

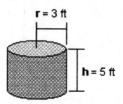

circumference

Circumference is the distance around a circle. To find the circumference, multiply the diameter of the circle by π (or approximately 3.14).
Circumference = πd, where d is the diameter of the circle.
Circumference = $2\pi r$ where r is the radius of the circle.

✎ *Example*

To find the surface area of the cylinder above:

Area of 2 circular faces	$3.14\ (3^2) = 28.26\ \text{ft}^2$
	$3.14\ (3^2) = 28.26\ \text{ft}^2$
Area of rectangular section	$+\ 2(3.14)(3) \times 5 = 94.20\ \text{ft}^2$
	───────────────
Total surface area	$150.72\ \text{ft}^2$

 Check Your Understanding 5.4.10

Put a check (✓) next to the correct answers in the answer column.

Question	Answer
1. Finding the surface area of a cylinder is the same process as finding the area of two circles and a rectangle and adding them together.	___ true ___ false
2. The rectangular section of a cylinder has one side that is equal to the circumference of the circular section.	___ true ___ false

3. Figure the surface area of the cylinder.

____ 9,809.36 sq ft

____ 11,329.12 sq ft

____ 12,456.32 sq ft

radius = 22 ft

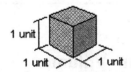

60 ft

5.4.11 Cubic Units (units^3)

Cubic units are used to measure **volume**, just as **square units** are used to measure **area**.

1 cubic unit

1 unit

1 unit   1 unit

▶ To understand cubic units, think of a **cube**. A cube has six identical square faces. If the edge of each square face measures one unit, the cube represents one cubic unit.

✏️ *Example*

A cube that measures one inch along each edge has a volume of one cubic inch (1 inch^3).

▶ The volumes of three-dimensional figures are measured in cubic units (unit^3).

---

volume

Volume is the measure of the interior space of a three-dimensional figure. Volume is measured in cubic units.

square units

A square unit is the unit of measure for the area of a two-dimensional figure. For example, the area of a square that measures one inch along each side is a square inch (1 in^2).

area

Area is the measure of the region within a closed 2-dimensional figure.

cube

A cube is a closed three-dimensional figure with six identical square faces.

Check Your Understanding 5.4.11

Draw a line to connect each item in the match column with the correct answer in the answer column.

Question	Match	Answer
What unit of measure would you use to show the volume of these objects?	1. A cube 3 in by 5 in by 7 in. 2. A rectangular prism 70 mm by 120 mm by 400 mm. 3. A rectangular building 20 ft by 40 ft by 10 ft. 4. A large box 1 meter by 3 meters by 4 meters.	feet³ feet² inches³ meters² meters³ millimeters millimeters³

5.4.12 Understanding Volume

The **volume** of an object is the number of **cubic units** that completely fill the space inside the object.

📝 *Example*

This **cube** is filled with 27 smaller cubes that each have the volume of one cubic inch. The volume of the larger cube is 27 cubic inches or 27 inch³.

---

cubic unit

A cubic unit (unit³) is the unit of measure for the volume of three-dimensional objects. You can think of a cubic unit as a cube with edges that are one unit long. The volume of this cube is 1 unit³.

cube

A cube is a closed three-dimensional figure with six identical square faces.

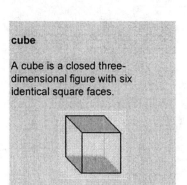

Check Your Understanding 5.4.12

Put a check (✓) next to the correct answers in the answer column.

Question	Answer
1. How many cubic inches are in the prism below? 1 in 4 in 4 in	___ 16 cu in ___ 8 cu in ___ 16 sq in
2. What is the volume of the prism? 3 in 4 in 4 in	___ 32 cu in ___ 48 cu in ___ 28 cu in

5.4.13 Volume of a Rectangular Prism

The **volume** of a **rectangular prism** is the number of **cubic units** that can fit inside the prism.

▶ To find the volume of any prism:

    1. Find the area of the **base (B)** of the prism.
    2. Multiply that number by the **height (H)** of the prism.

volume

Volume is the measure of the interior space of a three-dimensional figure. Volume is measured in cubic units.

rectangular prism

A rectangular prism is a closed three-dimensional figure with six rectangular faces. A cereal box is an example of a rectangular prism.

cubic unit

A cubic unit (unit^3) is the unit of measure for the volume of three-dimensional objects. You can think of a cubic unit as a cube with edges that are one unit long. The volume of this cube is 1 unit^3.

▶ The base of a rectangular prism is a rectangle. To find B (the area of the rectangular base), use the formula: **area = length x width**.

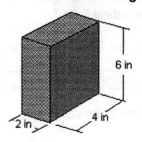

6 in

4 in

2 in

Volume = Area of Base x Height of Prism

base of a prism

The two opposite, congruent, and parallel faces of a prism are the bases. For example, the two shaded faces of the triangular prism shown below are its bases.

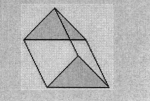

✍ *Example*

To find the volume of the rectangular prism above:

Area of Base	= l x w
	= 4 inches x 2 inches
	= 8 inches^2
Height of Prism	= 6 inches
Volume	= B x H
	= area of base x height of prism
	= 8 inches^2 x 6 inches
	= 48 inches^3

---

height of a prism

The height of a prism is the perpendicular distance between the two bases.

Check Your Understanding 5.4.13

Put a check (✓) next to the correct answers in the answer column.

Question	Answer
1. What is the volume of this prism?	___ 3 cu in ___ 4 cu in ___ 12 cu in
2. Now imagine stacking an additional two prisms of identical size on the prism shown in problem 1. What would the volume be now?	___ 12 cu in ___ 24 cu in ___ 36 cu in
3. What is the volume of this prism?	___ 420 cm³ ___ 820 cm³ ___ 18,040 cm³

volume

Volume is the measure of the interior space of a three-dimensional figure. Volume is measured in cubic units.

triangular prism

A triangular prism is a prism with two triangular faces as the bases and with three rectangular faces as the sides.

cubic unit

A cubic unit (unit^3) is the unit of measure for the volume of three-dimensional objects. You can think of a cubic unit as a cube with edges that are one unit long. The volume of this cube is 1 unit^3.

height of a prism

The height of a prism is the perpendicular distance between the two bases.

5.4.14 Volume of a Triangular Prism

The **volume** of a **triangular prism** is the number of **cubic units** that can fit inside the prism.

▶ To find the volume of any prism:

    1 Find the area of the **base (B)** of the prism.

    2 Multiply that number by the **height (H)** of the prism.

▶ The base of a triangular prism is a triangle. To find B (the area of the triangular base), use the formula:

$$\text{area} = \tfrac{1}{2}bh$$

where **b** = the base of the triangle, and **h** = the height of the triangle.

📝 *Example*

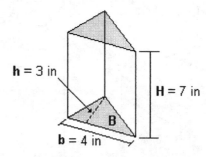

h = 3 in

H = 7 in

b = 4 in

B

To find the volume of this rectangular prism:

Area of base	= ½bh
	= ½(4 inches x 3 inches)
	= 6 inches²
Height of prism	= 7 inches
Volume	= **B x H**
	= area of base x height of prism
	= 6 inches² x 7 inches
	= 42 cubic inches (inches³)

Check Your Understanding 5.4.14

Put a check (✓) next to the correct answers in the answer column.

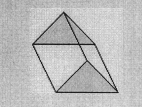

Question	Answer
1. The base of a triangular prism is a triangle.	____ true ____ false
2. The formula for finding the area of the base is (b x h).	____ true ____ false
3. Figure the volume of the prism. H= 8 in h = 2 in b = 6 in	____ 24 cubic inches ____ 48 cubic inches ____ 92 cubic inches
4. Figure the volume of the prism. b = 30 cm h = 3 cm H = 25 cm	____ 1,125 cm³ ____ 2,250 cm³ ____ 1,725 cm³

cylinder

A cylinder is a solid that has two circular bases. The bases are in parallel planes. A juice can is a good example of a cylinder.

prism

A prism is a solid with two bases that are polygons. The bases are in parallel planes. The sides of the prism are parallelograms.

volume

Volume is the measure of the interior space of a three-dimensional figure. Volume is measured in cubic units.

5.4.15 Volume of a Cylinder

A **cylinder** can be thought of as a circular **prism**. The **volume** of a cylinder is the number of **cubic units** that can fit inside it.

▶ To find the volume of any prism or cylinder:

    1. Find the area of the **base (B)** of the prism.

    2. Multiply that number by the **height (H)** of the prism.

▶ The base of a cylinder is a circle. To find **B** (the area of the circular base), use the formula:

$$\textbf{area} = \pi r^2$$

where **pi (π)** = 3.14 and **r** = the radius of the circle.

📝 *Example*

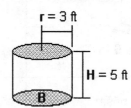

r = 3 ft

H = 5 ft

B

To find the volume of this cylinder:

Area of Base	=	πr^2
	=	3.14 (3 feet)^2
	=	28.26 feet^2
Height of cylinder	=	5 feet
Volume	=	Area of base x height of cylinder
	=	28.26 feet^2 x 5 feet
	=	141.3 cubic feet (feet^3)

---

cubic unit

A cubic unit (unit^3) is the unit of measure for the volume of three-dimensional objects. You can think of a cubic unit as a cube with edges that are one unit long. The volume of this cube is 1 unit^3.

Check Your Understanding 5.4.15

Draw a line to connect each item in the match column with the correct answer in the answer column.

Question	Match	Answer
Match the following statements.	1. Base of a cylinder 2. Area of a circle 3. π 4. Volume of a cylinder	3.14 circle area of base x height of cylinder πr^2

Put a check (✓) next to the correct answers in the answer column.

Question	Answer
5. Find the volume of the cylinder. r = 2 ft H = 10 ft	___ 12.56 cu ft ___ 125.6 cu ft ___ 62.8 cu ft
6. Calculate the volume of the cylinder. r = .5 in H = 3 in	___ 2.355 cu in ___ 4.71 cu in ___ 9.42 cu in

height of a prism

The height of a prism is the perpendicular distance between the two bases.

pi (π)

Pi (π) is the ratio of the circumference of a circle to its diameter. This ratio is the same for any circle, and is approximately equal to 3.14.

5.5 Answers to Questions

Answers to 5.1.1

Correct Answer	Explanation
1. 70°	To find the measure of angle *a* you must determine where side *ab* crosses the protractor scale.
2. 50°	Use the outside scale. Determine where side *ab* crosses the scale.
3. 40°	The m ∠ d = 70° - 30° = 40° (using the inside scale).
4. 140°	The m ∠ x = 150° - 10° = 140° (using the inside scale).

Answers to 5.1.2

Correct Answer	Explanation
1. a. ∠ ABC --- straight b. ∠ DEF --- obtuse c. ∠ GHI --- acute d. ∠ LKJ --- cannot say	∠ ABC = 180°. ∠ DEF is greater than 90°. ∠ GHI is less than 90°. ∠ LKJ could be less than or greater than 90°.
2. e. ∠ E --- acute f. ∠ F --- cannot say g. ∠ G --- acute	∠ E is less than 90° ∠ F could be less than or greater than 90° ∠ G is less than 90°

Answers to 5.1.3

Correct Answer	Explanation
1. 30°	m ∠ DBE = 180° - (90° + 60°) = 30°
2. 35°	m ∠ XWY = 180° - (50° + 95°) = 35°

3. 145°	m ∠ FGH = 180° - (20° + 15°) = 145°
4. 135°	m ∠ MPO = m ∠ MNO = 135° (Opposite diagonal angles of parallelograms are equal.)

Answers to 5.1.3.1

Correct Answer	Explanation
1. m ∠ f = 90° m ∠ g = 90°	When two parallel lines are crossed by another line, the vertical angles formed at each intersection have equal measures. This means that angles a, c, e, and g have equal measures, as do angles b, d, f, and h.
2. m ∠ a = 30° m ∠ b = 150°	Vertical angles a, c, e, and g have the same measure. Angles b, d, f, and h also have the same measure.
3. m ∠ c = 135° m ∠ d = 45°	Vertical angles a, c, e, and g have the same measure. Likewise, vertical angles f, h, b, and d have equal measures.

Answers to 5.1.4

Correct Answer	Explanation
1. ∠ a --- 90° ∠ b --- 45° ∠ c --- 30° ∠ d --- 60°	First find the 90° angle, since it will be easiest to recognize. Next find the 45° angle, since you can estimate what one-half of the 90° angle should be. Of the two remaining angles, the one just smaller than the 45° angle will be the 30° angle. The last angle will be 60°.

Answers to 5.1.5

Correct Answer	Explanation
1. ∠ d = 45° ∠ e = 60° ∠ f = 30° ∠ p = 22 1/2° ∠ q = 45° ∠ r = 60° ∠ s = 30° ∠ t = 180°	Find or draw a familiar angle, such as a 90° angle. Bisect this angle to get a 45° angle. This can then be halved again to get 22 1/2°. With these angles, it should be easy to estimate the remaining angles. **Note:** Your estimates do not need to match these angle measurements exactly, but they should be close to these numbers.

Answers to 5.1.6

Correct Answer	Explanation
1. right	The triangle has one right angle.
2. isosceles	The triangle has two equal sides.
3. equilateral	The triangle has three equal sides.
4. scalene	The triangle has an obtuse angle.
5. false	None of the angles are greater than 90°.
6. true	Triangle D contains one angle greater than 90°.

Answers to 5.2.1

Correct Answer	Explanation
1. true	By definition, quadrilaterals are four-sided polygons.
2. false	All quadrilaterals are polygons, but not the reverse.

3. false	Trapezoids have only two sides that are parallel. Parallelograms have two sets of sides parallel.
4. false	A rhombus does not always have four equal angles.
5. true	Parallelograms are quadrilaterals in which the opposite sides are parallel. Squares, rectangles, and rhombuses all fit that definition.

Answers to 5.2.1.1

Correct Answer	Explanation
1. a and d	These figures have four equal sides and four right angles.
2. All squares are polygons.	A polygon has three or more straight sides.
All squares are rhombuses.	Rhombuses have four equal sides. Squares do, too.
All squares are rectangles.	Rectangles have four right angles and opposite sides that are equal in length. So do squares.

Answers to 5.2.1.2

Correct Answer	Explanation
1. figures e, f, and h	Figures e, f, and h have four right angles and the opposite sides are equal in length. Remember that a square can also be a rectangle.
2. All rectangles are parallelograms.	Parallelograms have opposite sides that are equal in length. So do rectangles.

Answers to 5.2.1.3

Correct Answer	Explanation
1. figures k and l	Figures k and l have four sides equal in length.

2. All rhombuses are quadrilaterals.	Quadrilaterals have four sides, as do rhombuses.
All rhombuses are parallelograms.	Opposite sides of a parallelogram are parallel. Opposite sides of a rhombus are parallel as well.

Answers to 5.2.1.4

Correct Answer	Explanation
1. figures n and p	Figures n and p have only two sides that are parallel, and they are not the same length.
2. Trapezoids are quadrilaterals.	By definition, quadrilaterals are polygons with four sides. Trapezoids have four sides.

Answers to 5.2.1.5

Correct Answer	Explanation
1. figures s and u	These figures both have two sets of parallel sides.
2. Squares, rectangles, and rhombuses are parallelograms.	A parallelogram is a polygon with two sets of opposite sides that are parallel. Squares, rectangles, and rhombuses all fit that definition.

Answers to 5.2.2

Correct Answer	Explanation
1. figures a and c	Figures a and c have a circular base and one vertex.
2. true	By definition, a cone has a circular base.
3. false	A cone has only one vertex.

Answers to 5.2.3

Correct Answer	Explanation
1. figures f and g	Both f and g have two identical circular bases that are parallel.
2. false	A cylinder has no vertices.
3. true	The two bases of a cylinder are always parallel.

Answers to 5.2.4

Correct Answer	Explanation
1. figures i, k, and l	Figures i, k, and l, all have polygons for bases, parallelograms for sides, and bases in parallel planes. Figure j does not have parallelograms for sides.
2. false	The bases of a prism are always polygons, sometimes quadrilaterals.
3. false	The sides of a prism are always parallelograms, sometimes rectangles.

Answers to 5.2.5

Correct Answer	Explanation
1. figures m and p	Figures m and p have a polygon for a base, their sides are all triangular, and their sides share one vertex.
2. true	Pyramids have only triangular sides.
3. true	Pyramids have polygonal bases.

Answers to 5.2.6

Correct Answer	Explanation
1. figures r and s	These figures changed position, not shape.
2. false	Some transformations change shape, but we will not study them in LearningPlus.
3. true	By definition, transformation occurs when a figure changes its position.

Answers to 5.2.6.1

Correct Answer	Explanation
1. figures t and v	The corresponding vertices in figures t and v are all the same distance from the rotation point.
2. false	A rotation is a type of transformation.
3. true	All vertices remain the same distance from the point of rotation for any rotation.

Answers to 5.2.6.2

Correct Answer	Explanation
1. figures y and z	Figures y and z are mirror images.
2. true	By definition, a reflection is a mirror image.
3. true	A reflection is one type of transformation.

Answers to 5.2.6.3

Correct Answer	Explanation
1. figure a	Figure a is the only slide, because it is the only one that moved in a straight line and did not also rotate.

2. true	A transformation occurs when a geometric figure changes its position, but not its shape.
3. false	A slide is a transformation in which a figure slides along a straight line.

Answers to 5.3.1

Correct Answer	Explanation
1. A = 10 1/4 inches B = 2 cm	A. Find the inch scale and read the number of inches. Since the end of the pencil falls between two inch marks, determine how many parts each inch is divided into. On this scale each inch is divided into four equal parts, so each mark is equal to 1 in ÷ 4 = 1/4 in. B. Find the centimeter scale. On this scale each mark equals one centimeter, so it is easy to determine the length simply bv counting the marks.

2. C = 8 3/4 inches
   D = 12 cm
   E = 17 cm
	D. 34 cm - 17 cm = 17 cm

3. F = 6 1/4 inches
   G = 3 3/4 inches
   H = 19 cm
   I = 27 cm	

Answers to 5.3.2

Correct Answer	Explanation
1. 2,000	1 ton = 2,000 pounds
2. 5,280	1 mile = 5,280 feet
3. 16	1 pound = 16 ounces

4. 4	1 gallon = 4 quarts

Answers to 5.3.3

Correct Answer	Explanation
1. kilometer	Since a kilometer is the closest metric unit to a mile, this would be the best choice.
2. milliliter	The amount of contact lens solution needed to cover one lens is quite small so milliliters would be a good choice since 5 milliliters is about one teaspoon.
3. gram	A letter in a standard-size envelope weighs very little; therefore, a gram would be the best choice.
4. centimeter	A centimeter is used for measuring shorter objects.

Answers to 5.3.4

Correct Answer	Explanation
1. longer	Since one yard is only .9144 meters, you know that a yard is shorter than a meter; therefore, 100 yards will also be shorter than 100 meters.
2. no	Jason's luggage weighs 130 lbs. One kilogram equals 2.2 lbs. To find the weight of Jason's luggage in kilograms, divide 130 by 2.2 . 130 ÷ 2.2 = 59.09 kilograms
3. 45 liters	Maria's tank holds 12 gallons. Using the conversion factor of one gallon equals 3.785 liters, her tank will hold 12 x 3.785 liters, or 45.42 liters.

Answers to 5.3.5

Correct Answer	Explanation
1. 38 cm	The perimeter of this figure is equal to the sum of all the sides. Starting at the top and moving clockwise, add the following: 10 + 6 + 2 + 3 + 6 + 3 + 2 + 6 = 38 cm.
2. 20 inches	Adding the lengths of each side gives a perimeter of 8 + 8 + 4 = 20 inches. (An isosceles triangle has two equal sides.)
3. 1,058.5 feet	Add the lengths of all sides.

Answers to 5.3.6

Correct Answer	Explanation	
1. About 100 feet	C = π d	C = 3.14 x 32 = 100.48 feet
2. About 88 inches	C = 2πr	C = 2 x 3.14 x 14 = 87.92 inches
3. About 9.5 feet	C = πd	C = 3.14 x 3 = 9.42 feet

Answers to 5.3.7

Correct Answer	Explanation
1. 10	scale factor = $\dfrac{\text{actual size}}{\text{model size}}$ = $\dfrac{20 \text{ ft}}{2 \text{ ft}}$ = 10
2. 2	scale factor = $\dfrac{\text{actual size}}{\text{model size}}$ = $\dfrac{8 \text{ in}}{4 \text{ in}}$ and $\dfrac{12 \text{ in}}{6 \text{ in}}$ = 2
3. 5 feet by 8 feet	First convert 1 1/4 inches and 2 inches to quarter-inches. 1 1/4 inches = 5/4 inches and 2 inches = 8/4 inches. Since every quarter-inch on the drawing equals one foot, simply multiply 5 x 1 ft and 8 x 1 ft. The actual room size is 5 feet by 8 feet.

Answers to 5.4.1

Correct Answer	Explanation
1.--- square yards 2.--- square feet 3.--- square inches 4.--- square miles	1. 36" = 1 yard 2. 12" = 1 foot

Answers to 5.4.2

Correct Answer	Explanation
1. measured in square units	By definition, area is measured in square units.

Answers to 5.4.3

Correct Answer	Explanation
1. 48 sq in	Area of a rectangle = length x width Area = 12 in x 4 in = 48 square inches.
2. 12 sq ft	Area = 6 ft x 2 ft = 12 square feet.
3. 3,000 sq yds	Area = 100 yards x 30 yards = 3,000 square yards.
4. 3.75 cm^2	Area = 1.5 cm x 2.5 cm = 3.75 square centimeters.

Answers to 5.4.4

Correct Answer	Explanation
1. 12.25 square inches	Area of a square = length of one side squared. Area = 3.5 in x 3.5 in = 12.25 square inches.
2. 32 sq ft	The area of the shaded region is equal to the area of the large square minus the area of the small square: (6 ft x 6 ft) - (2 ft x 2 ft) = 32 square feet.

Answers to 5.4.5

Correct Answer	Explanation
1. 7 sq in	Area of a triangle = 1/2 base x height. Area = 1/2 (2 in x 7 in) = 7 square inches.
2. 54 cm²	Area = 1/2 (6 cm x 18 cm) = 54 cm²

Answers to 5.4.6

Correct Answer	Explanation
1. 3.14 x 3²	Area of a circle = πr^2 Area = 3.14 x 3²
2. 314 sq in	Area = 3.14 x 10² = 314 square inches
3. 28.26 cm²	Area = 3.14 x 3² = 28.26 square centimeters (Remember that radius = 1/2 diameter.)

Answers to 5.4.7

Correct Answer	Explanation
1. true	Area is measured in square units by definition.
2. false	Surface area is the sum of the areas of the faces of an object.
3. false	Perimeter is the distance around the outside of a two-dimensional object.
4. true	Surface area is the sum of the areas of each face of an object.

Answers to 5.4.8

Correct Answer	Explanation

1. 242 sq millimeters	The surface area of a rectangular prism equals the sum of the areas of the six sides. Keep in mind that opposite faces of the prism are identical, so once you find the areas of the front, top, and side views, you can simply multiply this total by 2 to find the total surface area.
	
	Area of top = 7 x 10 = 70 sq mm
	Area of side = 7 x 3 = 21 sq mm
	Area of front = <u>3 x 10 = 30 sq mm</u>
	                       121 sq mm
	Double this amount: <u>x 2</u>
	                   242 sq mm

2. 62 sq feet	Area of top = 2 x 3 = 6 sq ft
	Area of side = 5 x 2 = 10 sq ft
	Area of front = <u>3 x 5 = 15 sq ft</u>
	                    31 sq ft
	Double this amount: <u>x 2</u>
	                 62 sq ft

Answers to 5.4.9

Correct Answer	Explanation
1. false	A triangular prism has two triangular faces and three rectangular faces.
2. false	Its the sum of the five faces, not six.

3. 127 sq in	Add the areas of the five faces.
	
	Area of the two triangular faces: $1/2(5 \times 2) = 5$ in^2
	                                    $1/2(5 \times 2) = 5$ in^2
	
	Area of the 3 rectangular faces: $9 \times 5 = 45$ in^2
	                                $9 \times 2 = 18$ in^2
	                                <u>$9 \times 6 = 54$ in^2</u>
	
	                                     127 in^2

Answers to 5.4.10

Correct Answer	Explanation
1. true	The surface area of a cylinder is found by adding the two circular areas to that of the rectangular area.
2. true	Since the rectangular area is rolled into a circular tube, one side has the same length as the circumference of the circles.
3. 11,329.12 sq ft	To find the surface area of a cylinder: **1.** Find the area of 2 circular faces. $A = (\pi r^2)$ $3.14 \times 22^2 = 1,519.76$ sq feet $3.14 \times 22^2 = 1,519.76$ sq feet **2.** Find the area of the rectangular section. (find the circumference of the circular faces first) $C = 2\pi r = 2 \times 3.14 \times 22 = 138.16$ ft (then multiply this by the height) $138.16 \times 60 = 8,289.60$ sq ft **3.** Find the total of the three areas. Total of 3 areas: 11,329.12 sq ft

Answers to 5.4.11

Correct Answer	Explanation
1.--- inches³ 2.--- millimeters³ 3.--- feet³ 4.--- meters³	In each case, look at the unit of measurement and decide how many dimensions are being multiplied to find the answer: two or three. If two, then the answer is unit². If three, then the answer is unit³.
2. cubic	Volume is measured in cubic units.
3. cubic feet	Volume is measured in cubic units.

4. cubic meters	Volume is measured in cubic units.

Answers to 5.4.12

Correct Answer	Explanation
1. 16 cubic inches	Simply count the number of cubes, since there is only one layer and it is one inch high. Or, multiply 1 in x 4 in x 4 in = 16 cu in
2. 48 cubic inches	First, count the number of cubic inches on the top layer. (Or multiply as shown above.) Because there are two more identical layers, multiply the cubic inches on the first layer by 3 to get (3 x 16 cu. in) 48 cubic inches.

Answers to 5.4.13

Correct Answer	Explanation
1. 12 cu in	The volume of a rectangular prism equals the area of the base times the height of the prism. area of base = length x width = 4 x 3 = 12 height of prism = 1 in Volume = 12 x 1 = 12 cubic inches
2. 36 cu in	The volume of a rectangular prism equals the area of the base times the height of the prism. area of base = length x width = 4 x 3 = 12 height of prism = 3 in Volume = 12 x 3 = 36 cubic inches
3. 18,040 cm³	The volume of a rectangular prism equals the area of the base times the height of the prism. area of base = length x width = 41 x 20 = 820 height of prism = 22 cm Volume = 820 x 22 = 18,040 cubic centimeters

Answers to 5.4.14

Correct Answer	Explanation
1. true	The shape of the base determines the type of prism.
2. false	area of the base = 1/2 b x h
3. 48 cubic inches	The volume of a triangular prism equals the area of the base times the height of the prism. area of base = 1/2 b x h area of base: 1/2 x 6 x 2 = 6 Volume = 6 x 8 = 48 cubic inches
4. 1,125 cm³	The volume of a triangular prism equals the area of the base times the height of the prism. area of base = 1/2 b x h area of base: 1/2 x 30 x 3 = 45 Volume = 45 x 25 = 1125 cubic centimeters

Answers to 5.4.15

Correct Answer	Explanation
1.--- circle 2.--- πr^2 3.--- 3.14 4.--- area of base x height of cylinder	1. The base of a cylinder is a circle. 2. area of a circle = πr^2 3. pi = 3.14 4. by definition of the volume of a cylinder
5. 125.6 cu ft	The volume of a cylinder equals the area of the base times the height of the cylinder. area of circle = πr^2 = 3.14 x 2² = 12.56 volume = 12.56 x 10 = 125.6 cu ft

| 6. 2.355 cu in | The volume of a cylinder equals the area of the base times the height of the cylinder.

area of circle = πr^2 = 3.14 x $.5^2$ = .785

volume = .785 x 3 = 2.355 cu in |

Chapter 6

Logical Reasoning

6.1   Logic Term: all 408

6.2   Logic Term: some 410

6.3   Logic Term: no/none 412

6.4   Logic Term: and 414

6.5   Logic Term: or...416

6.6   Logic Terms: if and then 419

6.7   Venn Diagrams 422

6.8   Deductive Reasoning...423

6.9   Inductive Reasoning 425

6.10 Answers to Questions 426

Learn how to use logical language, Venn diagrams, and deductive and inductive reasoning.

Do **all** dogs chase cats?

6.1 Logic Term: *all*

logic term

A logic term is a word that has a specific meaning when used in logic statements.

The **logic term** *all* is used when referring to an entire group of items, with the same **attribute** or attributes.

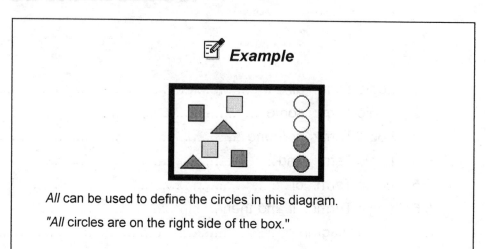

✏️ *Example*

All can be used to define the circles in this diagram.

"*All* circles are on the right side of the box."

attribute

An attribute is a property or a characteristic of something. For example, a small, clear triangle has three separate attributes: small, clear, and triangle.

Refer to the diagram above to answer the following questions.

✔️ **Check Your Understanding 6.1a**

Put a check (✓) next to the correct answers in the answer column.

Question	Answer
1. Which statement is true for the diagram above?	____ *All* circles and triangles are on the left side of the box. ____ *All* squares and circles are on the left side of the box. ____ *All* squares and triangles are on the left side of the box.
2. Which statement is true for the diagram above?	____ *All* squares are darkly shaded. ____ *All* triangles are darkly shaded. ____ *All* circles are darkly shaded.

Check Your Understanding 6.1b

Refer to the diagram below to answer the following questions.

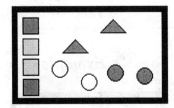

Put a check (✓) next to the correct answers in the answer column.

Question	Answer
1. Which statement is true for the diagram above?	____ *All* circles are on the left side of the box. ____ *All* squares are on the left side of the box. ____ *All* triangles are on the left side of the box.
2. Which statement is true for the diagram above?	____ *All* squares are above circles. ____ *All* circles are above squares. ____ *All* triangles are above circles.

logic term

A logic term is a word that has a specific meaning when used in logic statements.

6.2 Logic Term: *some*

The **logic term** *some* is used when referring to one item, a few items or every item in a group with the same **attribute** or attributes.

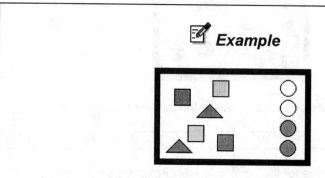

📝 *Example*

▶ *Some* can be used to describe every triangle in this diagram.
   "*Some* triangles are darkly shaded."

▶ *Some* can also be used to describe part of the circles in the diagram.
   "*Some* circles are clear."

attribute

An attribute is a property or a characteristic of something. For example, a small, clear triangle has three separate attributes: small, clear, and triangle.

Refer to the diagram above to answer the following questions.

 Check Your Understanding 6.1.2a

Put a check (✓) next to the correct answers in the answer column.

Question	Answer
1. Which statements are true for the diagram above? (Mark all that apply.)	___ *Some* squares are clear. ___ *Some* squares are lightly shaded. ___ *Some* triangles are darkly shaded.

2. Which statements are true for the diagram on the last page? (Mark all that apply.)	___ *Some* circles are darkly shaded. ___ *Some* circles are above some squares. ___ *Some* triangles are clear.

 Check Your Understanding 6.2b

Refer to the diagram below to answer the following questions.

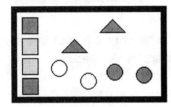

Put a check (✓) next to the correct answers in the answer column.

Question	Answer
1. Which statements are true for the diagram above? (Mark all that apply.)	___ *Some* circles are on the right of the squares. ___ *Some* squares are below the triangles. ___ *Some* triangles are below some of the circles.
2. Which statements are true for the diagram above? (Mark all that apply.)	___ *Some* triangles are on the left of the squares. ___ *Some* circles are above the triangles. ___ *Some* squares are above the circles.

6.3 Logic Term: *no/none*

The **logic terms** *no* or *none* are used when referring to items with the same **attribute** or attributes that are **not** in a group or do **not** belong in a group.

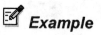 *Example*

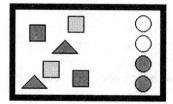

▶ *No* can be used to describe triangles that are not in this diagram.
   "*No* triangles are lightly shaded."

▶ *None* can also be used to describe the circles in the diagram.
   "*None* of the circles are on the left side of the box."

Refer to the diagram above to answer the following questions.

 Check Your Understanding 6.3a

Put a check (✓) next to the correct answers in the answer column.

Question	Answer
1. Which statements are true for the diagram above? (Mark all that apply.)	___ *None* of the triangles are clear. ___ *No* triangles are below some of the squares. ___ *None* of the circles are lightly shaded.

2. Which statements are true for the diagram above? (Mark all that apply.)	___ *No* triangles are on the right of the circles.
	___ *No* circles are below some of the squares.
	___ *None* of the squares are lightly shaded.

 Check Your Understanding 6.3b

Refer to the diagram below to answer the following questions.

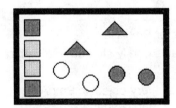

Put a check (✓) next to the correct answers in the answer column.

Question	Answer
1. Which statements are true for the diagram above? (Mark all that apply.)	___ *No* triangles are on the left of the squares.
	___ *None* of the squares are clear.
	___ *None* of the squares are on the left of the triangles.
2. Which statements are true for the diagram above? (Mark all that apply.)	___ *No* circles are clear.
	___ *None* of the triangles are to the right of the squares.
	___ *No* circles are above the triangles.

6.4 Logic Term: *and*

logic term

A logic term is a word that has a specific meaning when used in logic statements.

The **logic term** *and* is used to connect or link two or more **attributes** of items in a group.

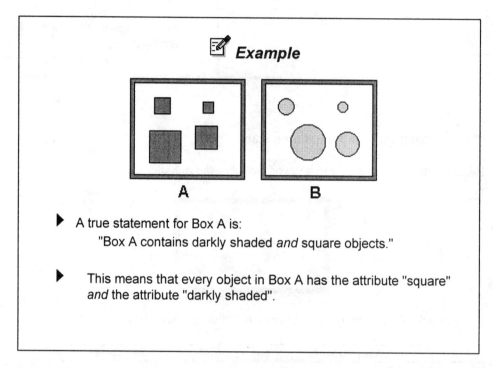

Example

A B

▶ A true statement for Box A is:
"Box A contains darkly shaded *and* square objects."

▶ This means that every object in Box A has the attribute "square" *and* the attribute "darkly shaded".

attribute

An attribute is a property or a characteristic of something. For example, a small, clear triangle has three separate attributes: small, clear, and triangle.

Refer to the diagram above to answer the following questions.

 Check Your Understanding 6.4a

Put a check (✓) next to the correct answers in the answer column.

Question	Answer
Which statement is true for the diagram above?	____ Box B contains circular *and* clear objects.
	____ Box B contains circular *and* lightly shaded objects.
	____ Box B contains triangular *and* lightly shaded objects.

Check Your Understanding 6.4b

Refer to the diagram below to answer the following questions.

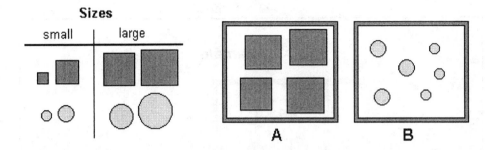

Put a check (✓) next to the correct answers in the answer column.

Question	Answer
1. Which statement is true for the diagram above?	____ The objects in box A are small, darkly shaded *and* square. ____ The objects in box A are large, darkly shaded *and* square. ____ The objects in box A are large, lightly shaded *and* square.
2. Which statements are true for the diagram above? (Mark all that apply.)	____ The objects in box B are large, lightly shaded *and* circular. ____ The objects in box B are small, clear *and* circular. ____ The objects in box B are small, lightly shaded *and* circular.

6.5 Logic Term: *or*

The **logic term** *or* is used to connect or link items with various **attributes** into a single group.

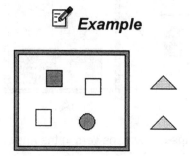

Example

▶ A true statement for this diagram is:

"Objects in the box are square *or* darkly shaded."

▶ Another way to write this statement is:

"The box contains square objects, darkly shaded objects, and square, darkly shaded objects."

▶ Both statements mean that the following objects are in the box:

- objects with the attribute square
- objects with the attribute darkly shaded
- objects with the attributes square and darkly shaded

Check Your Understanding 6.5a

Refer to the diagram below to answer the following questions.

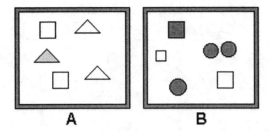

Put a check (✓) next to the correct answers in the answer column.

Question	Answer
1. Which statement is true for box A?	____ Objects in the box are square *or* clear. ____ Objects in the box are triangular *or* clear. ____ Objects in the box are triangular *or* lightly shaded.
2. Which statement is true for box B?	____ Objects in the box are circular *or* clear. ____ Objects in the box are clear *or* square. ____ Objects in the box are square *or* darkly shaded.

Check Your Understanding 6.5b

Refer to the diagram below to answer the following questions.

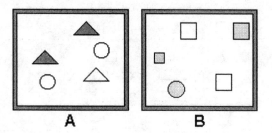

Put a check (✓) next to the correct answers in the answer column.

Question	Answer
1. Which statement is true for box A?	____ Objects in the box are circular *or* darkly shaded. ____ Objects in the box are triangular *or* clear. ____ Objects in the box are triangular *or* square.
2. Which statement is true for box B?	____ Objects in the box are circular *or* lightly shaded. ____ Objects in the box are clear *or* lightly shaded. ____ Objects in the box are clear *or* square.

6.6 Logic Terms: *if* and *then*

When the **logic terms** *if* and *then* are used, the objects in the set that have the first **attribute** must also have the second attribute.

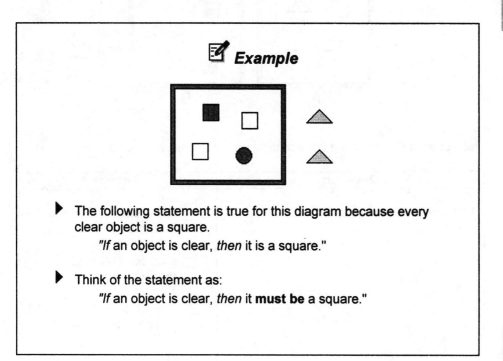

✎ *Example*

▶ The following statement is true for this diagram because every clear object is a square.

"*If* an object is clear, *then* it is a square."

▶ Think of the statement as:

"*If* an object is clear, *then* it **must be** a square."

Check Your Understanding 6.6a

Refer to the diagram below to answer the following questions.

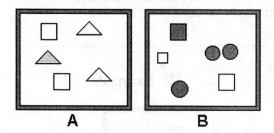

Put a check (✓) next to the correct answers in the answer column.

Question	Answer
1. Which statement is true for box A?	___ If an object is triangular, *then* it is lightly shaded. ___ If an object is square, *then* it is clear. ___ If an object is clear, *then* it is a square.
2. Which statement is true for box B?	___ If an object is circular, *then* it is darkly shaded. ___ If an object is darkly shaded, *then* it is circular. ___ If an object is square, *then* it is clear.

Check Your Understanding 6.6b

Refer to the diagram below to answer the following questions.

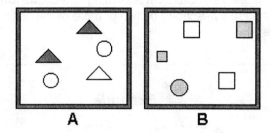

A   B

Put a check (✓) next to the correct answers in the answer column.

Question	Answer
1. Which statements are true for box A? (Mark all that apply.)	____ If an object is triangular, *then* it is darkly shaded. ____ If an object is circular, *then* it is clear. ____ If an object is clear, *then* it is a circular. ____ If an object is darkly shaded, *then* it is triangular.
2. Which statement is true for box B? (Mark all that apply.)	____ If an object is square, *then* it is clear. ____ If an object is lightly shaded, *then* it is circular. ____ If an object is clear, *then* it is square. ____ If an object is circular, *then* it is lightly shaded.

6.7 Venn Diagrams

attribute

An attribute is a property or a characteristic of something. For example, a small, clear triangle has three separate attributes: small, clear, and triangle.

A *Venn Diagram* is a useful method for showing relationships. Items are placed in the labeled rings of the Venn Diagram according to their **attribute** or attributes. If an item has the attributes described by two or more of the rings, it is placed where the rings overlap.

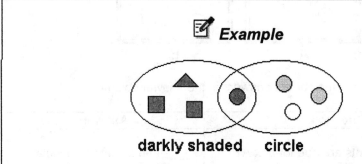

📝 ***Example***

darkly shaded   circle

This Venn diagram has two rings. The darkly shaded circle is the only object that can be placed in the overlapping area of the rings.

✔️ **Check Your Understanding 6.7a**

Put a check (✓) next to the correct answers in the answer column.

Question	Answer
1. Which Venn diagram can contain a darkly shaded circle in the overlapping area of the rings? **A** circle lightly shaded **B** clear triangle **C** circle darkly shaded	___ A ___ B ___ C
2. Which of the following objects would fit in the overlapping rings of this Venn Diagram? lightly shaded square ■ ☐ △ ☐ ○ A B C D E	___ A ___ B ___ C ___ D ___ E

Check Your Understanding 6.7b

Put a check (✓) next to the correct answers in the answer column.

Question	Answer
1. Which Venn diagram can contain a darkly shaded triangle in the overlapping area of the rings? **A** square / clear **B** triangle / darkly shaded **C** clear / triangle	___ A ___ B ___ C
2. Which of the following objects would fit in the overlapping rings of this Venn Diagram? clear circle ● ○ △ □ ○ **A B C D E**	___ A ___ B ___ C ___ D ___ E

6.8 Deductive Reasoning

Deductive reasoning is the process of reaching a **conclusion** from **statements** that are accepted as true. The conclusion is true only for the statements from which it was found.

> **conclusion**
>
> A conclusion is a statement that follows from other statements that are assumed to be true.

> **statement**
>
> A statement in logic is a fact or something that is assumed to be true.

📝 *Example*

If the two statements below are **assumed** to be true, then the conclusion found from those statements is also assumed to be true.

Statement 1: "All flowers have petals."

Statement 2: "Roses are flowers."

Conclusion: "Therefore, roses have petals."

Check Your Understanding 6.8

Put a check (✓) next to the correct answers in the answer column.

Question	Answer
1. What is the true conclusion, **assuming** that these statements are true? *The market for all vegetables has grown.* *Broccoli is a vegetable.* **A Therefore, all vegetables are broccoli.** **B Therefore, the market for broccoli has grown.** **C Therefore, the broccoli plant is growing bigger.**	__ A __ B __ C
2. What is the true conclusion, **assuming** that these statements are true? *All students take their finals in December.* *All freshmen are students.* **A Therefore, all freshmen take their finals in December.** **B Therefore, all freshmen take finals.** **C Therefore, all freshmen are nervous about taking their finals.**	__ A __ B __ C
3. What is the true conclusion, **assuming** that these statements are true? *All mammals feed their young with milk.* *All cows feed their calves with milk.* **A Therefore, all mammals are cows.** **B Therefore, all cows are mammals.** **C Therefore, all young who drink milk are calves.**	__ A __ B __ C

6.9 Inductive Reasoning

Inductive reasoning is the process of finding a rule after examining specific cases.
It often involves guessing and making predictions.

 *Example*

If two new buildings were built downtown every year for the past five
years, a person might use inductive reasoning to say that next year
two new buildings will be built downtown. This may not happen, but it
is a reasonable prediction.

 Check Your Understanding 6.9

Put a check (✓) next to the correct answers in the answer column.

statement

A statement in logic is a fact or
something that is assumed to be
true.

Question	Answer
1. From the following **statement**, which **conclusion** is inductive? *The Jammers soccer team hasn't won a road game all season.* **A The Jammers will win the next road game.** **B The Jammers will lose the next road game.** **C The Jammers will lose the next home game.**	___ A ___ B ___ C
2. From the following **statement**, which **conclusion** is inductive? *For the past 5 years, the annual rainfall was less than the average of 30 inches for the past 50 years.* **A Last year, the annual rainfall was less than 30 inches.** **B Next year the annual rainfall will be more than 50 inches.** **C Next year the annual rainfall will be less than 30 inches.**	___ A ___ B ___ C

3. From the following **statement**, which **conclusion** is inductive?

___ A
___ B
___ C

Over the past two years, the number of new homes built in the city was 420.

A **In the next year, approximately 400 new homes will be built.**

B **In the next year, approximately 200 new homes will be built.**

C **In the next two years, approximately 250 new homes will be built.**

conclusion

A conclusion is a statement that follows from other statements that are assumed to be true.

6.10 Answers to Questions

Answers to 6.1a

Correct Answer	Explanation
1. *All* squares and triangles are on the left side of the box.	The squares and triangles are all located in one part of the box. They are *all* on the left side of the box. 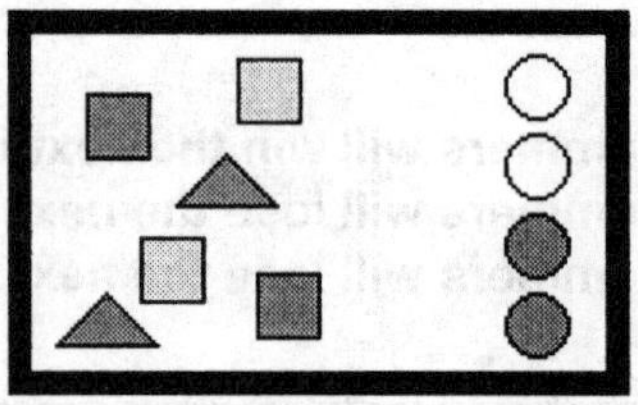
2. *All* triangles are darkly shaded.	There are only darkly shaded triangles in the diagram. Therefore, *all* **triangles are darkly shaded**.

Answers to 6.1b

Correct Answer	Explanation
1. *All* squares are on the left side of the box.	The squares are all located in one part of the box. They are *all* on the left side of the box.
2. *All* triangles are above circles.	The triangles are *all* located above the circles in the box.

Answers to 6.2a

Correct Answer	Explanation
1. *Some* squares are lightly shaded. *Some* triangles are darkly shaded.	Two of the four squares are lightly shaded. The other two are darkly shaded. Although every triangle is darkly shaded, *some* can be used to describe one, a few, or every triangle.
2. *Some* circles are above some squares. *Some* circles are darkly shaded.	Two of the circles are above two of the squares. Two of the circles are darkly shaded, and two are clear.

Answers to 6.2b

Correct Answer	Explanation
1. *Some* circles are on the right of the squares. *Some* squares are below the triangles.	Although every circle is on the right of the squares, *some* can be used to describe one, a few, or every circle. Two squares are below the triangles.
2. *Some* squares are above the circles.	Two squares are above the circles.

Answers to 6.3a

Correct Answer	Explanation
1. *None* of the triangles are clear. *None* of the circles are lightly shaded.	There are only darkly shaded triangles in this diagram. There are only clear and darkly shaded circles in this diagram.
2. *No* triangles are on the right of the circles.	The triangles are all on the left of the circles.

Answers to 6.3b

Correct Answer	Explanation
1. *No* triangles are on the left of the squares. *None* of the squares are clear.	The triangles are all on the right of the squares. There are only darkly shaded and lightly shaded squares in this diagram.
2. *No* circles are above the triangles.	All the circles are below the triangles in this diagram.

Answers to 6.4a

Correct Answer	Explanation
Box B contains circular *and* lightly shaded objects.	Box B contains items with both the attributes "circular" *and* "lightly shaded".

Answers to 6.4b

Correct Answer	Explanation
1. The objects in box A are large, darkly shaded, *and* square.	Box A contains items with the three attributes "large", "darkly shaded", *and* "square". **Sizes** small | large A B
2. The objects in box B are small, lightly shaded, *and* circular.	Box B contains items with the three attributes "small", "lightly shaded", *and* "circular".

Answers to 6.5a

Correct Answer	Explanation
1. Objects in the box are triangular *or* clear.	All objects in box A have one or both of these attributes: triangular or clear. A B
2. Objects in the box are square *or* darkly shaded.	All objects in box B have one or both of these attributes: square or darkly shaded.

Answers to 6.5b

Correct Answer	Explanation
1. Objects in the box are triangular *or* clear.	All objects in box A have one or both of these attributes: triangular or clear. A B
2. Objects in the box are clear *or* lightly shaded.	All objects in box B have one or both of these attributes: clear or lightly shaded.

Answers to 6.6a

Correct Answer	Explanation
1. If an object is square, *then* it is clear.	In box A every square is clear. If an object is a square, then it **must be** clear. A B
2. If an object is circular, *then* it is darkly shaded.	In box B every circle is darkly shaded. If an object is a circle, then it **must be** darkly shaded.

Answers to 6.6b

Correct Answer	Explanation
1. If an object is circular, *then* it is clear. If an object is darkly shaded, *then* it is triangular.	Both of these statements are true about the objects in box A. If an object is circular, then it **must be** clear. If an object is darkly shaded, then it **must be** triangular. A B
2. If an object is clear, *then* it is square. If an object is circular, *then* it is lightly shaded.	Both of these statements are true about the objects in box B. If an object is clear, then it **must be** a square. If an object is circular, then it **must be** lightly shaded.

Answers to 6.7a

Correct Answer	Explanation
1. C	The rings are labeled with two separate attributes, "circle" and "darkly shaded." Only a darkly shaded circle can be placed where the rings overlap. A B C circle lightly shaded clear triangle circle darkly shaded
2. B	The rings are labeled with two separate attributes, "lightly shaded" and "square." Only object B, a lightly shaded square, can be placed where the rings overlap. lightly shaded square A B C D E

Answers to 6.7b

Correct Answer	Explanation
1. B	The rings are labeled with two separate attributes, "triangle" and "darkly shaded." Only a darkly shaded triangle can be placed where the rings overlap. A B C square clear triangle darkly shaded clear triangle
2. E	The rings are labeled with two separate attributes, "clear" and "circle." Only object E, a clear circle, can be placed where the rings overlap. clear circle A B C D E

Answers to 6.8

Correct Answer	Explanation
1. B	If the market for vegetables has grown and broccoli is a vegetable, then you can deduce that the market for broccoli must have grown too.
2. A	If all students take their finals in December and all freshmen are students, then you can deduce that all freshmen take their finals in December.
3. B	If all mammals feed their young with milk and all cows feed their calves with milk, then you can deduce that all cows are mammals.

Answers to 6.9

Correct Answer	Explanation
1. B	**The Jammers will lose the next road game.** This is an inductive conclusion. It is a prediction, based on the fact that they haven't won a road game so far in the season.
2. C	**Next year the annual rainfall will be less than 30 inches.** This is an inductive conclusion. It is a prediction, based on the low rainfall over the past five years.
3. B	**In the next year, approximately 200 new homes will be built.** This is an inductive conclusion. It is a prediction, based on the number of new homes built over the past two years.

Glossary

acute: An acute angle is an angle that measures less than 90°. An acute triangle is a triangle that has only acute angles.

addend: An addend is a number that is added to another number. For example, in the equation 3 + 5 = 8, the addends are 3 and 5.

adjacent: Two objects that are adjacent are next to each other. For example, in a group of three dots (. . .), the first and second dots are adjacent, and the second and third dots are adjacent. However, the first and third dots are *not* adjacent.

area: Area is the measure of the region within a closed two-dimensional figure.

attribute: An attribute is a property or a characteristic of something. For example, a small, yellow triangle has three separate attributes: small, yellow, and triangle.

average: To find the average, or "arithmetic mean" of a group of numbers, first add the numbers, then divide the sum by the number of terms you added. For example, the average of 6, 7, and 2 is 5.

6 + 7 + 2 = 15   (Since you are adding 3 numbers, 3 is the number of terms.)

15 ÷ 3 = 5

base of a prism: The two opposite, congruent, and parallel faces of a prism are the bases. For example, the two shaded faces of the triangular prism shown below are its bases. Note that a prism is not always drawn as standing on its base.

base of a triangle: The base of a triangle is any one of its three sides. Therefore, every triangle has three bases.

base 10: A base 10 number system uses ten digits 0, 1, ..., 9 and powers of 10 to represent numbers. The number system we use is a base 10 system.

calculate: Calculating means using mathematical operations to determine an answer to a problem.

circumference: Circumference is the distance around a circle. To find the circumference, multiply the diameter of the circle by π (or approximately 3.14).

> The circumference equals πd, where d is the diameter of the circle.

> The circumference equals $2\pi r$ where r is the radius of the circle.

clockwise: Clockwise means in the same direction that the hands on a clock move.

cluster: A cluster is a group of two or more values on a plot.

clustering: Clustering is an estimation strategy that finds a number that all the numbers in a mathematics problem are close to in value. It is a good estimation strategy when adding long lists of numbers.

columns: Columns are vertical sections of a table. Columns are usually read from top to bottom.

common denominator: A common denominator is a multiple of the denominators of two or more fractions. For example, for the fractions 1/2 and 3/5, a common denominator is 10 because 10 is a multiple of both 2 and 5. Another common denominator is 20.

compatible numbers: Numbers that are easy to work with mentally are called compatible numbers. Compatible numbers can be number groupings that allow you to estimate an answer quickly. For example, in the expression 23 + 72 + 54 + 46, the compatible number groups are (23, 72) and (54,46). The value of each group is *about* 100, so the answer is *about* 100 x 2, or about 200.

conclusion: A conclusion is a statement that follows from other statements that are assumed to be true.

congruent: Two figures are congruent if they exactly match when superimposed.

constant: A constant is an amount or number that does not change. It remains the same for the purpose of performing specific calculations.

counterclockwise: Counterclockwise means in the opposite direction that the hands on a clock move.

cube: A cube is a closed three-dimensional figure with six identical square faces.

cubic unit: A cubic unit is the unit of measure (unit³) for the volume of three-dimensional objects. You can think of a cubic unit as a cube with edges that are one unit long. The volume of this cube is 1 unit³.

cylinder: A cylinder is a solid that has two circular bases. The bases are in parallel planes. A juice can is a good example of a cylinder.

data: Data is a collection of information such as facts or numbers. It is often used to form some sort of conclusion. For example, Company XYZ earned a profit of $5 million two years ago and $5.6 million the following year. From this data the company can conclude that during the second year, its profits increased by $0.6 million.

degree: A unit of angular measure is called a degree. There are 360 degrees in a full circle. The raised circle (°) means *degrees*. For example, $m \angle a = 40°$ is read "The measure of angle a equals 40 degrees."

denominator: The denominator is the number in a fraction that represents the number of parts that make a whole. For example, in the fraction 7/13, the denominator is 13.

diameter: A diameter is a line segment through the center of a circle with end points on the circle

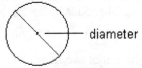

difference: Difference is the result of subtracting one quantity from another. Differences may be positive or negative, although a positive difference is usually preferred. To find the difference between two numbers, subtract one from the other. For example, the difference between 8 and 6 is either 2 or -2.

$$8 - 6 = 2$$
$$6 - 8 = -2$$

digit: A digit is any one of the 10 counting numbers: 0, 1, 2, 3, 4, 5, 6, 7, 8, 9. All rational numbers are expressed using one or more of these digits.

divisible: Divisible means the quality of being divided, *without* remainder, by another number. For example, 12 is divisible by 6 because 12 ÷ 6 =2. There is no remainder. By contrast, 12 is *not* divisible by 5 because 12 ÷ 5 = 2 *with a remainder of 2*.

equation: An equation is a statement of equality between two expressions. For example, 2b + 4 = 2(b + 2) is an equation. It is understood as meaning: 2b + 4 *is equal to* 2(b + 2).

equilateral: In an equilateral triangle, all three sides are the same length and all three angles have the same measure.

equivalent fractions: Fractions that name the same number are equivalent. For example, 12/24 and 15/30 are equivalent fractions. They are two ways of expressing 1/2.

equivalent: Equivalent means the same in amount, size, or value.

even: An integer which can be divided by 2 without leaving a remainder is said to be even. The last digit of an even number is always 0, 2, 4, 6, or 8. Some examples of even numbers are: 4, 8, 22, 36, and 130.

expression: An expression is a combination of numbers and symbols. For example, 5n + 3, (b + a), and 7 - y are expressions.

extremes: Extremes are the greatest and smallest values in a set of numbers.

face: A face is any of the flat surfaces of a three-dimensional figure or a solid. For example, a box has six flat sides. Each of these sides is a face of the box.

factor: A factor is an integer that divides another integer evenly, with no remainder. For example, 3 and 7 are factors of 21 because 3 x 7 = 21.

factoring: The process of finding a number's prime factors is called factoring. For example, factoring 24 results in 2 x 2 x 2 x 3. Both 2 and 3 are prime factors of 24.

fraction: A fraction is the quotient of two quantities. It is a symbol that tells us to divide one quantity by another. For example, 3/4 is the fraction that means divide 3 by 4.

front-end numbers: Front-end numbers refer to an estimation strategy that uses the first digit of the numbers you are working with. For example, in the expression 512 x 12, the front-end numbers are 500 x 10, or 5,000. The remaining numbers are 12 x 12, or about 10 x 10, or about 100. Add the numbers 5,000 and 100, the answer is about 5,100.

gap: A gap is the space between two clusters of data or between a cluster and an outlier.

greatest common factor: The largest factor that two or more numbers have in common is called the greatest common factor. For example, the common factors of 36 and 42 are 2, 3, and 6; and of these, 6 is the greatest.

height of a prism: The height of a prism is the perpendicular distance between the two bases.

height of a triangle: The perpendicular (or shortest) distance from one vertex (or corner) of a triangle to the opposite base is called the height of a triangle. Therefore, every triangle has three heights, one for each base.

hexagon: A hexagon is a polygon with exactly six sides.

horizontal axis: A straight line, that is the base line (or parallel to the base line) of a graph or chart. It goes from left to right. The horizontal axis of this graph is the one that shows days.

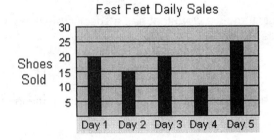

Fast Feet Daily Sales

improper fraction: A fraction that has a numerator that is larger than the denominator and represents a number greater than one is an improper fraction. An example of an improper fraction is 5/4.

inscribe: To inscribe is to construct a geometric figure inside another figure so that the two figures have points in common, but do not cross over each other. The figure below shows a square inscribed in a circle.

integer: An integer is any number in the set { . . . -3, -2, -1, 0, 1, 2, 3, . . . }. In other words, integers include all whole numbers, their negatives or opposites, and zero.

interest: Interest is money paid for borrowing money. This is usually a percentage of the money borrowed.

inverse operations: Operations that undo each other are called inverse operations. Subtraction and addition undo each other, and multiplication and division undo each other. For example, if you start with x, then add 3, the result is x + 3. Performing the inverse operation (subtract 3) undoes the addition: x + 3 - 3 = x + 0 = x. You end up as you started, with only x.

isosceles: An isosceles triangle has at least two sides that are the same length and two angles that have the same measure.

key: A key is a list of words, numbers, symbols, or combination of these that helps identify or explain items in a graph or chart. For example, a key for a circle graph might show what a fill pattern or color means.

least common denominator: The least common denominator is the smallest possible multiple of all the common denominators of two or more fractions. For example, the least common denominator of 1/2, 2/3, and 1/4 is 12. Twelve is the smallest possible common multiple of the denominators 2, 3, and 4.

length (l): The length is the measure of the longer side of a two-dimensional figure, or the measure of the longer side of the base of a three-dimensional figure.

logic term: A logic term is a word that has a specific meaning when used in logic statements.

lower extreme: The lower extreme is the lowest value in a set of data.

lower quartile: The lower quartile is the middle value in the lower half of a set of data.

lowest terms: A fraction is in lowest terms when the greatest common factor of the numerator and denominator is 1. For example, the fraction 3/5 is in lowest terms, because 1 is the greatest common factor of 3 and 5. The fraction 6/8 is not, because 2 is the greatest common factor of 6 and 8.

mean: A mean is another kind of average. To find the mean or arithmetic average of a group of numbers, first add the numbers, then divide the sum by the number of terms you added. For example, the mean of 6, 7, and 2 is 5.

> $6 + 7 + 2 = 15$ (Since you are adding 3 numbers, 3 is the number of terms.)
>
> $15 \div 3 = 5$

median: The median is the middle number of a set of numbers that are arranged in numerical order, or the average of the two middle numbers. For example, 7 is the median of 3, 4, 7, 8, 10; and 4.5 is the median of 1, 2, 4, 5, 8, 9.

metric system: The metric system is used worldwide for scientific measurement. The metric system uses measures such as centimeters, grams, and liters. In the metric system, all units of measure are related to each other by powers of 10.

mixed number: A number that has a whole-number part and a fraction part is called a mixed number. For example, 3 2/5 is a mixed number.

mode: The mode is the number in a set of numbers that occurs most often. For example, the mode of 2, 3, 6, 6, 6, 8, 8, 10, 11, 11 is 6.

multiple: A multiple is a number which is the product of a specific integer and another integer. For example, 15 is a multiple of 3 and 5 because 3 x 5 = 15 and 5 x 3 = 15. However, 15 is *not* a multiple of 4, because there is no integer that you can multiply 4 by that will equal 15.

negative numbers: All numbers less than zero are called negative numbers.

numerator: The numerator is the number in a fraction that represents part of one whole. For example, in the fraction 7/13, the numerator is 7.

obtuse: An angle that measures greater than 90° is called an obtuse angle. An obtuse triangle is a triangle that contains an obtuse angle.

odd: An odd integer leaves a remainder of 1 when divided by 2.

outlier: An outlier is a value that is significantly removed from other data.

parallel lines: When two lines are parallel, they remain a constant distance apart.

For example, these lines are parallel.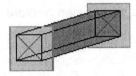

These lines are *not* parallel.

parallel planes: When two planes are parallel, they remain a constant distance apart.

For example, the bases of this solid are marked with an X. They are in parallel planes.

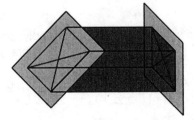

The faces of this solid that are marked with an X are *not* in parallel planes.

parallelogram: A parallelogram is a polygon with two sets of opposite sides that are parallel.

partition: To partition is to divide something into two or more areas or sections.

pentagon: A pentagon is a polygon with exactly five sides.

percent: A percent is a special kind of ratio. It compares a quantity to 100. The word **percent** (%) means "per one hundred."

perimeter: The perimeter is the distance around a closed two-dimensional figure. To find the perimeter of a figure, add the measures of the lengths of its sides.

pi (π): Pi is a value that represents the ratio of the circumference of a circle to its diameter. This ratio is the same for any circle and is approximately equal to 3.14.

$$\frac{\text{circumference}}{\text{diameter}} = \text{approximately } \frac{22}{7} = \text{approximately } 3.14$$

place value: Place value is the value assigned to a digit based on the place it holds relative to the decimal point. For example, in the number 87.35, the 8 has a place value of 8 tens or 80, the 7 has a place value of 7 *ones*, the 3 has a place value of 3 *tenths*, and the 5 has a place value of 5 *hundredths*.

plane: A geometric concept that can be thought of as a flat surface that has no bounds is called a plane.

polygon: A polygon is a closed two-dimensional figure with three or more straight sides (or edges). A polygon always has the same number of vertices (or corners) as it does sides. For example, these figures are polygons:

positive numbers: Numbers greater than zero are positive numbers.

prime: A prime number is an integer that has exactly two factors: itself and 1. In other words, the only integers a prime number can be evenly divided by are 1 and itself. For example, 2, 3, and 5 are prime numbers. The number 4 is *not* a prime number because it has *three* factors: 1, 2, and 4. The number 1 is *not* a prime number because it can only be factored by itself.

prism: A prism is a solid with two bases that are polygons. The bases are in parallel planes. The sides of the prism are parallelograms.

product: A product is the result of multiplying two or more numbers. For example, the product of 5 and 10 (5 x 10) is 50.

proportion: A statement of equality between two ratios is called a proportion. For example, 3/5 = 9/15 is a proportion.

protractor: A protractor is an implement used to measure angles. The scale of a protractor is marked in degrees.

quadrilateral: A polygon with exactly four sides is a quadrilateral.

quantity: A quantity is an amount or number.

quartile: In certain graphs, a median divides data in half; quartiles divide the halves into quarters.

quotient: The answer to a division problem is called a quotient. For example, 7 is the quotient of 35 and 5: $35 \div 5 = 7$.

radius: A radius is a line segment (or distance) from the center of a circle to a point on the edge of the circle.

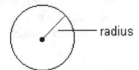

range (as a difference): A range is the *difference* between the highest value and the lowest value in a set of data. To find the range, subtract the smallest number from the largest number.

range (as a group): A range is a *group of numbers or values* that are defined by a high number and a low number. For example, the range of ages in my family is between 2 months and 75 years.

ratio: A ratio compares two or more quantities. For example, the ratio of *lightly-shaded* squares to *darkly-shaded* squares in the figure below is 2 to 6 (2:6). The ratio of *lightly-shaded* squares to *all* the squares is 2 to 8 (2:8). And the ratio of *darkly-shaded* squares to *all* the squares is 6 to 8 (6:8).

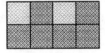

rectangle: A rectangle is a polygon with exactly four sides and four right angles. The lengths of the opposite sides of a rectangle are always equal.

rectangular prism: A rectangular prism is a closed three-dimensional figure with six rectangular faces. A cereal box is an example of a rectangular prism.

rhombus: A rhombus is a polygon with exactly four equal sides.

right triangle: A triangle that has one right (90°) angle is called a right triangle.

right angles: An angle that has a measure of 90 degrees is called a right angle. Sometimes right angles are called square angles.

rounding: Rounding is a way to write complex numbers in a simple form so they are easier to work with. To estimate the answer to $3,983,423 \times 4.88 = ?$ round the numbers to $4,000,000 \times 5$. The answer is about 20,000,000.

rows: The horizontal sections of a table are called rows. Rows are usually read from left to right.

scale: A scale is a line marked with ticks that are labeled with values. A scale is used, for example, on instruments that are designed to measure carefully defined attributes.

scale down: To scale down is to divide the numerator and the denominator of a fraction (or each part of the ratio) by the same number. For example, you can scale down 12/15 by dividing both 12 and 15 by 3.

$$\frac{12}{15} = \frac{12 \div 3}{15 \div 3} = \frac{4}{5}$$

scale up: To scale up is to multiply the numerator and the denominator of a fraction (or each part of the ratio) by the same number. For example, you can scale up 6/7 by multiplying both 6 and 7 by 3.

$$\frac{6}{7} = \frac{6 \times 3}{7 \times 3} = \frac{18}{21}$$

scalene: A scalene triangle has no sides equal in length and no angles equal in measure.

single value: A single value is one number. The single value of the expression 3 + 2 is the answer that you calculate, 5.

solid: A solid is a three-dimensional object that occupies space.

square: A square is a polygon with exactly four sides of equal length and four right angles.

square units: The square unit is the unit of measure for the area of a two-dimensional figure. For example, the area of a square that measures one inch along each side is a square inch (1 in²).

squared: A squared number is one that is multiplied by itself. The number 4 squared (4^2) is 4 x 4 or 16.

statement: A statement in logic is a fact or something that is assumed to be true.

stem: The stem is the left column of numbers on a stem-and-leaf plot. It serves as a type of scale.

sum: A sum is the result of the addition of two or more numbers or quantities. For example, the sum of 3 and 5 is 8.

surface area: The surface area is the total area of all outside surfaces of a three-dimensional object. For example, a box has six outside surfaces. They are the sides, or faces, of the box. To find the surface area, you must find the area of each face, then add the areas together.

terms: The numbers in a ratio or fraction that are being compared are called terms. For example, the terms of the ratio 5:3 are 5 and 3. The terms of the fraction 4/7 are 4 and 7.

title: The title is the first part of a table or graph that you should read. It tells you what is shown in the table or graph, and is usually above it.

transformation: A transformation occurs when a geometric figure changes its position.

trapezoid: A trapezoid is a polygon with four sides and one pair of opposite sides that are parallel. The parallel sides of a trapezoid are not the same length. For example, these figures are trapezoids.

triangle: A triangle is a polygon with exactly three sides.

triangular prism: A triangular prism has two triangular faces as the bases and three rectangular faces as the sides.

U.S. Customary System: The U.S. Customary System of measurement is used in the United States and some English-speaking countries.

upper extreme: The greatest value in a set of data is called the upper extreme.

upper quartile: The upper quartile is the middle value in the upper half of a set of data that is ordered.

variable: In algebra, a letter which represents any number from a specific set of numbers is called a variable. For example, the variable y in 2y < 5 can represent any number from the set {...-2,-1,0,1,2}.

vertex: The point where two sides of an angle meet is called the vertex. Some examples are shown below.

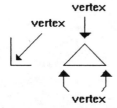

vertical axis: A vertical axis is a straight line that runs parallel to or makes up one of the sides (usually the left side) of a graph or chart. It goes from bottom to top. The vertical axis of this graph shows the number of shoes sold.

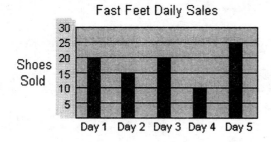

volume: Volume is the measure of the interior space of a 3-dimensional figure. Volume is measured in cubic units.

whole number: A whole number is any of the numbers in the set {. . . -3, -2, -1, 0, 1, 2, 3, . . .}. The whole-number part of the decimal number is to the left of the decimal point. For example, the whole-number part of 19.3498 is 19.

width (w): The width is the shorter dimension of a two-dimensional figure, or the number that is the measure of this dimension. Or, width can be the measure of the shorter side of the base of a three-dimensional figure.

Index

A

acute angles, 329
addends, 46
adding decimals, 89
addition, 76, 89
angles, 327-41
    angle relationships, 331
        vertical angles, 333
    classifying angles, 329
    classifying triangles, 339
    estimating angles, 337
    familiar angles, 335
    measuring angles, 327
area, 369-75, 376, 378, 379, 381
    area of a circle, 374
    area of a rectangle, 371
    area of a square, 372
    area of a triangle, 373
    square units, 369
    understanding area, 370
arithmetic mean, 179
assumptions, 423
attributes, 358, 408, 410, 412, 414, 416, 419, 422
average, 179, 181, 192, 193, 210, 226
    finding the average, 179

B

bar graphs, 190, 192, 209
    building bar graphs, 209
    double, 192, 210, 211
        reading double bar graphs, 192
    single, 210
        reading single bar graphs, 190
base 10, 94, 107
box-and-whisker plots, 227, 231, 237
    building box-and-whisker plots, 237
    comparing box-and-whisker plots, 231
    extremes, 237
    lower extreme, 231, 237
    lower quartile, 231, 237
    median, 231, 237
    quartiles, 237
    reading box-and-whisker plots, 227
    upper extreme, 231, 237
    upper quartile, 231, 237

C

calculate, 2
calculator, keys, 11
calculator, use of, 11, 90, 92, 93, 96, 105, 113, 114
cell, 172
characteristics of good problem solvers, 14
circle graphs, 219, 232
    building circle graphs, 232
    percents and circle graphs, 127
    reading circle graphs, 219

circles
    area of a circle, 374
    circumference, 366, 380
    diameter, 366
    perimeter, 366
    pi, 366, 374, 388
    radius, 366, 374, 388
circumference, 366, 380
classifying angles
    acute, 329
    obtuse, 329
    right, 329
    straight, 329
clock arithmetic
    adding in clock arithmetic, 51
    congruence in clock arithmetic, 49
    multiplying in clock arithmetic, 54
    subtracting in clock arithmetic, 53
    understanding clock arithmetic, 48
clockwise, 49, 51, 53
closed two-dimensional figure, 364
clustering, 6, 8, 10
clusters, 174, 222, 223, 224, 225
columns, 171, 172, 175
common denominators, 62, 69, 71, 76
common factors, 44
communication and problem solving, 14-16
    characteristics of good problem solvers, 14
    problem-solving strategies, 15
compatible numbers, 7, 8, 10
composite numbers, 40
conclusions, 423, 426
cones, 350
congruent, 49
constant, 363
converting measures, 363
counterclockwise, 53
cross multiplying, 283
cubes, 381, 382
cubic units, 381, 382, 383, 386, 388
cylinders, 351
    surface area, 379
    volume, 388

D

data, 169, 173, 177, 178, 195, 197, 198, 206, 207, 210, 211, 213, 214, 215, 219, 220, 222, 223, 225, 227, 229, 230, 231, 232, 234, 235, 237
decimals, 83-97
    adding and subtracting decimals, 89
    decimal numbers, 83
    decimal/percent equivalence, 107
    dividing decimals, 93
    fraction/decimal equivalence, 94
    multiplying decimals, 91
    ordering decimals, 85
    place value and decimals, 84

decimals (*continued*)
  rounding decimals, 87
    rules for rounding, 88
deductive reasoning, 423
degrees, 327
denominators, 56, 57, 58, 60, 61, 62, 64, 66, 67, 68, 69, 72, 74, 76, 80, 94, 96, 101, 103, 104, 105, 111, 113, 114, 283, 285, 286
  common denominators, 62, 69, 71, 72, 76
diameter, 366
difference, 27, 292
digits, 23, 30, 31, 32, 33, 34, 35, 84, 86, 87, 92, 115
divisibility, 41
divisibility tests, 30-35
divisible, 30, 31, 32, 33, 34, 35
division, 81, 93
divisor, 44

E

equations, 296, 301, 303, 305
equivalent fractions, 57, 58, 60, 61, 73, 77, 94, 103, 104
equivalent measures, 363
equivalent percents, 103, 104
estimating angles, 337
estimating fractions, 75
estimating percents, 121
estimation, 1-10, 70
  by clustering, 6
  by rounding, 5
  by using compatible numbers, 7
  by using front-end numbers, 8
estimation strategies, 10
estimation, using, 2
even numbers, 30, 46, 181
  adding with even numbers, 46
  multiplying with even numbers, 47
  rule for multiplying with even numbers, 47
exponents, 307
expressions, 298, 299, 301
extremes, 229, 237
  lower extreme, 231, 237
  upper extreme, 231, 237

F

faces, 375, 376, 378
factor tree, 42
factoring, 41
factors, 36, 37, 39, 41, 44, 47, 103
  common factors, 44
  greatest common factor, 44, 61
familiar angles, 335
fractions, 56-82, 101
  adding and subtracting fractions, 76
  as part of a whole, 56
  common denominators, 62
  comparing fractions to 1, 67
  comparing fractions to fractions, 68
    using a common denominator, 72
    using reasoning and estimation, 70
  dividing fractions, 81

fractions (*continued*)
  equivalent fractions, 57, 58, 60, 61, 73, 77, 104
  estimating equivalent fractions, 74
  estimating fractions, 75
  expressing percents as fractions, 101
  fraction/decimal equivalence, 94
  fraction/percent equivalence, 103
  improper fractions, 64, 66
  in lowest terms, 61, 75
  mixed numbers, 64
  multiplying fractions, 79
  scaling down fractions, 60, 94, 104
  scaling up fractions, 58, 94
front-end numbers, 8, 10

G

gaps, 174
graphs, 188-218, 219-38
  bar graphs
    building bar graphs, 209
    reading double bar graphs, 192
    reading single bar graphs, 190
  box-and-whisker plots
    building box-and-whisker plots, 237
    comparing box-and-whisker plots, 231
    reading box-and-whisker plots, 227
  circle graphs
    building circle graphs, 232
    reading circle graphs, 219
  clusters, 223
  extremes, 229
  gaps, 224
  line graphs
    building line graphs, 213
    reading line graphs, 195
  line plots
    building line plots, 234
    reading line plots, 220
  outliers, 225
  pictographs
    building pictographs, 206
    reading pictographs, 188
  quartiles, 230
  scatter plots
    building scatter plots, 215
    elimination with scatter plots, 199
    plotting points on a graph, 203
    reading scatter plots, 197
  stem-and-leaf plots
    building stem-and-leaf plots, 235
    reading stem-and-leaf plots, 222
  trends in graphs, 202
greatest common factor, 44, 61, 273

H

hexagons, 342
horizontal axis, 190, 193, 195, 197, 204, 213

I

improper fractions, 64, 66
inductive reasoning, 425

integers, 23-55, 64
    adding in clock arithmetic, 51
    adding negative numbers, 26
    adding with odd and even numbers, 46
    composite numbers, 40
    congruence in clock arithmetic, 49
    divisibility tests, 30-35
        divisibility test for 10, 35
        divisibility test for 2, 30
        divisibility test for 3, 31
        divisibility test for 4, 32
        divisibility test for 5, 33
        divisibility test for 9, 34
    factoring, 41
    factors, 36
    greatest common factors, 44
    magnitude, 23
    multiples, 37
    multiplying and dividing negative
    numbers, 28
    multiplying in clock arithmetic, 54
    multiplying with odd and even numbers,
    47
    place value, 23
    prime factorization, 42
    prime numbers, 39
    subtracting in clock arithmetic, 53
    subtracting negative numbers, 27
    understanding clock arithmetic, 48
    understanding negative numbers, 24
interest, 122
inverse operations, 296

K

key, 188, 193, 207, 212, 219, 233, 235

L

leaves, 235
length, 371
line graphs, 195, 202, 213
    building line graphs, 213
    reading line graphs, 195
    trends in graphs, 202
line plots, 220, 223, 224, 225, 234
    building line plots, 234
    reading line plots, 220
linear units, 369
logic terms, 408-21
    all, 408
    and, 414
    if and *then*, 419
    no/none, 412
    or, 416
    some, 410
logical reasoning, 16

M

magnitude, 23
mean, 179
measurement, 358-65
    converting measures, 363
    metric units of measure, 361
        metric system, 361
    standard units of measure, 359

measurement (*continued*)
    units of measure, 358
        metric system, 358
        U.S. Customary System, 358
median, 180, 181, 226, 230, 231, 237
    finding the median, 180
metric system, 361
metric units of measure, 361
mixed numbers, 64, 66
mode, 184
    finding the mode, 184
multiples, 31, 32, 34, 37, 41, 63, 74, 104
multiplication, 54, 79, 81, 91

N

negative numbers, 24, 26, 27, 28
    adding negative numbers, 26
    multiplying and dividing negative
    numbers, 28
    rules for multiplying and dividing negative
    numbers, 29
    subtracting negative numbers, 27
    understanding negative numbers, 24
number patterns, 290-95
    patterns in figures, 290
    patterns in sequences, 292
        relationships involving differences,
        292
        relationships involving products, 292
        relationships involving sums, 292
    patterns in tables, 294
numerators, 56, 57, 58, 60, 61, 64, 66, 67,
68, 72, 74, 76, 80, 94, 96, 105, 111, 113,
114, 283

O

obtuse angles, 329
odd numbers, 46, 181
    adding with odd numbers, 46
    multiplying with odd numbers, 47
    rule for multiplying with odd numbers, 47
operations, order of, 12
operations, series of, 12
outliers, 174, 224, 225

P

parallel, 333, 348, 349
parallel planes, 351, 352
parallelograms, 342, 343, 349, 352
    rectangles, 342, 349
    rhombuses, 342, 349
    squares, 349
    sum of angle measures, 331
patterns, 173
pentagons, 343
percent, 288
percent of increase, 288
percents, 98-129
    calculating percents, 113
    calculations using percents, 117
    decimal/percent equivalence, 107
    estimating percents, calculations, 119

percents (*continued*)
    estimating percents, common sense, 121
    expressing percents as fractions, 101
    fraction/percent equivalence, 103
    meaning of percent, 98
    percent as part of a whole, 99
    percent decrease, 125
    percent increase, 123
    percents and circle graphs, 127
    percents greater than 100%, 109
    percents less than 1%, 110
    rounding percents, 115
perimeter, 364-68
    circumference, 366
    closed two-dimensional figure, 364
    understanding scale factors, 367
pi, 366, 374, 388
    decimal value, 366
pictographs, 188
    building pictographs, 206
    reading pictographs, 188
place value, 23, 83
polygons, 342-49, 352
    hexagons, 342
    parallelograms, 349
    pentagons, 343
    quadrilaterals, 342, 343
    rectangles, 346
    rhombuses, 347
    squares, 345
    trapezoids, 348
    triangles, 342
positive numbers, 24, 26, 27, 28, 186
predictions, 425
prime factorization, 42
prime factors, 42
prime numbers, 39, 40
prism, rectangular
    surface area, 376
prism, triangular
    surface area, 378
prisms, 352
problem solvers, 14
problem solving
    characteristics of good problem solvers,
    14
    problem-solving strategies, 15
problem-solving strategies, 14, 15
product, 2, 7, 36, 47, 292
proportions, 276, 285, 288
    cross multiplying, 283
    definition, 276
    scaling down, 281
    scaling up, 280
    setting up proportions, 278
protractor, 327
    base of, 327
pyramids, 353

Q

quadrilaterals, 342, 343
    parallelograms, 342, 343
    rectangles, 343
    rhombuses, 343
    squares, 343

quadrilaterals (*continued*)
    trapezoids, 342, 343
quantity, 113, 114, 190, 192, 206, 209, 213,
265, 266, 268, 270, 271, 278, 285
quartiles, 230, 237
    lower quartile, 231, 237
    upper quartile, 231, 237
quotient, 5, 51, 54

R

radius, 366, 374
range, 2, 186, 190, 193, 197, 227
    finding the range, 186
ratios, 113, 114, 265, 266, 268, 275, 276,
278, 280, 285, 286, 288, 367
    definition, 265
    equivalent ratios, 275
    four-part ratios, 271
    in lowest terms, 273
    part to part ratios, 266
    part to whole ratios, 268
    three-part ratios, 270
ratios and proportions, 265-89
ratios to percents, calculator, 286
ratios to percents, proportions, 285
reasoning, 70, 423-26
    deductive, 423
    inductive, 425
rectangles, 342, 343, 346, 349, 373
    area of a rectangle, 371
    squares, 342, 346
rectangular prisms
    surface area, 376
    volume, 383
reflections, 356
rhombuses, 342, 343, 347, 349
    squares, 342, 347
right angles, 329, 337, 343, 345, 346
rotations, 355
rounding, 5, 8, 10, 12, 87, 91, 115, 216
    rules, 12
rounding decimals, 87
rounding percents, 115
rows, 170, 172, 175, 188

S

scale, 211, 214, 217, 234, 237
scale factors, 367
scaling, 94
scaling down, 60, 94, 101, 103, 113, 281,
367
scaling up, 58, 94, 103, 111, 114, 280, 367
scatter plots, 197, 199
    building scatter plots, 215
    elimination with scatter plots, 199
    plotting points on a graph, 203
    reading scatter plots, 197
single operations, 11
single values, 2
slides, 357
solids, 350, 351, 353
square units, 369, 371, 372, 374, 375, 381
squares, 342, 343, 345, 346, 347, 349
    area of a square, 372

standard units of measure, 359
    U.S. Customary System, 359
statements, 423, 426
stem, 235
stem-and-leaf plots, 222, 235
    building stem-and-leaf plots, 235
    leaves, 235
    reading stem-and-leaf plots, 222
    stem, 235
straight angles, 329, 331
strategies
    problem-solving, 15
subtracting decimals, 89
subtraction, 53, 76, 89
sum, 6, 7, 26, 46, 54, 179, 292, 364, 375
surface area, 369, 375-81
    of a cylinder, 379
    of a rectangular prism, 376
    of a triangular prism, 378
    understanding surface area, 375

T

table headings, 175
tables and charts, 169-79
    creating table headings, 175
    generating table data, 178
    organizing data, 177
    patterns in data, 173
    reading schedules and tables, 172
    understanding columns, 171
    understanding rows, 170
    understanding titles, 169
three-dimensional figures, 350-57
    cones, 350
    cylinders, 351
    prisms, 352
    pyramids, 353
        pentagonal pyramids, 353
        rectangular pyramids, 353
        square pyramids, 353
        triangular pyramids, 353
    transformations, 354
        reflections, 356
        rotations, 355
        slides, 357
title
    graphs, 188, 190, 192, 197
    tables, 172
transformations, 354-57
trapezoids, 342, 343, 348
triangles, 342
    acute, 340
    area of a triangle, 373
    classifying triangles
        equilateral, 339
        isosceles, 340
        right, 339
        scalene, 340
    obtuse, 340
triangular prism
    surface area, 378
    volume, 386
two-dimensional figures, 342-49
    polygons, 342

V

variables, 305
variables, expressions, and equations, 295-307
    evaluating equations with variables, 305
    evaluating expressions, 298
    exponents, 307
    manipulating equations, 303
    recognizing equivalent expressions, 299
    solving for unknowns, 296
    understanding equations, 301
Venn Diagrams, 422
vertex, 327, 350, 353, 355
vertical angles, 333
vertical axis, 190, 191, 193, 195, 197, 204, 214
volume, 381-89
    cubic units, 381
    understanding volume, 382
    volume of a cylinder, 388
    volume of a rectangular prism, 383
    volume of a triangular prism, 386

W

whole numbers, 83, 85, 89, 91, 93
width, 371